OPTIMAL DECISION RULES FOR GOVERNMENT AND INDUSTRY

STUDIES IN MATHEMATICAL AND MANAGERIAL ECONOMICS

Editor

HENRI THEIL

VOLUME 1

1964

NORTH-HOLLAND PUBLISHING COMPANY - AMSTERDAM

RAND McNALLY & COMPANY - CHICAGO

OPTIMAL DECISION RULES FOR GOVERNMENT AND INDUSTRY

by

H. THEIL

Professor of Econometrics
Netherlands School of Economics

in association with

P. J. M. VAN DEN BOGAARD †

assisted by

A. P. BARTEN / J. C. G. BOOT / C. VAN DE PANNE

Econometric Institute of the
Netherlands School of Economics, Rotterdam

1964

NORTH-HOLLAND PUBLISHING COMPANY - AMSTERDAM

RAND McNALLY & COMPANY - CHICAGO

Sole distributors for U.S.A. and Canada
RAND McNALLY & COMPANY - CHICAGO

PRINTED IN THE NETHERLANDS

INTRODUCTION TO THE SERIES

This is a series of books concerned with the quantitative approach to problems in the behavioural science field. The studies are in particular in the overlapping areas of mathematical economics, econometrics, operational research, and management science. Also, the mathematical and statistical techniques which belong to the apparatus of modern behavioural science have their place in this series. A well-balanced mixture of pure theory and practical applications is envisaged, which ought to be useful for Universities and for research workers in business and government.

The Editor hopes that the volumes of this series, all of which relate to such a young and vigorous field of research activity, will contribute to the exchange of scientific information at a truly international level.

THE EDITOR

PREFACE

Linear decision rules are a powerful tool for handling dynamic decision problems in the face of uncertainty. It is true that their applicability requires that certain conditions be satisfied (quadratic preferences and linear constraints), which correspond only approximately with most real-world situations. But when the approximation is satisfactory the method provides a simple and elegant guidance for decision-making, for the evaluation of the decision-making process, and for the allocation of research resources.

This book deals both with the theory of linear decision rules and with its application at the microeconomic and the macroeconomic level. The underlying research started as a continuation of the work done for *Economic Forecasts and Policy*, for which a grant was obtained from the Netherlands Organization for Pure Research (Z.W.O.). Mr. P. J. M. van den Bogaard was to have been a co-author, but this was prevented by his sudden death in January, 1962. The task of actually writing the book was therefore left to me. In the months following this heartfelt loss Mr. A. P. Barten helped me greatly; the computations reported in Chapter 6 are largely his work. Most of the applications referring to the paint factory of Chapter 5 are due to Mr. C. van de Panne; I am indebted to Mr. J. C. G. Boot for his work on these applications during the period which Mr. Van de Panne spent at the Carnegie Institute of Technology, Pittsburgh, Penn.

I am indebted to Mr. Thomas Rothenberg, now of Northwestern University, for his assistance regarding the English language; to Miss C. A. Berger for her fast and accurate typewriting of the manuscript; and to several of my younger colleagues at the Econometric Institute and the International Center for Management Science for reading the proofs, in particular Mr. J. I. Vorst.

Rotterdam, July 1963 H. THEIL

ABBREVIATED CONTENTS

TABLE OF CONTENTS

LIST OF TABLES

Chapter 3

Chapter 4

Chapter 5

Chapter 6 *

* Tables 6.1 through 6.10 refer to the American application in Section 6.1; Tables 6.11 through 6.25 to the Dutch application in Sections 6.2 and 6.3 and the Appendix.

Chapter 7

LIST OF FIGURES

Chapter 1

Chapter 2

Chapter 3

Chapter 4

Chapter 5

Chapter 6 *

* Figures 6.1 through 6.4 refer to the American application in Section 6.1; Figures 6.5 through 6.8 to the Dutch application in Sections 6.2 and 6.3.

CHAPTER 1

Introduction

1.1. QUADRATIC PREFERENCES AND LINEAR CONSTRAINTS

1.1.1. Linear Constraints

In this book we shall consider certain problems of a decision maker who pursues certain objectives within a given framework. This will be made more specific by postulating (i) that the pursuing of these objectives amounts to the maximization of a quadratic preference function in certain variables and (ii) that this framework can be represented by a certain number of linear equations in these variables.

Naturally, this specification reduces the applicability of the analysis. To illustrate this we shall start by considering the framework restriction (which is, as was mentioned, in terms of linear equations). Perhaps the most general procedure is to postulate that the decision maker's choice is confined to a subset of a larger set. For example, he may wish to establish a school in a certain city and there is a set S of locations which are in principle suitable for that purpose; but some of these are too expensive or have been reserved for other purposes, etc., so the choice of the location is restricted to some subset S' of the original set S.

It will be noticed that this formulation involves no restriction on the nature of the variables; in particular, such a set formulation does not necessarily imply that these variables should be real-valued. But the variables with which we shall deal in this book do have this property: they are production, inventories and work force of a factory and employment, consumption and wage shares in a national economy, and so on. When this is the case, it is appropriate to take it into account, because it enables us to obtain more specific results. The framework which the decision maker has to face can then usually be represented by a set of equations or inequalities. An example of a constraint in equational form is that in each time period the change in inventories equals the excess of production over shipments (which is an identity). Another example: the change in consumption is 0.7 times the change in income (which is a behavioural relation). Inequality constraints take this form: a cattle feed is to be designed such that its protein content should be at least 10 per cent, its water content should be at most 30 per cent, etc. In this book we shall not consider any inequality constraints, which means either that it is assumed that there are no such constraints or that the solution which one derives while disregarding these constraints does satisfy them.

We shall be concerned with real-valued variables which are constrained in terms of a set of equations. But such equations can in principle have any form; in particular, they may be linear, they may be not. However, one can argue that there is an intermediate possibility: an equation is nonlinear but can be linearized to a sufficient degree of accuracy. Taylor's theorem provides a justification for this procedure, at least in principle; whether or not the approximation is sufficiently accurate is of course a question that can be settled only on empirical grounds. This is a topic to which we shall have to return on several occasions.

1.1.2. Quadratic Preferences

By making more and more specific assumptions we exclude an increasing number of practical problems to which the analysis can be applied; on the other hand, we raise the number of interesting things that can be said about the problems that can still be handled by the analysis. To see that the harvest is meagre in case our investment of assumptions is modest, let us return to the school location example of the second paragraph of 1.1.1. Then S is the set of all conceivable locations, S' the set which is available. Suppose then that the decision maker is able to specify for any pair of locations in S (say, A and B) whether he prefers A to B or B to A or whether he is indifferent between them. Suppose also that he is consistent in the sense that if he prefers A to B and B to C, he prefers A to C as well (for all locations $A, B, C, \ldots$ in S; and similarly for indifference). In that case he is able to formulate a complete ranking of all locations in S according to decreasing preference. The conclusions are then as follows:

(i) The decision made is that location in the subset S' which is highest on the preference ladder. For example, let S consist of five locations: A, B, C, D and E; let A be preferred to B, B to C, and so on; let the set of available locations (S') consist of B, C and E. Then the decision made – the location chosen – is B. (This will be referred to as the first example.)

(ii) The solution may be a multiple one, viz., when there are two or more locations in S' which are equally high on the ladder, while all other locations are lower. We have such a case when we modify the first example to the extent that there is now indifference between B and C, all other specifications of that example remaining unchanged. Then (B, C) is the multiple solution. (This will be referred to as the second example.)

(iii) When there is a change in the decision maker's framework implying that some element of S' is no longer available, this affects the decision made only if this element is the solution (i) or part of the solution (ii). Thus, let us remove C from the set of available locations, then this does not affect the solution of the first example; but in the second the solution is reduced to the single location B.

(iv) When there is a change implying that some element of S but not in S' becomes available, this affects the decision only if this element ranks higher on the utility ladder than (or as high as) the original decision. Thus, let A become available, then the new solution is A; but the solution is not changed if D becomes available (in both examples).

That is all that can be said; it is not much. To be able to formulate more interesting conclusions we should be willing to introduce stronger assumptions. Now given our decision to work with real-valued variables, an obvious procedure is to introduce a preference (or utility) function of which these variables are the arguments. Regarding its mathematical form, this function may be the linear objective function of linear programming; it may be the quadratic objective function of quadratic programming; it may be the arbitrary convex objective function of convex programming. As to its economic interpretation, it may be the arbitrary (but convex and differentiable) utility function of the classical theory of consumer's demand; it may be a cost function which a factory manager tries to minimize; it may be a social welfare function which a government policy maker tries to maximize.

In this book we shall try to be general with respect to the field of application, which implies that the analysis should be applicable in principle to the consumer, the factory manager, and the government policy maker. But we shall be more restrictive with respect to the form of the preference function. The simplest form is undoubtedly the linear objective function, which is one of the bases of linear programming. If we accept this form and take the derivatives with respect to the various arguments, we obtain the marginal utilities which are constants. By taking the ratio of any pair of marginal utilities we obtain the marginal rate of substitution, which is then constant too. This will be realistic in a number of cases, but one would ordinarily expect that a decreasing marginal rate of substitution is more realistic. For let utility depend on two desirable things, D_1 and D_2, and let us write $\bar{D}_1$, $\bar{D}_2$ for the present level of the D's, and let us suppose that a decrease of D_1 by one unit compensated by an increase of D_2 by c units leaves the decision maker at the same indifference level. Then, if in a new situation D_1 takes a smaller value than $\bar{D}_1$ while D_2 takes the old level $\bar{D}_2$, one should expect that in most cases a D_2-increase of somewhat more than c units is necessary to compensate a unit decrease in D_1 from this new level.

There are many functional forms of preference functions which satisfy the requirement of decreasing marginal rates of substitution, but the quadratic is probably simplest. In fact, it has a long standing in many fields of applied mathematics. For example, the procedure of minimum-variance estimation in statistics is essentially based on a quadratic preference function and the same holds for the procedure of minimum mean-squared error prediction which is so popular in engineering. To illustrate the most important properties of this function, let us consider the special case of only one argument (z, say), so that it takes the form

$$w(z) = a_0 + a_1 z + \tfrac{1}{2} a_2 z^2, \quad (a_2 < 0) \tag{1.1}$$

which can also be written in the form:

$$w(z) = \left(a_0 - \frac{a_1^2}{2a_2}\right) + \tfrac{1}{2} a_2 (z - z^0)^2 \quad \text{where } z^0 = -\frac{a_1}{a_2}. \tag{1.2}$$

Given $a_2 < 0$, it follows immediately from (1.2) that $w(z)$ takes the highest level for $z = z^0$, which means that z^0 is the best value. As soon as z differs from z^0 there is a utility reduction below the attainable maximum. We conclude from (1.2) that (i) this reduction increases with the size of the difference and it does so more than proportionally, viz., quadratically (when $z - z^0 = 1$, the reduction is $\frac{1}{2}a_2$; when $z - z^0 = 10$, it is $50a_2$); and (ii) the value of the utility reduction depends only on the absolute value of $z - z^0$, i.e., it is the same when z equals $z^0 + b$ or $z^0 - b$, for whatever value of b. In many cases it will be realistic to assume that the seriousness of a discrepancy increases more than proportionally with the discrepancy itself, but it is of course not necessarily true that this relationship is quadratic. Also, it is not self-evident that discrepancies of the same size but opposite sign have identical consequences. As in the case of linear constraints, we should say that the proof of the pudding is in the eating. It will be noted, parenthetically, that the Taylor expansion argument is also applicable here: if we differentiate the preference function with respect to its arguments we obtain the marginal utilities which are functions of the same arguments. By expanding these functions in Taylor series and retaining only the linear terms, we do in fact proceed with a quadratic utility function. It will indeed turn out that the matrix

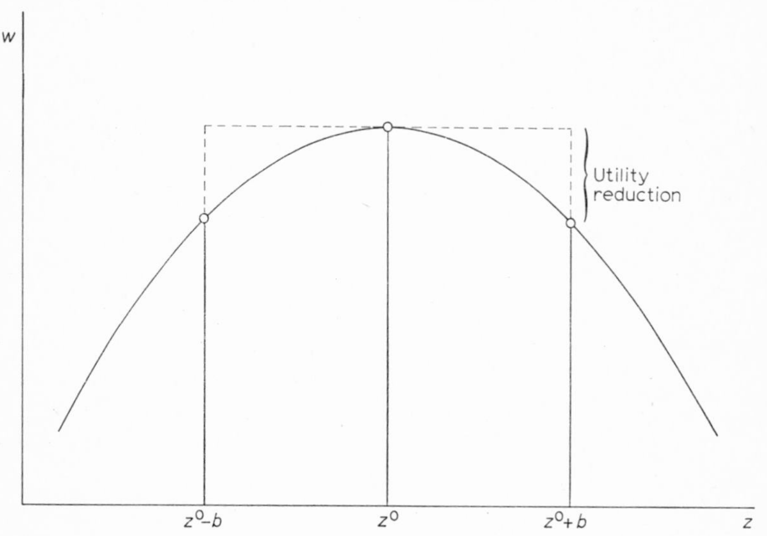

Figure 1.1. A quadratic preference function in one argument (z)

of multiplicative coefficients of these marginal utility functions plays a role which is in many respects similar to that of the matrix of multiplicative coefficients of the linear equations, while the same is true for the two vectors of constant terms.

1.2. SOME ELEMENTARY MATRIX ALGEBRA

1.2.1. Definition of Matrices; Transposition and Addition

The most elegant way to handle quadratic preference functions and linear constraints is in terms of matrix algebra. Since the matrix operations carried out in this book are very elementary (apart from a few isolated places), it may be convenient for the reader to have an informal summary of what he is supposed to know.[1]

[1] The reader is advised to go quickly through the following pages until the moment when he finds something with which he is unfamiliar. The same advice applies to Section 1.3, which contains an elementary account of some relevant results of probability theory.

A matrix can be described as a rectangular array of elements, arranged in m rows and n columns; it is said to be of order $m \times n$. These elements may be numbers, variables, etc. For example:

$$(2.1) \qquad \begin{bmatrix} 3 & 7 \\ 4 & 0 \\ 1 & -5 \end{bmatrix}, \quad \begin{bmatrix} 3 & 4 & 1 \\ 7 & 0 & -5 \end{bmatrix}, \quad \begin{bmatrix} a & b \\ b & c \end{bmatrix}, \quad \begin{bmatrix} x \\ y \\ z \end{bmatrix}.$$

The last matrix has $n = 1$, in which case we call it a column vector. The second can be obtained from the first by interchanging the role of rows and columns, which is the operation of transposition. The usual notation of a matrix is by a bold-face capital letter, e.g. $\mathbf{A}$, and its typical $(i, j)^{\text{th}}$ element (in the ith row and j^{th} column) is denoted by a_{ij}. One also writes $\mathbf{A} = [a_{ij}]$, which means that the matrix is indicated by its typical element. Transposition implies that $[a_{ij}]$ is replaced by $[a_{ji}]$, for which one frequently writes $\mathbf{A}'$. When $m = n$ we have a square matrix; if moreover such a matrix remains unchanged after transposition, it is called symmetric. The third matrix of (2.1) is square and symmetric. The fourth matrix (the three-element column vector), when transposed, gives a row vector. We shall adopt the usage of indicating a column by a bold-face lower-case letter, e.g. $\mathbf{z}$, so that a row vector is written as $\mathbf{z}'$. Sometimes, in order to save space, a column is written in the horizontal form $\{x\ y\ z\}$; the curled brackets serve to indicate that it is a column, not a row.

Two matrices $[a_{ij}]$ and $[b_{ij}]$ are said to be equal if they are of the same order and if the elements on corresponding places are pairwise equal: $a_{ij} = b_{ij}$ for all (i, j). When two matrices are of the same order we can add them and their sum is defined as the matrix whose elements are the sum of the corresponding elements of the original two matrices: $[a_{ij} + b_{ij}]$. For example:

$$(2.2) \qquad \begin{bmatrix} 3 & 7 \\ 4 & 0 \\ 1 & -5 \end{bmatrix} + \begin{bmatrix} 1 & -8 \\ 2 & 5 \\ 1 & 9 \end{bmatrix} = \begin{bmatrix} 4 & -1 \\ 6 & 5 \\ 2 & 4 \end{bmatrix}; \qquad \begin{bmatrix} a \\ b \\ c \end{bmatrix} + \begin{bmatrix} 0 \\ 0 \\ 0 \end{bmatrix} = \begin{bmatrix} a \\ b \\ c \end{bmatrix}.$$

In the second example we add a matrix (a column vector in this case) which consists of zeros and the result is that we obtain the original matrix. We write $\mathbf{0}$ for a matrix of zeros (a zero matrix); there is a zero matrix of every order. It is further easily verified that $(\mathbf{A}+\mathbf{B})' = \mathbf{A}'+\mathbf{B}'$, i.e., the transposed sum of two matrices is equal to the sum of the two transposed matrices.

1.2.2. Multiplication and Linear Equation Systems

There are two kinds of multiplication. The simplest is scalar multiplication, which deals with multiplying some matrix $[a_{ij}]$ by some ordinary number (a scalar) p. This is defined according to the rule $p[a_{ij}] = [pa_{ij}]$, i.e., every individual element is multiplied by the scalar. Matrix multiplication is of the form $\mathbf{C} = \mathbf{AB}$ where $\mathbf{A}$ and $\mathbf{B}$ are both matrices. It is defined only when the number of columns of the premultiplying matrix $\mathbf{A}$ is equal to the number of rows of the postmultiplying matrix $\mathbf{B}$, i.e., when $\mathbf{A}$ is of order $m \times n$ and $\mathbf{B}$ of order $n \times p$. The typical $(i, j)^{\text{th}}$ element of the product matrix $\mathbf{C}$ is defined as

$$c_{ij} = \sum_{h=1}^{n} a_{ih} b_{hj}, \tag{2.3}$$

i.e., one takes the ith row of $\mathbf{A}$ and the jth column of $\mathbf{B}$, multiplies the first element of that row by the first element of that column, does the same with the second elements, and so on, and adds. For example:

$$\begin{bmatrix} 1 & 2 \\ 3 & 4 \end{bmatrix} \begin{bmatrix} 5 & 6 \\ 7 & 8 \end{bmatrix} = \begin{bmatrix} 1\times5+2\times7 & 1\times6+2\times8 \\ 3\times5+4\times7 & 3\times6+4\times8 \end{bmatrix} = \begin{bmatrix} 19 & 22 \\ 43 & 50 \end{bmatrix}. \tag{2.4}$$

It is easily seen that $\mathbf{AB}$ is of order $m \times p$ when $\mathbf{A}$ is $m \times n$ and $\mathbf{B}$ is $n \times p$. $\mathbf{BA}$ does not exist unless $m = p$, in which case it is of order $n \times n$. This order is in general different from that of $\mathbf{AB}$, hence the two product matrices need not be the same even if both exist. When $m = n = p$ the two matrices $\mathbf{A}$ and $\mathbf{B}$ are square and of the same order and this holds also for their products $\mathbf{AB}$ and $\mathbf{BA}$. But even then these products need not be the same:

$$\begin{bmatrix} 5 & 6 \\ 7 & 8 \end{bmatrix} \begin{bmatrix} 1 & 2 \\ 3 & 4 \end{bmatrix} = \begin{bmatrix} 23 & 34 \\ 31 & 46 \end{bmatrix},$$

which is to be compared with (2.4).

Consider again the product $\mathbf{C} = \mathbf{AB}$ and suppose that we are interested in the transpose of that product, $\mathbf{C}' = (\mathbf{AB})'$. It follows from (2.3) that the $(i, j)^{\text{th}}$ element of that matrix is

$$c_{ji} = \sum_{h} a_{jh} b_{hi} = \sum_{h} b_{hi} a_{jh}.$$

But the sum behind the second equation sign can be obtained from the right-hand side of (2.3) by replacing a_{ih} by b_{hi} and b_{hj} by a_{jh}; in other words, by interchanging $\mathbf{A}$ and $\mathbf{B}$ and taking their transposes. Hence:

$$(\mathbf{AB})' = \mathbf{B}'\mathbf{A}', \tag{2.5}$$

and, more generally: $(\mathbf{ABC})' = \mathbf{C}'\mathbf{B}'\mathbf{A}'$, etc. In words: the transpose of a product is equal to the product of the transposes but in reverse order.

An important special case of matrix multiplication is illustrated by the following example:

$$\begin{bmatrix} 5 & -7 & 1 \\ 4 & 8 & 0 \end{bmatrix} \begin{bmatrix} 1 & 0 & 0 \\ 0 & 1 & 0 \\ 0 & 0 & 1 \end{bmatrix} = \begin{bmatrix} 5 & -7 & 1 \\ 4 & 8 & 0 \end{bmatrix}.$$

The product is the same as the premultiplying matrix. This can be written in the form $\mathbf{AI} = \mathbf{A}$ and $\mathbf{I}$ is known as the unit matrix: units on the diagonal (from upper left to lower right), zeros elsewhere. The unit matrix is always square but otherwise it may be of any order $n \times n$. It can be easily verified that $\mathbf{IA} = \mathbf{A}$ also holds but in that case the number of rows and columns of $\mathbf{I}$ should be equal to the number of rows of $\mathbf{A}$. The unit matrix is a special case of a so-called diagonal matrix, which is square and has zero off-diagonal elements. A diagonal matrix is always symmetric. If a diagonal matrix has equal elements on the diagonal, it is called a scalar matrix; it is then of the form $c\mathbf{I}$ where c is a scalar.

We can use these results to write a system of linear equations in matrix notation. Consider the following set of n equations in n variables:

$$\begin{aligned} a_{11}z_1 + a_{12}z_2 + \ldots + a_{1n}z_n &= h_1 \\ a_{21}z_1 + a_{22}z_2 + \ldots + a_{2n}z_n &= h_2 \\ &\vdots \\ a_{n1}z_1 + a_{n2}z_2 + \ldots + a_{nn}z_n &= h_n. \end{aligned} \tag{2.6}$$

A more compact notation is:

$$\sum_{j=1}^{n} a_{ij}z_j = h_i \qquad \text{for } i = 1, \ldots, n. \tag{2.7}$$

A still more compact notation can be found as soon as we realize that the right-hand sides of the system (2.6) are the elements of a column vector $\mathbf{h}$. In the same way the left-hand sides are the elements of the product $\mathbf{Az}$ where $\mathbf{A} = [a_{ij}]$ and $\mathbf{z}$ is the n-element column vector $[z_i]$; this is easily seen if we compare the left-hand side of (2.7) with (2.3), from which it follows immediately that this left-hand side is the ith element of the column $\mathbf{Az}$. Now (2.6) specifies that the corresponding elements of the vectors $\mathbf{Az}$ and $\mathbf{h}$ are pairwise equal, hence (2.6) can be written in the following simple form:

$$\mathbf{Az} = \mathbf{h}. \tag{2.8}$$

1.2.3. Inversion; The Rank of a Matrix

The question arises whether we can use (2.8) to obtain an explicit solution for the elements of **z**. The answer is affirmative provided that **A** is square [which is true for (2.6), its order being $n \times n$] and provided that one additional condition is fulfilled (to be described in the next paragraph). The procedure can be explained conveniently with the following numerical example:

$$\begin{bmatrix} 1 & 2 \\ 2 & 5 \end{bmatrix} \begin{bmatrix} 5 & -2 \\ -2 & 1 \end{bmatrix} = \begin{bmatrix} 1 & 0 \\ 0 & 1 \end{bmatrix}. \tag{2.9}$$

Suppose that $n = 2$ in (2.6) and let the matrix **A** be the second matrix on the left in (2.9). Then (2.9) specifies that if we premultiply **A** by the first matrix on the left—call it **B**—we obtain the unit matrix: $\mathbf{BA} = \mathbf{I}$. If we apply this to (2.8) we obtain $\mathbf{BAz} = \mathbf{Bh}$ or $\mathbf{Iz} = \mathbf{Bh}$ or $\mathbf{z} = \mathbf{Bh}$, which is indeed an explicit solution for **z**.

Evidently, the problem is to find for any given square matrix **A** a matrix **B** such that $\mathbf{BA} = \mathbf{I}$. This **B** is known as the inverse of **A**, written $\mathbf{A}^{-1}$, and it is of the following form:

$$\mathbf{A}^{-1} = \frac{1}{|\mathbf{A}|} \begin{bmatrix} |\mathbf{A}_{11}| & |\mathbf{A}_{21}| & \cdots & |\mathbf{A}_{n1}| \\ |\mathbf{A}_{12}| & |\mathbf{A}_{22}| & \cdots & |\mathbf{A}_{n2}| \\ \vdots & \vdots & & \vdots \\ |\mathbf{A}_{1n}| & |\mathbf{A}_{2n}| & \cdots & |\mathbf{A}_{nn}| \end{bmatrix}, \tag{2.10}$$

where $|\mathbf{A}|$ is the determinant value of **A** and $|\mathbf{A}_{ij}|$ is the cofactor of its $(i, j)^{\text{th}}$ element.[1] In other words, we transpose the matrix **A**, so that $[a_{ij}]$ becomes $[a_{ji}]$, then we replace elements by cofactors, so that $[a_{ji}]$ becomes $[|\mathbf{A}_{ji}|]$, and finally we divide by the determinant of **A**:

$$\mathbf{A}^{-1} = \left[\frac{|\mathbf{A}_{ji}|}{|\mathbf{A}|}\right]. \tag{2.11}$$

This procedure is of course possible only if **A** has a nonzero determinant value, which is the condition alluded to in the preceding paragraph. To verify that $\mathbf{A}^{-1}$ does satisfy the condition $\mathbf{A}^{-1}\mathbf{A} = \mathbf{I}$ we consider the $(i, j)^{\text{th}}$ element of $\mathbf{A}^{-1}\mathbf{A}$:

$$\frac{1}{|\mathbf{A}|} \sum_k |\mathbf{A}_{ki}| a_{kj}.$$

---

[1] The minor of the $(i, j)^{\text{th}}$ element is the determinant value after the ith row and the jth column are deleted. The cofactor of that element is equal to the corresponding minor if $i+j$ is even, it is equal to minus the minor if $i+j$ is odd.

Using the wellknown expansion of a determinant according to own and alien cofactors, we find that the sum over k of $|\mathbf{A}_{ki}|a_{kj}$ is equal to $|\mathbf{A}|$ if $i = j$ and to 0 if $i \neq j$. Hence the $(i, j)^{\text{th}}$ element of $\mathbf{A}^{-1}\mathbf{A}$ is 1 if $i = j$ and 0 if $i \neq j$, in other words $\mathbf{A}^{-1}\mathbf{A} = \mathbf{I}$. It is also easily verified that $\mathbf{A}\mathbf{A}^{-1} = \mathbf{I}$; that the inverse of a unit matrix is the unit matrix of the same order; that the inverse of a symmetric matrix (with nonvanishing determinant) is also symmetric; and that the inverse of a diagonal matrix is also diagonal and that the diagonal elements of the inverse are the reciprocals of the corresponding elements of the original matrix, provided of course that the latter elements are all different from zero. Another interesting property is

$$(\mathbf{AB})^{-1} = \mathbf{B}^{-1}\mathbf{A}^{-1}, \tag{2.12}$$

provided that both $\mathbf{A}$ and $\mathbf{B}$ have an inverse [compare also (2.5)]. Proof: $\mathbf{B}^{-1}\mathbf{A}^{-1}(\mathbf{AB}) = \mathbf{B}^{-1}\mathbf{IB} = \mathbf{B}^{-1}\mathbf{B} = \mathbf{I}$.

An $n \times n$ matrix $\mathbf{A}$ does not have an inverse if its determinant $|\mathbf{A}|$ vanishes; it is then said to be singular, the word nonsingular being used for square matrices whose determinant differs from zero. If an $n \times n$ matrix has a zero determinant we can always find a lower-order determinant of order $r \times r$ whose value differs from zero (except when it is a zero matrix). For example, the matrix

$$\begin{bmatrix} 2 & 0 \\ 0 & 0 \end{bmatrix} \tag{2.13}$$

has a zero determinant value, but the leading 1×1 determinant is 2 and hence different from zero. More generally, consider an arbitrary $m \times n$ matrix $\mathbf{A}$, not necessarily square; then the rank of $\mathbf{A}$ is defined as the largest number r such that an $r \times r$ subdeterminant of $\mathbf{A}$ differs from zero.[1] We have $r = n$ when $\mathbf{A}$ is a nonsingular $n \times n$ matrix; we have $r = 1$ for the 2×2 matrix (2.13); and when $\mathbf{A}$ is of order $m \times n$, then r is at most equal to the smaller of m and n as is easily verified.[2] An $m \times n$ matrix is said to be of full rank when r is equal to the smaller of m and n. Finally, it can be shown that the rank of a product matrix $\mathbf{AB}$ is at most equal to the smaller of the ranks of the constituent matrices $\mathbf{A}$ and $\mathbf{B}$.

---

[1] An $r \times r$ subdeterminant of an $m \times n$ matrix $\mathbf{A}$ is obtained by striking $m-r$ rows and $n-r$ columns of $\mathbf{A}$ and computing the determinant value of the resulting submatrix of $\mathbf{A}$. The subject of submatrices and operations on these is considered in more detail in 1.2.5 below.

[2] A zero matrix has no nonvanishing subdeterminants; its rank is defined to be zero.

1.2.4. Quadratic Forms; Definite and Semi-Definite Matrices

When we have a vector $\mathbf{z}$ of certain variables, a homogeneous linear function of these variables can be written in the form $\mathbf{a}'\mathbf{z} = \sum a_i z_i$ where $\mathbf{a} = [a_i]$ is the column vector of coefficients of this linear function. A homogeneous quadratic function of the same variables takes the form:

$$(2.14) \qquad \sum_i \sum_j a_{ij} z_i z_j = [z_1 \ldots z_n] \begin{bmatrix} \sum_j a_{1j} z_j \\ \vdots \\ \sum_j a_{nj} z_j \end{bmatrix}$$

$$= [z_1 \ldots z_n] \begin{bmatrix} a_{11} & \ldots & a_{1n} \\ \vdots & & \vdots \\ a_{n1} & \ldots & a_{nn} \end{bmatrix} \begin{bmatrix} z_1 \\ \vdots \\ z_n \end{bmatrix} = \mathbf{z}'\mathbf{A}\mathbf{z}.$$

A quadratic function $\mathbf{z}'\mathbf{A}\mathbf{z}$ is known as a quadratic form with $\mathbf{A}$ as matrix and $\mathbf{z}$ as vector. It can be assumed without loss of generality that the matrix of any quadratic form is symmetric; for the product $z_i z_j (i \neq j)$ is multiplied by $a_{ij} + a_{ji}$ in the quadratic form (2.14) and if a_{ij} and a_{ji} differ from each other, we can replace each of them by the common value $\frac{1}{2}(a_{ij} + a_{ji})$ without affecting the value of the quadratic form. By so doing we make the matrix of a quadratic form unique.

Sometimes we have a matrix $\mathbf{A}$ such that any quadratic form $\mathbf{z}'\mathbf{A}\mathbf{z}$ is positive for whatever vector $\mathbf{z}$, provided only that $\mathbf{z}$ is not a zero vector. An example is the unit matrix. We have $\mathbf{z}'\mathbf{I}\mathbf{z} = \mathbf{z}'\mathbf{z} = \sum z_i^2$, which means that this quadratic form is simply the sum of squares of the $\mathbf{z}$-elements and hence positive unless all these elements are zero. The following example is also instructive:

$$(2.15) \qquad \mathbf{z}'\mathbf{A}\mathbf{z} = [z_1 \quad z_2] \begin{bmatrix} 1 & \rho \\ \rho & 1 \end{bmatrix} \begin{bmatrix} z_1 \\ z_2 \end{bmatrix} = z_1^2 + z_2^2 + 2\rho z_1 z_2 .$$

It is easily verified that this quadratic form is always positive for any $\mathbf{z} \neq \mathbf{0}$ (as in the unit matrix example), provided that $-1 < \rho < 1$. The matrix of the quadratic form is then said to be positive definite. When $\rho = -1$ or 1 the quadratic form is either zero or positive, which is expressed by saying that the matrix is then positive semi-definite. For example, when $\rho = 1$ we have $\mathbf{z}'\mathbf{A}\mathbf{z} = 0$ for any $\mathbf{z}$ which satisfies $z_1 + z_2 = 0$ but $\mathbf{z}'\mathbf{A}\mathbf{z} > 0$ for any $\mathbf{z}$ which does not satisfy this condition. When $\rho > 1$ or < -1 the quadratic form may be positive, zero or negative and the matrix is then said to be indefinite. By replacing the units on the diagonal of $\mathbf{A}$ in (2.15) by -1 we obtain examples of negative (semi) definiteness. The quadratic form is then $-z_1^2-z_2^2+2\rho z_1 z_2$, which is always negative for any $\mathbf{z} \neq \mathbf{0}$ when $-1 < \rho < 1$ (negative definiteness) and either negative or zero for any $\mathbf{z}$ when $\rho = -1$ or 1 (negative semi-definiteness). It is easily seen that a diagonal matrix is positive definite (negative definite) when all its diagonal elements are positive (negative); that it is positive semi-definite (negative semi-definite) when some of its diagonal elements are zero and all others positive (negative); and that it is indefinite when some elements are positive and some negative. Note that the diagonal elements of a positive definite matrix are always positive. This is seen by taking a vector $\mathbf{z}$ of which one element is 1 and all others zero. Furthermore, when $\mathbf{A}$ is singular it is never definite and hence either positive or negative semi-definite or indefinite. The reason is that when $\mathbf{A}$ has a zero determinant value, one of its columns must be zero or such a column can be expressed as a linear function of other columns. Hence $\mathbf{Az} = \mathbf{0}$ for some $\mathbf{z} \neq \mathbf{0}$; which, on premultiplication by $\mathbf{z}'$, means $\mathbf{z}'\mathbf{Az} = 0$ for some $\mathbf{z} \neq \mathbf{0}$. The possibility of a definite $\mathbf{A}$ is then excluded. Therefore, if $\mathbf{A}$ is positive definite, $\mathbf{A}^{-1}$ exists and we have for all $\mathbf{z} \neq \mathbf{0}$:

$$0 < (\mathbf{A}^{-1}\mathbf{z})'\mathbf{A}(\mathbf{A}^{-1}\mathbf{z}) = \mathbf{z}'\mathbf{A}^{-1}\mathbf{A}\mathbf{A}^{-1}\mathbf{z} = \mathbf{z}'\mathbf{A}^{-1}\mathbf{z}, \quad (\mathbf{A} \text{ symmetric})$$

which means that if $\mathbf{A}$ is positive definite, so is $\mathbf{A}^{-1}$. A similar result holds for negative definiteness.

1.2.5. Partitioned Matrices

In this book we shall deal rather frequently with partitioned matrices. An example is

$$\left[\begin{array}{cc|ccc} 7 & 2 & 0 & 5 & -8 \\ -8 & 4 & -3 & 9 & 4 \\ 0 & 1 & 4 & 12 & -10 \\ \hline 3 & 0 & 6 & 7 & -2 \\ 0 & 5 & -2 & 1 & 0 \end{array}\right] = \begin{bmatrix} \mathbf{A}_1 & \mathbf{A}_2 \\ \mathbf{A}_3 & \mathbf{A}_4 \end{bmatrix}.$$

This matrix is of order 5×5 and it is partitioned into four submatrices: $\mathbf{A}_1$ which is of order 3×2, $\mathbf{A}_2$ which is of order 3×3, and $\mathbf{A}_3$ and $\mathbf{A}_4$ which are of order 2×2 and 2×3 respectively. It is not difficult to apply the ordinary rules of matrix algebra to partitioned matrices, but one should be careful with respect to the numbers of rows and columns.

For example:

$$\left[\begin{array}{cc:c} 3 & 4 & -2 \\ 2 & 0 & 8 \\ \hdashline 7 & 3 & -1 \end{array}\right] + \left[\begin{array}{cc:c} 4 & 2 & 2 \\ 7 & 8 & 1 \\ \hdashline 1 & 0 & 1 \end{array}\right] = \left[\begin{array}{cc:c} 7 & 6 & 0 \\ 9 & 8 & 9 \\ \hdashline 8 & 3 & 0 \end{array}\right],$$

more generally:

$$\begin{bmatrix} \mathbf{A}_1 & \mathbf{A}_2 \\ \mathbf{A}_3 & \mathbf{A}_4 \end{bmatrix} + \begin{bmatrix} \mathbf{B}_1 & \mathbf{B}_2 \\ \mathbf{B}_3 & \mathbf{B}_4 \end{bmatrix} = \begin{bmatrix} \mathbf{A}_1+\mathbf{B}_1 & \mathbf{A}_2+\mathbf{B}_2 \\ \mathbf{A}_3+\mathbf{B}_3 & \mathbf{A}_4+\mathbf{B}_4 \end{bmatrix},$$

provided that $\mathbf{A}_i$ and $\mathbf{B}_i$ are of the same order, $i = 1, \ldots, 4$. We have a similar result for multiplication:

$$\left[\begin{array}{cc:c} 3 & 1 & 4 \\ 2 & -1 & 5 \end{array}\right] \left[\begin{array}{cc} 1 & 2 \\ 6 & -5 \\ \hdashline 0 & -1 \end{array}\right]$$

$$= \begin{bmatrix} (3\times 1+1\times 6)+4\times 0 & (3\times 2-1\times 5)-4\times 1 \\ (2\times 1-1\times 6)+5\times 0 & (2\times 2+1\times 5)-5\times 1 \end{bmatrix}$$

$$= \begin{bmatrix} 3\times 1+1\times 6 & 3\times 2-1\times 5 \\ 2\times 1-1\times 6 & 2\times 2+1\times 5 \end{bmatrix} + \begin{bmatrix} 4\times 0 & -4\times 1 \\ 5\times 0 & -5\times 1 \end{bmatrix},$$

more generally:

$$[\mathbf{A}_1 \quad \mathbf{A}_2] \begin{bmatrix} \mathbf{B}_1 \\ \mathbf{B}_2 \end{bmatrix} = \mathbf{A}_1\mathbf{B}_1 + \mathbf{A}_2\mathbf{B}_2,$$

provided that the number of columns of $\mathbf{A}_i$ is equal to the number of rows of $\mathbf{B}_i$, $i = 1, 2$. For example, consider the quadratic form:

$$[\mathbf{x}' \quad \mathbf{y}'] \begin{bmatrix} \mathbf{A} & \mathbf{C} \\ \mathbf{C}' & \mathbf{B} \end{bmatrix} \begin{bmatrix} \mathbf{x} \\ \mathbf{y} \end{bmatrix} = [\mathbf{x}' \quad \mathbf{y}'] \begin{bmatrix} \mathbf{Ax}+\mathbf{Cy} \\ \mathbf{C}'\mathbf{x}+\mathbf{By} \end{bmatrix} = \mathbf{x}'\mathbf{Ax}+\mathbf{x}'\mathbf{Cy}+\mathbf{y}'\mathbf{C}'\mathbf{x}+\mathbf{y}'\mathbf{By}.$$

When $\mathbf{x}$ is an m-element and $\mathbf{y}$ an n-element column vector, $\mathbf{A}$, $\mathbf{B}$ and $\mathbf{C}$ should be of order $m \times m$, $n \times n$, and $m \times n$ respectively. This result shows that when the vector of a quadratic form is partitioned into two subvectors, the form can be written as the sum of two quadratic forms in these subvectors ($\mathbf{x}'\mathbf{Ax}$ and $\mathbf{y}'\mathbf{By}$) plus a so-called bilinear form in these vectors, $\mathbf{x}'\mathbf{Cy}+\mathbf{y}'\mathbf{C}'\mathbf{x}$. It will be noted that $\mathbf{x}'\mathbf{Cy}$ and $\mathbf{y}'\mathbf{C}'\mathbf{x}$ are equal because they are each other's transpose and both symmetric (since they are both scalars).

We conclude by considering the inverse of a symmetric matrix which is partitioned into four submatrices. Thus, our objective is to find the submatrices of $\mathbf{B}$ from

$$\text{(2.16)} \qquad \mathbf{BA} = \begin{bmatrix} \mathbf{B}_1 & \mathbf{B}_2 \\ \mathbf{B}_2' & \mathbf{B}_3 \end{bmatrix} \begin{bmatrix} \mathbf{A}_1 & \mathbf{A}_2 \\ \mathbf{A}_2' & \mathbf{A}_3 \end{bmatrix} = \begin{bmatrix} \mathbf{I} & \mathbf{0} \\ \mathbf{0} & \mathbf{I} \end{bmatrix},$$

where it will be supposed that both $\mathbf{A}$ and its submatrix $\mathbf{A}_3$ are non-singular. The orders of $\mathbf{A}_1$, $\mathbf{B}_1$ and the leading unit matrix on the right are $m \times m$; those of $\mathbf{A}_3$, $\mathbf{B}_3$ and the lower right-hand unit matrix $n \times n$; and those of $\mathbf{A}_2$, $\mathbf{B}_2$ and the upper right-hand zero matrix $m \times n$. It will be noted that the $\mathbf{B}$-partitioning of (2.16) uses the fact that the inverse of a symmetric matrix is also symmetric. Then, on multiplying according to the rules of partitioned matrices, we obtain:

$$\text{(2.17)} \qquad \mathbf{B}_1 \mathbf{A}_1 + \mathbf{B}_2 \mathbf{A}_2' = \mathbf{I} \qquad (m \times m)$$

$$\text{(2.18)} \qquad \mathbf{B}_1 \mathbf{A}_2 + \mathbf{B}_2 \mathbf{A}_3 = \mathbf{0} \qquad (m \times n)$$

$$\text{(2.19)} \qquad \mathbf{B}_2' \mathbf{A}_1 + \mathbf{B}_3 \mathbf{A}_2' = \mathbf{0} \qquad (n \times m)$$

$$\text{(2.20)} \qquad \mathbf{B}_2' \mathbf{A}_2 + \mathbf{B}_3 \mathbf{A}_3 = \mathbf{I} \qquad (n \times n).$$

On postmultiplying (2.18) by $\mathbf{A}_3^{-1}$ (which exists because $\mathbf{A}_3$ is non-singular) we obtain $\mathbf{B}_2 = -\mathbf{B}_1 \mathbf{A}_2 \mathbf{A}_3^{-1}$. We substitute this into (2.17) and obtain $\mathbf{B}_1(\mathbf{A}_1 - \mathbf{A}_2 \mathbf{A}_3^{-1} \mathbf{A}_2') = \mathbf{I}$ and hence

$$\text{(2.21)} \qquad \mathbf{B}_1 = (\mathbf{A}_1 - \mathbf{A}_2 \mathbf{A}_3^{-1} \mathbf{A}_2')^{-1}.$$

Using $\mathbf{B}_2 = -\mathbf{B}_1 \mathbf{A}_2 \mathbf{A}_3^{-1}$ we find

$$\text{(2.22)} \qquad \mathbf{B}_2 = -(\mathbf{A}_1 - \mathbf{A}_2 \mathbf{A}_3^{-1} \mathbf{A}_2')^{-1} \mathbf{A}_2 \mathbf{A}_3^{-1}.$$

On substituting this result into (2.20) we find:

$$\text{(2.23)} \qquad \begin{aligned} \mathbf{B}_3 &= [\mathbf{I} + \mathbf{A}_3^{-1} \mathbf{A}_2' (\mathbf{A}_1 - \mathbf{A}_2 \mathbf{A}_3^{-1} \mathbf{A}_2')^{-1} \mathbf{A}_2] \mathbf{A}_3^{-1} \\ &= \mathbf{A}_3^{-1} + \mathbf{A}_3^{-1} \mathbf{A}_2' (\mathbf{A}_1 - \mathbf{A}_2 \mathbf{A}_3^{-1} \mathbf{A}_2')^{-1} \mathbf{A}_2 \mathbf{A}_3^{-1}. \end{aligned}$$

1.3. SOME ELEMENTARY PROBABILITY THEORY

1.3.1. Univariate Distributions; Mean and Variance

A considerable part of this book is devoted to the problem of decision-making under uncertainty. The use of probabilities is very convenient to handle the uncertainty aspect and we shall therefore give an informal summary of probability theory and statistics as far as this is relevant for our purpose.

We say that X is a random variable if it is subject to a probability distribution. Such a distribution is usually either discrete or continuous.

We shall start with the former case, which implies that X takes a number of values (possibly an infinite number):

$$x_1 \quad x_2 \quad x_3 \quad \ldots$$

with certain probabilities:

$$p_1 \quad p_2 \quad p_3 \quad \ldots$$

For short:

$$P[X = x_i] = p_i \quad \text{for} \quad i = 1, 2, \ldots, \tag{3.1}$$

in words: the probability is p_i that the random variable X takes the value x_i. These probabilities are constrained to be nonnegative and to add up to 1:

$$p_i \geqq 0 \quad \text{for all } i; \quad \sum_i p_i = 1 \text{ (sum over all } i\text{)}. \tag{3.2}$$

There are several measures to describe the most important features of a distribution. One is the mean or expectation of X, which is the weighted average of all the values which it can take, weighted by the probabilities:

$$\mathscr{E}X = \sum p_i x_i. \tag{3.3}$$

The mean is a measure of central tendency of the distribution. Another important feature is the dispersion of the distribution, which is frequently measured by its variance. This is the weighted average of the squares of the values which the random variable can take with the understanding that these values are to be measured as deviations from the mean:

$$\operatorname{var} X = \sum p_i (x_i - \mathscr{E}X)^2. \tag{3.4}$$

The variance is obviously always positive except for the degenerate case of an X which takes only one value; in that case this single x_i-value must coincide with the mean $\mathscr{E}X$ and hence the variance is zero. It will be noted that the right-hand side of (3.4) can be written as

$$\sum p_i [x_i^2 - 2x_i \mathscr{E}X + (\mathscr{E}X)^2] = \sum p_i x_i^2 - 2\mathscr{E}X \sum p_i x_i + (\mathscr{E}X)^2 \sum p_i$$
$$= \sum p_i x_i^2 - (\mathscr{E}X)^2$$

and hence:

$$\operatorname{var} X = \mathscr{E}(X^2) - (\mathscr{E}X)^2, \tag{3.5}$$

where $\mathscr{E}(X^2) = \sum p_i x_i^2$ is known as the second moment (about zero) of X; it is the weighted average of the squares of the X-values. We should mention that the mean, variance and second moment need not be finite when X takes an infinite number of values. In this book the assumption of a finite variance will always be made; the mean and the second moment are then necessarily finite.

1.3.2. Bivariate Distributions; The Marginal Distribution and the Covariance

A pair of random variables (X, Y) is defined by its bivariate probability distribution:

$$P[X = x_i, Y = y_j] = p_{ij} \quad \text{for} \quad i, j = 1, 2, \ldots \tag{3.6}$$

This is the probability that both $X = x_i$ and $Y = y_j$. Again, the probabilities are nonnegative and add up to 1:

$$p_{ij} \geqq 0; \qquad \sum_i \sum_j p_{ij} = 1. \tag{3.7}$$

Suppose now that we are interested in the probability that $X = x_i$, the value taken by Y being considered irrelevant. This means that we want the probability of the event "$X = x_i$ and ($Y = y_1$ or $Y = y_2$ or $Y = y_3 \ldots$)," in other words:

$$\begin{aligned} P[X = x_i] &= P[(X = x_i, Y = y_1) \text{ or } (X = x_i, Y = y_2) \text{ or} \ldots] \\ &= P[X = x_i, Y = y_1] + P[X = x_i, Y = y_2] + \ldots = \sum_j p_{ij} = p_{i\cdot} \quad \text{say,} \end{aligned} \tag{3.8}$$

where use is made of the postulate that if A and B are events which cannot occur at the same time, the probability of "A or B" is equal to the probability of A plus the probability of B. The result (3.8) defines the so-called marginal distribution of X; this random variable takes the values $x_1, x_2, \ldots$ with probabilities $p_{1\cdot}, p_{2\cdot}, \ldots$. The mean and variance of X are defined as the mean and the variance of its marginal distribution:

$$\mathscr{E}X = \sum_i p_{i\cdot} x_i = \sum_i \sum_j p_{ij} x_i$$

$$\text{var } X = \sum_i p_{i\cdot}(x_i - \mathscr{E}X)^2 = \sum_i \sum_j p_{ij}(x_i - \mathscr{E}X)^2.$$

For Y we proceed in precisely the same fashion; its marginal distribution is such that it takes the values y_j with probabilities $p_{\cdot j}$, the latter being defined as the sum of all p_{ij} over i. The mean and variance of Y are:

$$\mathscr{E}Y = \sum_j p_{\cdot j} y_j = \sum_i \sum_j p_{ij} y_j$$

$$\text{var } Y = \sum_j p_{\cdot j}(y_j - \mathscr{E}Y)^2 = \sum_i \sum_j p_{ij}(y_j - \mathscr{E}Y)^2.$$

The mean and variance concepts are therefore straightforward extensions of the theory of one single random variable. A new concept is the covariance, which is the weighted average of the products of the values taken by X and Y (all measured as deviations from the respective means):

$$\text{cov}(X, Y) = \sum_i \sum_j p_{ij}(x_i - \mathscr{E}X)(y_j - \mathscr{E}Y). \tag{3.9}$$

The covariance plays a role in the analysis of linear combinations of random variables, say $\alpha X + \beta Y$ where α and β are fixed and nonstochastic (non-random) numbers. The mean of this combination is

$$\begin{aligned} \mathscr{E}(\alpha X + \beta Y) &= \sum_i \sum_j p_{ij}(\alpha x_i + \beta y_j) \\ &= \alpha \sum_i \sum_j p_{ij} x_i + \beta \sum_i \sum_j p_{ij} y_j = \alpha \mathscr{E}X + \beta \mathscr{E}Y, \end{aligned} \tag{3.10}$$

i.e., the mean is equal to the same linear combination of the separate means $\mathscr{E}X$ and $\mathscr{E}Y$. For the variance we find:

$$\begin{aligned} \text{var}(\alpha X + \beta Y) &= \sum_i \sum_j p_{ij}[\alpha x_i + \beta y_j - (\alpha \mathscr{E}X + \beta \mathscr{E}Y)]^2 \\ &= \sum_i \sum_j p_{ij}[\alpha^2(x_i - \mathscr{E}X)^2 + \beta^2(y_j - \mathscr{E}Y)^2 + 2\alpha\beta(x_i - \mathscr{E}X)(y_j - \mathscr{E}Y)] \\ &= \alpha^2 \text{ var } X + \beta^2 \text{ var } Y + 2\alpha\beta \text{ cov}(X, Y), \end{aligned} \tag{3.11}$$

i.e., the variance is equal to a linear combination of the two separate variances and the covariance, the weights of the former (α^2 and β^2) being nonnegative. Suppose now that we take α and β as the reciprocals of the square roots of var X and var Y respectively. Then we obtain from (3.11):

$$\text{var}\left(\frac{X}{(\text{var } X)^{\frac{1}{2}}} + \frac{Y}{(\text{var } Y)^{\frac{1}{2}}}\right) = 2\left(1 + \frac{\text{cov}(X, Y)}{(\text{var } X \text{ var } Y)^{\frac{1}{2}}}\right).$$

The left-hand side is nonnegative because it is a variance; hence the covariance should be at least equal to minus the geometric mean of var X and var Y. In the same way, if we take α equal to minus the reciprocal of the square root of var X (while β remains as before), we find that the covariance is at most plus the geometric mean. Hence:

$$-1 \leqq \frac{\text{cov}(X, Y)}{(\text{var } X \text{ var } Y)^{\frac{1}{2}}} \leqq 1.$$

This ratio is known as the correlation coefficient of X and Y (usually written as ρ with appropriate subscripts like ρ_{XY}) and is therefore at most 1 in absolute value. The limits are attained when the two random variables are linearly related (1 when the relationship is increasing, -1 when it is decreasing). Two random variables are said to be uncorrelated when their covariance vanishes. We also note:

$$\sum_i\sum_j p_{ij}(x_i-\mathscr{E}X)(y_j-\mathscr{E}Y) = \sum_i\sum_j p_{ij}x_iy_j-\mathscr{E}X\sum_i\sum_j p_{ij}y_j$$
$$-\mathscr{E}Y\sum_i\sum_j p_{ij}x_i+\mathscr{E}X\mathscr{E}Y\sum_i\sum_j p_{ij} = \sum_i\sum_j p_{ij}x_iy_j-\mathscr{E}X\mathscr{E}Y$$

and hence:

(3.12) $$\operatorname{cov}(X, Y) = \mathscr{E}(XY)-\mathscr{E}X\mathscr{E}Y,$$

where $\mathscr{E}(XY) = \sum\sum p_{ij}x_iy_j$ is called the cross-moment (of the second order) of X and Y. This result is to be compared with (3.5).

1.3.3. Multivariate Distributions; The Covariance Matrix

Triples of random variables like (X, Y, Z) can be handled by introducing probabilities of the type p_{ijk}. The further extension is therefore a matter of more indices and is left to the reader's imagination. In the general case we have an n-element column vector $\mathbf{x} = [X_h]$ of random variables, the expectation of which is defined as the vector of separate expectations:

(3.13) $$\mathscr{E}\mathbf{x} = \mathscr{E}\begin{bmatrix} X_1 \\ \vdots \\ X_n \end{bmatrix} = \begin{bmatrix} \mathscr{E}X_1 \\ \vdots \\ \mathscr{E}X_n \end{bmatrix}.$$

Consider then a linear combination of the $\mathbf{x}$-elements, $\mathbf{a}'\mathbf{x} = \sum a_h X_h$ where the weight vector $\mathbf{a} = [a_h]$ is supposed to consist of fixed and non-stochastic elements. Following the rule that the mean of a linear combination equals the same linear combination of the separate means [see (3.10)], we have

(3.14) $$\mathscr{E}(\mathbf{a}'\mathbf{x}) = \mathscr{E}\left(\sum a_h X_h\right) = \sum a_h \mathscr{E}X_h = \mathbf{a}'\mathscr{E}\mathbf{x}.$$

Let us write $\mathbf{V}$ for the matrix of all variances and covariances:

(3.15) $$\mathbf{V} = \begin{bmatrix} \operatorname{var} X_1 & \operatorname{cov}(X_1, X_2) & \dots & \operatorname{cov}(X_1, X_n) \\ \operatorname{cov}(X_2, X_1) & \operatorname{var} X_2 & \dots & \operatorname{cov}(X_2, X_n) \\ \vdots & \vdots & & \vdots \\ \operatorname{cov}(X_n, X_1) & \operatorname{cov}(X_n, X_2) & \dots & \operatorname{var} X_n \end{bmatrix}.$$

This matrix contains the variances in the diagonal and the covariances in the off-diagonal elements; it is symmetric because cov (X_1, X_2) = cov (X_2, X_1) and similarly for all other pairs of indices. It is of some interest to note that $\mathbf{V}$ can be expressed elegantly in terms of $\mathbf{x}$ and the expectation operator. Consider:

$$(\mathbf{x}-\mathscr{E}\mathbf{x})(\mathbf{x}-\mathscr{E}\mathbf{x})' = \begin{bmatrix} X_1-\mathscr{E}X_1 \\ X_2-\mathscr{E}X_2 \\ \vdots \\ X_n-\mathscr{E}X_n \end{bmatrix} [X_1-\mathscr{E}X_1 \quad X_2-\mathscr{E}X_2 \dots X_n-\mathscr{E}X_n]$$

$$\begin{bmatrix} (X_1-\mathscr{E}X_1)^2 & (X_1-\mathscr{E}X_1)(X_2-\mathscr{E}X_2) \dots & (X_1-\mathscr{E}X_1)(X_n-\mathscr{E}X_n) \\ (X_2-\mathscr{E}X_2)(X_1-\mathscr{E}X_1) & (X_2-\mathscr{E}X_2)^2 \quad \dots & (X_2-\mathscr{E}X_2)(X_n-\mathscr{E}X_n) \\ \vdots & \vdots & \vdots \\ (X_n-\mathscr{E}X_n)(X_1-\mathscr{E}X_1) & (X_n-\mathscr{E}X_n)(X_2-\mathscr{E}X_2) \dots & (X_n-\mathscr{E}X_n)^2 \end{bmatrix}.$$

Then take the expectation of this matrix, i.e., consider the $n \times n$ matrix of the expectations of the separate elements. For the leading element we obtain the mean of $(X_1-\mathscr{E}X_1)^2$, which is nothing else than the variance of X_1 in view of (3.4). For the second element in the first row we obtain the mean of $(X_1-\mathscr{E}X_1)(X_2-\mathscr{E}X_2)$, which is the covariance of X_1 and X_2, see (3.9). And so on. Hence:

$$\mathbf{V} = \mathscr{E}[(\mathbf{x}-\mathscr{E}\mathbf{x})(\mathbf{x}-\mathscr{E}\mathbf{x})']. \tag{3.16}$$

This result can be used to express the variance of a linear combination $\mathbf{a}'\mathbf{x}$ in terms of the covariance matrix $\mathbf{V}$ of $\mathbf{x}$. This variance is by definition the mean of the square of $\mathbf{a}'\mathbf{x}$ after subtraction of its own mean, $\mathbf{a}'\mathscr{E}\mathbf{x}$, see (3.14). Hence we should take the square of $\mathbf{a}'\mathbf{x}-\mathbf{a}'\mathscr{E}\mathbf{x} = \mathbf{a}'(\mathbf{x}-\mathscr{E}\mathbf{x})$ and take the mean. This square is

$$[\mathbf{a}'(\mathbf{x}-\mathscr{E}\mathbf{x})]^2 = \{\sum a_h(X_h-\mathscr{E}X_h)\}^2 = \sum\sum a_h a_k(X_h-\mathscr{E}X_h)(X_k-\mathscr{E}X_k),$$

which is a linear function of the variables $(X_h-\mathscr{E}X_h)(X_k-\mathscr{E}X_k)$ with weights $a_h a_k$. Taking the mean we find:

$$\text{var}\,(\mathbf{a}'\mathbf{x}) = \sum_h \sum_k a_h a_k \mathscr{E}[(X_h-\mathscr{E}X_h)(X_k-\mathscr{E}X_k)] = \mathbf{a}'\mathbf{V}\mathbf{a}, \tag{3.17}$$

i.e., the variance of a linear combination $\mathbf{a}'\mathbf{x}$ is a quadratic form with $\mathbf{V}$ as matrix and $\mathbf{a}$ as vector. In the special case when all the $\mathbf{x}$-elements are uncorrelated, $\mathbf{V}$ is diagonal and the variance of $\mathbf{a}'\mathbf{x}$ is then a weighted sum of squares of the form $\sum a_h^2 \text{ var } X_h$. We also note that the covariance matrix $\mathbf{V}$ is positive definite or semi-definite; this follows from $\mathbf{a}'\mathbf{V}\mathbf{a}$ = var $(\mathbf{a}'\mathbf{x}) \geqq 0$ for any vector $\mathbf{a}$.

1.3.4. *Conditional Distributions and Stochastic Independence*

We return to the random pair (X, Y) of 1.3.2 and ask: what is the probability that $X = x_i$ when it is known that $Y = y_j$? This is a so-called conditional probability, written $P[X = x_i | Y = y_j]$, which is defined implicitly as follows:

$$P[X = x_i, Y = y_j] = P[X = x_i | Y = y_j] P[Y = y_j],$$

in words: the probability that both $X = x_i$ and $Y = y_j$ is equal to the conditional probability that $X = x_i$ under the condition $Y = y_j$, multiplied by the probability of the condition. Assuming that the last probability differs from zero, we obtain:

$$P[X = x_i | Y = y_j] = \frac{P[X = x_i, Y = y_j]}{P[Y = y_j]} = \frac{p_{ij}}{p_{\cdot j}}. \tag{3.18}$$

Hence, under the condition $Y = y_j$ the random variable X takes the values $x_1, x_2, \ldots$ with probabilities $p_{1j}/p_{\cdot j}, p_{2j}/p_{\cdot j}, \ldots$ This is the conditional distribution of X given $Y = y_j$, which has a mean:

$$\mathscr{E}(X | Y = y_j) = \frac{1}{p_{\cdot j}} \sum_i p_{ij} x_i,$$

and also a variance, etc. In the same way we define the conditional probability of $Y = y_j$ given $X = x_i$ as

$$P[Y = y_j | X = x_i] = \frac{P[X = x_i, Y = y_j]}{P[X = x_i]} = \frac{p_{ij}}{p_{i\cdot}}. \tag{3.19}$$

Such conditional distributions enable us to use the knowledge that a certain condition holds when formulating probability statements about the random variable in which we are interested. Thus, when we know nothing about Y, the random variable X is considered to follow its marginal distribution, i.e., it takes the values $x_1, x_2, \ldots$ with the probabilities $p_{1\cdot}, p_{2\cdot}, \ldots$; but when we know that $Y = y_j$ holds, it takes these values with the probabilities $p_{1j}/p_{\cdot j}, p_{2j}/p_{\cdot j}, \ldots$, which are in general different. However, suppose now that the following is true:

$$p_{ij} = p_{i\cdot} p_{\cdot j} \text{ for all pairs } (i, j). \tag{3.20}$$

In that case $p_{ij}/p_{\cdot j} = p_{i\cdot}$, so that we conclude from (3.18) and (3.8) that the conditional probability of $X = x_i$ given $Y = y_j$ is equal to the (unconditional) probability of $X = x_i$, for all pairs (i, j). In the same way we have $p_{ij}/p_{i\cdot} = p_{\cdot j}$ from (3.20), so that the conditional probability of $Y = y_j$ given $X = x_i$ is equal to the unconditional probability of $Y = y_j$. If (3.20) is true, we say that X and Y are (stochastically) independent. In that case any knowledge about Y (like $Y = y_j$) is worthless for the formulation of probability statements about X and vice versa.

When X and Y are independent, their covariance vanishes and they are therefore uncorrelated. For we have from (3.9) and (3.20):

$$\sum_i \sum_j p_{ij}(x_i - \mathscr{E}X)(y_j - \mathscr{E}Y) = \sum_i p_{i\cdot}(x_i - \mathscr{E}X) \sum_j p_{\cdot j}(y_j - \mathscr{E}Y)$$

$$= (\mathscr{E}X - \mathscr{E}X)(\mathscr{E}Y - \mathscr{E}Y) = 0.$$

The converse is not true in general: when X and Y are uncorrelated they need not be independent.

The concept of stochastic independence is extended to three and more random variables in a straightforward manner. When we have a random triple (X, Y, Z) taking values (x_i, y_j, z_k), we call these variables independent as soon as the probability that (X, Y, Z) takes the value (x_i, y_j, z_k) is equal to the product of the probabilities of the three separate events: $X = x_i$, $Y = y_j$, $Z = z_k$, for all triples (i, j, k). When all elements of a random vector $\mathbf{x}$ are independent, they are also uncorrelated; hence the covariance matrix of $\mathbf{x}$ is then diagonal.

1.3.5. On Statistical Estimation

We proceed to consider an application of probability theory and return to the distribution (3.1). Suppose we draw at random n elements from the population corresponding to this distribution, which means that we have n independent random variables $X_1, \ldots, X_n$, all of which follow the same distribution (3.1). Suppose also that we wish to use the outcomes of this sample to draw inferences about the mean (3.3) of the distribution, which is regarded as unknown; we shall write μ for it in what follows. An obvious procedure is to use the sample mean, $(1/n)\sum X_i = m$ say, to approximate μ. Such a function of random variables which serves to approximate an unkown parameter is called an estimator of that parameter.[1] Since it is a function of random variables it is random itself and therefore subject to a distribution, the so-called sampling distribution. The quality of the estimator as an approximation to the

---

[1] The word estimate is normally used for the numerical value which the estimator takes for a sample of which the components are specified numerically.

unknown parameter is determined by the degree to which the sampling distribution is concentrated around that parameter.

Considering our example, we note that

$$\mathscr{E}m = \mathscr{E}[(1/n)\sum X_i] = (1/n)\sum \mathscr{E}X_i = \mu, \tag{3.21}$$

where use is made of the fact that (i) the expectation of a linear combination of random variables is equal to the same linear combination of the individual expectations and (ii) that the latter expectations are all equal to μ, since all X_i are assumed to follow the same distribution (3.1). Equation (3.21) states that the expectation of the estimator is equal to the parameter which it serves to estimate, which is expressed by saying that the estimator is unbiased. We can also write (3.21) in the form $\mathscr{E}(m-\mu) = 0$, which states that the sampling error is zero on the average.

When the sampling error has zero mean we know that there is no systematic error, but this does not prevent the errors from being large in an appreciable number of cases. To see to what extent this is the case we consider the sampling variance, which is the variance of the sampling distribution:

$$\begin{aligned}\text{var } m &= \mathscr{E}(m-\mu)^2 = \mathscr{E}\left\{\frac{1}{n}\sum X_i - \mu\right\}^2 = \frac{1}{n^2}\mathscr{E}\{\sum (X_i-\mu)\}^2 \\ &= \frac{1}{n^2}\sum_i\sum_j \mathscr{E}[(X_i-\mu)(X_j-\mu)] = \frac{1}{n^2}\sum_i \mathscr{E}(X_i-\mu)^2 = \frac{\sigma^2}{n},\end{aligned} \tag{3.22}$$

where use is made of the fact that the X's are independent and hence have zero covariances, while σ^2 stands for the common variance of all X's. The result (3.22) specifies that the sampling variance of the sample mean as an estimator of the population mean is equal to the population variance (σ^2) divided by the sample size (n). Hence the quality of m as an estimator of μ when measured by the sampling variance turns out to be better when the population variance is smaller and when the sample size is larger.

These results can be extended in a straightforward manner to the case in which one desires to estimate a vector $\boldsymbol{\xi}$ of unknown parameters from a random sample. The estimator is then also a vector, $\mathbf{x}$ say, which is said to be unbiased when $\mathscr{E}\mathbf{x} = \boldsymbol{\xi}$, and there is then a matrix of sampling variances and covariances. An extension in another direction is that of conditional unbiased estimation; the parameter estimated is then equal to the mean of the estimator with respect to a particular conditional distribution.

1.3.6. On Utility and Expected Utility

The expected-utility hypothesis can be regarded as another application of probability theory. This subject can be approached conveniently by returning to the example of 1.1.2, in which a decision maker had to evaluate the merits of a number of alternatives, $A, B, C, \ldots$ Two assumptions are then usually made, as was already mentioned in 1.1.2: one dealing with comparability (the decision maker prefers either A to B or B to A or he is indifferent between them) and the other with transitivity (if A is preferred to B and B to C, then A is preferred to C as well, and similarly for indifference). When these two conditions are satisfied the decision maker is able to rank these alternatives according to decreasing preference; and this automatically[1] implies that a preference function w exists such that $w(A) > w(B)$ when A is preferred to B and $w(A) = w(B)$ when there is indifference. The decision maker's objective may then be described by saying that he maximizes w over the set of alternatives available to him.

The situation becomes more complicated as soon as there is uncertainty, for the decision maker has then to face alternatives of the type $(A, B; p, 1-p)$ where p is a number between 0 and 1; that is, "A with probability p and B with the remaining probability $1-p$." To take a very simple example, let A be the prospect of getting a car and B the prospect of a grant of \$ 1000. Then $(A, B; p, 1-p)$ stands for an uncertain prospect; if the decision maker decides on it he cannot be sure to get the car nor to get \$ 1000. He can only be sure to receive either the car or \$ 1000 and he knows that the probability of the former alternative is p and that of the latter $1-p$.

Assuming that the decision maker's uncertainty is of this probabilistic type, our problem is now how to rank probability distributions of outcomes such as $Z = (A_1, A_2, \ldots; p_1, p_2, \ldots)$. [Thus, if the decision maker decides on Z, he knows that the probability is p_i that A_i will be realized $(i = 1, 2, \ldots; p_i \geqq 0, \sum p_i = 1)$.] This problem was considered by VON NEUMANN and MORGENSTERN, who formulated an axiomatic approach, which will be outlined here in the form given by MARSCHAK.[2]

[1] For more detailed considerations, see G. DEBREU, "Representation of a Preference Ordering by a Numerical Function," Chapter XI of *Decision Processes*, edited by R. M. Thrall, C. H. Coombs and R. L. Davis (New York–London, 1954).

[2] J. VON NEUMANN and O. MORGENSTERN, *Theory of Games and Economic Behavior*, Third Edition (Princeton, 1953), pp. 617–632; J. MARSCHAK, "Rational Behavior, Uncertain Prospects, and Measurable Utility," *Econometrica*, Vol. 18 (1950), pp. 111–141. [Marschak's three alternative Postulates III (pp. 117–118) will not be discussed here.]

First, we assume comparability and transitivity of prospects, both sure and unsure. Thus, let Z_1 and Z_2 be $(A_1, A_2, \ldots; p_1, p_2, \ldots)$ and $(B_1, B_2, \ldots; q_1, q_2, \ldots)$ respectively, where the p's and q's are all nonnegative and add up to 1. Then the decision maker should be able to state whether he prefers Z_1 to Z_2 or Z_2 to Z_1 or that he is indifferent; also, if there is a third prospect Z_3 (sure or unsure) such that Z_1 is preferred to Z_2 and Z_2 to Z_3, then he should prefer Z_1 to Z_3. In this way we ensure that the decision maker is able to rank probability distributions of outcomes according to decreasing preference.

But it is worthwhile not to stop here, because it appears that when two other, equally plausible, postulates are introduced, a very convenient result emerges. We consider a "mixture" of two or more Z's, e.g. $Z = (Z_1, Z_2; p, 1-p)$ where $Z_i = (A_i, B_i; q_i, 1-q_i)$ for $i = 1, 2$. For example, let Z_1 be the prospect of having \$ 1000 with probability $q_1 = \frac{1}{2}$ and a car with probability $1-q_1 = \frac{1}{2}$; let Z_2 be the prospect of having a house (with certainty, $q_2 = 1$); and let p be 0.7. Then Z is the prospect of having a house with probability 0.3, \$ 1000 with probability $0.7 \times \frac{1}{2} = 0.35$, and a car with probability $0.7 \times \frac{1}{2} = 0.35$. Hence there are three possible outcomes of Z and exactly one of these will be realized. Using the A_i, B_i, p, q_i-notation, we can write:

$$Z = [A_1, B_1, A_2, B_2; pq_1, p(1-q_1), (1-p)q_2, (1-p)(1-q_2)].$$

The sum of the four probabilities behind the semicolon is 1, which is as it should be.

Two assumptions with respect to such mixtures are made. Consider any two indifferent Z's, say Z_1 and Z_2, and an arbitrary third, Z_3. The first assumption is that any mixture of Z_1 and Z_3 should be indifferent to the same mixture of Z_2 and Z_3; i.e., $(Z_1, Z_3; p, 1-p)$ and $(Z_2, Z_3; p, 1-p)$ should be indifferent for any p between 0 and 1. An example: suppose a man is indifferent between a car (Z_1) and \$ 1000 (Z_2). Then the prospect of having a car with probability p and a house with probability $1-p$ is equivalent to the prospect of having \$ 1000 with the same probability p and that house with probability $1-p$, for whatever value of p and for whatever house (which may even be replaced by anything else including cars and \$ 1000 bills). The second assumption amounts to "continuity" of the preference ordering and can be explained as follows. Consider any triple of Z's such that Z_1 is preferred to Z_2 and Z_2 to Z_3; hence Z_2 is "between" Z_1 and Z_3 as far as the preference ordering is concerned. Now it seems intuitively obvious that $Z' = (Z_1, Z_3; p, 1-p)$

is also "in between" as long as $0 < p < 1$. The assumption made is related to this idea and implies that there exists a p such that the corresponding Z' is indifferent to Z_2.

To explain the consequences of these assumptions we go back to the end of the first paragraph, where it was stated that the decision maker's preferences can be represented by a function w and that he behaves as if he maximizes that function. This result was confined to decision-making under certainty, but when the three assumptions of the last three paragraphs are satisfied, it can be extended as follows: there exists a preference function w such that, if the decision maker has to decide about uncertain prospects, he behaves as if he maximizes the expectation of that function. Hence, if he faces two uncertain prospects, $(A_1, B_1; p, 1-p)$ and $(A_2, B_2; q, 1-q)$, he will choose the former if

$$pw(A_1)+(1-p)w(B_1) > qw(A_2)+(1-q)w(B_2)$$

and the latter if the reverse is true. Note that maximizing expected utility is in general not equivalent to maximizing the utility of the expected outcome of the uncertain prospect. For example, let A be a gain of 10 million dollars, B a loss of 2 million dollars, and C a gain of 1 million. The choice is between $(A, B; \frac{1}{2}, \frac{1}{2})$ and C. The expected gain of the unsure prospect is $\frac{1}{2}\times 10+\frac{1}{2}\times(-2) = 4$ millions, which is considerably larger than the sure C-gain. Hence maximizing the utility of the expected outcome would imply that C is rejected in favour of the A, B-gamble. But one would of course expect that most people would act differently; and indeed, maximizing expected utility does not at all imply that the gamble is chosen. We may, e.g., have $w(A) = 2$, $w(B) = -2$, $w(C) = 1$; then the expected utility of the gamble is 0 and hence $< w(C)$. This is a case of "risk aversion," which means that the expected utility of the gamble is smaller than the utility of the expected outcome of the gamble.

There is a considerable amount of freedom in the choice of a preference function which has to represent a given preference ordering, in particular when we consider only sure prospects. Then w may be replaced by any monotonically increasing function of itself and still represent the original preference ordering; examples are w^2 and $\log w$ (at least when $w > 0$). The reason is that such a transformation preserves the ranking of the alternatives according to decreasing preference. But the preference function to which the calculus of expectations is applicable is much more restricted. We may replace it by a linear function of itself and that is all; it is uniquely determined as soon as a zero and a unit of measurement are fixed. It will therefore be clear that if we introduce quadratic preference conditions (as will indeed be done), this is more restrictive with respect to unsure prospects than with respect to sure ones.

1.3.7. On Continuous Distributions

Up till now we confined ourselves to discrete distributions and hence to random variables which can take certain particular values only (although their number may be infinite). There are also random variables which can take any real value or possibly any real value in a finite interval. It will be sufficient for our purpose to give a very short sketch of continuous distribution theory.

The chance that a (continuously distributed) random variable X lies in the infinitesimal interval $(x, x+dx)$ is $f(x)dx$, where f is the probability density function. The density function is nonnegative for any values of its arguments and its integral from $-\infty$ to ∞ is 1:

$$f(x) \geqq 0, \qquad \int_{-\infty}^{\infty} f(x)dx = 1.$$

This is analogous to (3.2). In fact, the continuous analysis appears to be a straightforward extension of its discrete predecessor, the probabilities p_i being replaced by the density function (multiplied by the differential dx) and sums by integrals. Examples are the mean and the variance:

$$\mathscr{E}X = \int_{-\infty}^{\infty} xf(x)dx, \qquad \text{var } X = \int_{-\infty}^{\infty} (x-\mathscr{E}X)^2 f(x)dx.$$

For a pair of random variables (X, Y) we write $f(x, y)dx\,dy$ to indicate the probability that X lies in $(x, x+dx)$ and Y in $(y, y+dy)$, where $f(x, y)$ stands for the bivariate density function. This is also nonnegative and its double integral (from $-\infty$ to ∞) is 1. The marginal density functions are

$$f_1(x) = \int_{-\infty}^{\infty} f(x, y)dy \quad \text{and} \quad f_2(y) = \int_{-\infty}^{\infty} f(x, y)dx,$$

so that the mean of X is:

$$\mathscr{E}X = \int_{-\infty}^{\infty} xf_1(x)dx = \int_{-\infty}^{\infty}\int_{-\infty}^{\infty} xf(x, y)dxdy,$$

while $\mathscr{E}Y$, var X and var Y are defined similarly. The covariance is

$$\text{cov}(X, Y) = \int_{-\infty}^{\infty}\int_{-\infty}^{\infty} (x-\mathscr{E}X)(y-\mathscr{E}Y)f(x, y)dxdy.$$

All these definitions are straightforward extensions of those given in 1.3.2. For the expectation of a linear combination we have:

$$\mathscr{E}(\alpha X+\beta Y) = \int_{-\infty}^{\infty}\int_{-\infty}^{\infty}(\alpha x+\beta y)f(x, y)dxdy$$

$$= \alpha\int_{-\infty}^{\infty}\int_{-\infty}^{\infty}xf(x, y)dxdy+\beta\int_{-\infty}^{\infty}\int_{-\infty}^{\infty}yf(x, y)dxdy = \alpha\mathscr{E}X+\beta\mathscr{E}Y.$$

In fact, the calculus of expectations (including quadratic forms in covariance matrices) is completely applicable to random variables which are subject to a continuous distribution.[1] The most wellknown example of this category is the normal distribution, whose density function is

$$f(x) = \frac{1}{\sigma\sqrt{2\pi}}\exp\left[-\tfrac{1}{2}(x-\mu)^2/\sigma^2\right],$$

where $\exp[k]$ stands for e^k, μ for the mean, and σ^2 for the variance. The density function of an n-element vector $\mathbf{x}$ whose components are simultaneously normally distributed is

$$f(\mathbf{x}) = \frac{1}{|\mathbf{\Sigma}|^{\frac{1}{2}}(2\pi)^{\frac{1}{2}n}}\exp\left[-\tfrac{1}{2}(\mathbf{x}-\boldsymbol{\mu})'\mathbf{\Sigma}^{-1}(\mathbf{x}-\boldsymbol{\mu})\right], \tag{3.23}$$

where $\mathbf{\Sigma}$ is the covariance matrix, $|\mathbf{\Sigma}|$ its determinant value, and $\boldsymbol{\mu}$ the column vector of means. For $n = 1$, (3.23) reduces to the one-dimensional normal density function as is easily verified.

For a pair (X, Y) the conditional probability density function of X given $Y = y$ is defined as $f(x, y)/f_2(y)$ provided that $f_2(y) > 0$. X and Y are said to be independent if

$$f(x, y) \equiv f_1(x)f_2(y),$$

in which case the conditional density function just mentioned is equal to $f_1(x)$, i.e., to the marginal density function of X. A similar result holds when X and Y are interchanged. The definition of independence is generalized in an obvious manner when we have three or more random variables. As an illustration we consider the normal density function (3.23) for the case in which all components of $\mathbf{x}$ are uncorrelated. Then $\mathbf{\Sigma}$ is diagonal (with diagonal elements σ_i^2, say); $\mathbf{\Sigma}^{-1}$ is diagonal too (with diagonal

[1] For continuous distributions, too, the mean and variance may be infinite, but in this book we shall assume that they are finite.

elements $1/\sigma_i^2$) and $|\mathbf{\Sigma}|$ is the product $\sigma_1^2\sigma_2^2\ldots\sigma_n^2$. Hence:

$$f(\mathbf{x}) = \frac{1}{\prod_{i=1}^{n}(\sigma_i\sqrt{2\pi})}\exp\left[-\tfrac{1}{2}\sum_{i=1}^{n}(x_i-\mu_i)^2/\sigma_i^2\right]$$

$$= \prod_{i=1}^{n}\frac{1}{\sigma_i\sqrt{2\pi}}\exp\left[-\tfrac{1}{2}(x_i-\mu_i)^2/\sigma_i^2\right] = f_1(x_1)f_2(x_2)\ldots f_n(x_n),$$

where f_i is the one-dimensional normal density function with mean μ_i (the ith element of $\boldsymbol{\mu}$)and variance σ_i^2. The conclusion is that if we have a multivariate normal distribution and if the random variables are all uncorrelated, the joint density function is the product of all n one-dimensional marginal density functions; and hence normal random variables are independent as soon as they are uncorrelated. Note that this is a characteristic of the normal distribution; if random variables are not normal they may be uncorrelated without being independent.

1.4. SURVEY OF CONTENTS

1.4.1. An Overview of Chapters 2-7

In Chapter 2 we shall consider a decision maker who controls certain variables (instruments) and is interested in certain other variables (noncontrolled variables). This interest is formalized by means of a quadratic preference function; both sets of variables are arguments of this function. The preference function is maximized subject to constraints in the form of a linear equation system; each equation describes one noncontrolled variable in terms of the instruments. As long as there is no uncertainty this is a straightforward conditional maximization problem, although several interesting things can be said about it; e.g., about what happens in case the decision made is suboptimal. This suboptimality plays of course a greater role in case there is no certainty. In that case expected utility is maximized and considerable attention is paid to certainty equivalence. This means that by replacing some unsure prospect by an appropriate sure prospect the decision maker arrives at the same decision as in case he maximizes expected utility.

Chapter 2 is static in the sense that a decision has to be made now and that later-period decisions do not enter into the picture. The results of that chapter are illustrated in Chapter 3 by means of two examples. One is a simplified case of macroeconomic planning; it represents an effort to show how the depression of the nineteen-thirties in the United States might have been brought to an end. There are three instruments and three noncontrolled variables, which are connected by a small econometric equation system. This system supplies the constraints subject to which a quadratic social welfare function is maximized; and this maximization problem is formulated in terms of the minimization of the sum of squares of the discrepancies between actual and desired values. The other example is of the microeconomic category and deals with the minimization of a quadratic cost function of a factory. The constraints are very simple in this case and specify only that the change in inventories is equal to the excess of production over shipments.

Although these examples are treated in a static manner in Chapter 3, they are essentially dynamic: the government policy maker thinks in terms of a series of successive decisions by which he will approach his goal and the factory manager wishes to minimize costs over time. This subject is approached from the theoretical point of view in Chapter 4. The quadratic preference function depends on instruments and noncontrolled variables as before, but these variables are now "dated:" there is a decision to be made now, another one period later, and so on. Maximizing expected utility amounts then to finding an appropriate strategy or decision rule, i.e., a rule which specifies the decision for each future period as a function of the information which will be available at the moment when the decision has to be made. It turns out that under certain assumptions the decision which has to be made for the period immediately ahead is identical with the decision that would be made if all unsure prospects are replaced by certain sure prospects (first-period certainty equivalence). There are some other dynamic generalizations of the static theory, most of which are straightforward.

This dynamic theory is applied in Chapter 5 to the factory manager example. His objective is to find the production level and the size of the work force, month after month, in such a way that, given the information which is available to him at the beginning of each month, expected total costs are minimized over time. In this case the information amounts to previous shipments and to expected shipments in future periods; it turns out that the decision rules for production and work force are linear in expected future shipments. The analysis covers also the implications of alternative horizons (including the case in which the manager takes an indefinite future into account) as well as the losses due to suboptimal decisions, to imperfect sales forecasts, and to an incorrect specification of the coefficients of the cost function.

Chapter 6 contains two macroeconomic applications, the first of which is the American depression example which was introduced in Chapter 3. This is elaborated in some detail for a four-year horizon; the discussion includes the loss due to suboptimal decisions and the expected losses due to the random variability of the disturbances of the equation system and to the sampling errors of the coefficients of one of the equations. Another interesting feature is the discussion of forecasts of the future development of instruments and noncontrolled variables. The point is that the strategy approach supplies not only information about what is to be done in the period immediately ahead, but also unbiased forecasts of future instrument and noncontrolled values. This is pursued in greater detail in the second example, which is based on three alternative social welfare functions for The Netherlands in the years 1957–1959. Each of these is maximized subject to the constraints implied by a rather large econometric model. The sources of uncertainty which are taken into account in this example include the disturbances of the model, the prediction errors of future exogenous values (as far as they are not under the policy maker's control), and the estimation errors of past realizations.

In Chapter 7 the scene is changed and we consider no longer one single decision maker but several. The analysis includes the case of a research manager who adjusts his research programme such that the objectives of a decision maker (his boss) are satisfied as well as possible; the case of a team of persons working for a common goal; that of a committee of persons who are jointly responsible for the manipulation of all instruments but who have conflicting preferences; and that of a group of persons with conflicting preferences controlling different variables. The committee decision problem is considered in more detail than the other three.

1.4.2. Some Technical Notes

Each chapter is divided into sections and these into subsections. The last subsection of every section gives a summary of the main findings of that section without the use of mathematical symbols.

Formulas are indicated by three numbers, the first of which is the number of the chapter, the second that of the section, while the third indicates the order of occurrence in the section. Thus the last formula of Section 1.3 is (1.3.23). In fact, it was indicated there as (3.23), the number of the chapter being deleted. We shall continue to delete such chapter numbers as long as such a formula is referred to in its own chapter.

Matrices consisting of algebraic (rather than numerical) elements will be denoted typographically in two ways: x, y, A, B, . . . as against **x**, **y**, **A**, **B**, . . . The former type is used mainly for static concepts, the latter for dynamic concepts. Therefore, the first type dominates in Chapters 2 and 3, while the other will appear in Chapter 4. The latter type is used throughout for matrices with purely numerical elements, such as **0** and **I**.

CHAPTER 2

Static Theory of Quadratic Preferences and Linear Constraints

2.1. BEHAVIOUR UNDER CERTAINTY

2.1.1. Introductory

We shall start with some examples of quadratic preferences and linear constraints.

The classical analysis of consumer's demand is based on the idea that the consumer behaves as if he maximizes a utility function which depends on the consumption of all possible commodities, x_1, $x_2, \ldots$, and that he does so subject to the constraint that his disposable income is exactly spent. Supposing that the utility function is quadratic, we can write it in the form

$$(1.1) \quad u(x_1, x_2, \ldots) = a_0 + a_1 x_1 + a_2 x_2 + \ldots + \tfrac{1}{2}(a_{11} x_1^2 + a_{22} x_2^2 + \ldots + 2a_{12} x_1 x_2 + \ldots).$$

Furthermore, we write $p_1, p_2, \ldots$ for the prices of the commodities and M for disposable income; they are all considered as given numbers, at least from the consumer's point of view. The constraint takes then the form:

$$(1.2) \qquad p_1 x_1 + p_2 x_2 + \ldots = M,$$

which is linear because the coefficients (the p's and M) are taken as constant and hence do not depend on the x's. The problem is then: to find the values of x_1, $x_2, \ldots$ which maximize the quadratic utility function (1.1) subject to the linear budget constraint (1.2).

A second example deals with cost minimization over time. Suppose our decision maker is a factory manager who produces a single product and whose objective is to minimize the combined costs of production and of inventory holding over a period of T months. Let us denote the production of month t by P_t and suppose that the associated costs are quadratic: $a + bP_t + cP_t^2$. Similarly, we denote the inventory level at the end of month t by I_t and assume the associated costs to be quadratic: $a'+b'I_t+c'I_t^2$. The combined costs over the T-month period are then

$$(1.3)\quad C(P_1,\ldots,P_T;I_1,\ldots,I_T)=\sum_{t=1}^{T}(a+bP_t+cP_t^2+a'+b'I_t+c'I_t^2).$$

But production and inventories are not unrelated. They are connected by the condition that for each month the change in inventories equals the excess of production over shipments. Hence:

$$(1.4)\quad \begin{aligned} I_1-I_0 &= P_1-S_1\\ I_2-I_1 &= P_2-S_2\\ &\vdots\\ I_T-I_{T-1} &= P_T-S_T, \end{aligned}$$

where S_t stands for the shipments in month t and I_0 for the inventory level at the beginning of the first month. The problem is therefore: to find the values $P_1,\ldots,P_T$, $I_1,\ldots,I_T$ which minimize the quadratic cost function (1.3) subject to the T linear constraints (1.4). [For simplicity's sake, we disregard the value of I_T-I_0, i.e., the value of the change in inventories during the period as a whole.]

These examples are convenient to illustrate the following remarks. First, we may have either one constraint, as in (1.2), or any larger number, like in (1.4). The analysis which follows will be general in this respect and is therefore based on an arbitrary (finite) number of constraints. Second, the decision problem may take a static or a dynamic form. The first example is static: there is a decision to be made for one period only, and that is all. The second is however dynamic, for decisions for T successive periods enter into the picture. This chapter will be confined to static decision-making; the dynamic generalization will be presented in Chapter 4. Third, there may or may not be uncertainty. There is no uncertainty in the consumer example if we take the coefficients of the utility function and prices and income as fixed and given. But there is uncertainty in the factory manager example if we make the (realistic) assumption that the shipments in the T future months are not known with certainty. In addition, the coefficients of the cost function (a, b, c, a', b', c') may have to be estimated from engineering or statistical data, in which case there is an additional source of uncertainty. In the present section it will be assumed that there is no uncertainty; this restrictive condition will be removed in Sections 2.2 and 2.3.

2.1.2. First Set of Assumptions on Preferences and Constraints

In the general static theory we shall assume that there are m real-valued variables, $x_1, \ldots, x_m$, which are under the decision maker's control. They will be written as a column vector, x; and they will be called *instruments* or *controlled variables*. Further, we shall suppose that there are n real-valued variables, $y_1, \ldots, y_n$, which are interesting from the decision maker's point of view because his preference level depends on them but which are not controlled by him; or at least, which are beyond the decision maker's control to a sufficiently appreciable degree. For example, in the factory manager's case we take next month's production as a controlled variable but the inventory level at the end of that month as noncontrolled; the reason being that this inventory level is beyond the manager's control as far as it is determined by next month's sales. Such *noncontrolled variables*, too, will be written in the form of a column vector, y. Our first assumption is that the decision maker's preferences are quadratic in all $m+n$ variables:

ASSUMPTION 2.1. *All vectors* $x = [x_h]$, $y = [y_i]$ *of instruments and noncontrolled variables, respectively, are real-valued and ordered according to the decision maker's preference such as to allow a representation by means of a quadratic preference function*:

$$w(x, y) = a'x + b'y + \tfrac{1}{2}(x'Ax + y'By + x'Cy + y'C'x), \tag{1.5}$$

where $a = [a_h]$, $b = [b_i]$, $A = [a_{hk}]$, $B = [b_{ij}]$, $C = [c_{hi}]$ *are vectors and matrices of fixed elements and of appropriate order.* A *and* B *are symmetric.*

The second assumption deals with the constraints, which are supposed to be linear. We assume that each of the noncontrolled variables depends linearly on all instruments, the coefficients of these linear relations being fixed. If the decision maker would know these fixed values, he would be able to control his "noncontrolled" variables indirectly (by means of his instruments) and there would be very little difference between the two sets of variables. However, in a later part of the analysis we shall wish to take account of the possibility that these coefficients are unknown to him; we shall even introduce the assumption that they are random rather than fixed. But this does not interest us at the present stage, so we introduce:

ASSUMPTION 2.2. *The vectors* x, y *are connected by a linear equation system,*

$$y = Rx + s, \tag{1.6}$$

where $R = [r_{ih}]$ *is a matrix of fixed elements describing the multiplicative structure of the constraints and* $s = [s_i]$ *a vector of fixed elements describing the additive structure.*

These assumptions can be illustrated conveniently by means of the two examples of 2.1.1. Considering the factory manager example first, we observe that it can be reduced to the static case by putting $T = 1$. The cost function takes then the form

$$a+bP+cP^2+a'+b'I+c'I^2,$$

where the index 1 of P_1 and I_1 is deleted for notational simplicity. Production is taken as controlled and the inventory level as uncontrolled. Hence $m = n = 1$ in this case, and x and y are simply one-element vectors:

$$x = [P]; \qquad y = [I]. \tag{1.7}$$

On comparing this cost function with the preference function (1.5), we find further:

$$a = [-b]; \quad b = [-b']; \quad A = [-2c]; \quad B = [-2c']; \quad C = [0], \tag{1.8}$$

the minus signs being due to the fact that the cost function is to be minimized, and hence minus the cost function to be maximized. Further, there is now only one constraint, which we write as

$$I = P+(I_0-S),$$

S being the shipments of the month which we are considering. On comparing this with (1.6), we see that both R and s consist of one element only:

$$R = [1]; \qquad s = [I_0-S]; \tag{1.9}$$

and it will be noted that the assumption of fixed s-elements implies that S is taken as fixed (which is not necessarily realistic). It will also be noted, parenthetically, that the constant term of the quadratic cost function $(a+a')$ is irrelevant for the purpose of finding the extremum; this is the reason why no constant term has been introduced into the preference function (1.5).

The consumer example needs a minor adjustment in order to be brought within the present framework. Let us write $m+1$ for the total number of commodities; then the consumer is free in the choice of m of the x's while the last follows from the budget constraint. We choose "savings," say, for this last commodity; then

$$x = \begin{bmatrix} x_1 \\ \vdots \\ x_m \end{bmatrix}; \qquad y = [x_{m+1}], \tag{1.10}$$

and hence, on comparing this with (1.1) and (1.5):

$$(1.11) \qquad a = \begin{bmatrix} a_1 \\ \vdots \\ a_m \end{bmatrix}; \qquad b = [a_{m+1}]; \qquad A = \begin{bmatrix} a_{11} & \dots & a_{1m} \\ \vdots & & \vdots \\ a_{m1} & \dots & a_{mm} \end{bmatrix};$$

$$B = [a_{m+1,\,m+1}]; \qquad C = \begin{bmatrix} a_{1,\,m+1} \\ \vdots \\ a_{m,\,m+1} \end{bmatrix}.$$

The budget constraint is written in the form

$$x_{m+1} = -\frac{p_1}{p_{m+1}}x_1 - \dots - \frac{p_m}{p_{m+1}}x_m + \frac{M}{p_{m+1}},$$

so that R of (1.6) is now a row vector and s a scalar:

$$(1.12) \qquad R = -\frac{1}{p_{m+1}}[p_1 \dots p_m]; \qquad s = [M/p_{m+1}].$$

The asymmetric way in which we handled the last example may seem artificial to the reader. In fact, this procedure is artificial as long as we are only interested in finding those values of our variables which maximize the preference function subject to the constraints; and this is indeed the topic of the present section. But, as mentioned above, such an analysis is considered here as preliminary to the problem of finding the "best" decision in the case when there is uncertainty. Suppose then that the consumer is uncertain about the income which he is going to earn in the period considered, while the prices are taken as given as before; suppose also that he decides on $x_1, \dots, x_m$ at the beginning of the period, so that x_{m+1} (saving) is determined by this decision and by this unknown income. In that case there is indeed a marked asymmetry between x_{m+1} and the other x's.

2.1.3. First and Second-Order Maximum Conditions

We proceed to consider the conditions which a numerically specified vector pair (x^0, y^0) should meet in order to maximize the preference function subject to the constraints. This can be done in two alternative ways: either one treats all instruments and noncontrolled variables symmetrically by applying the Lagrangean technique, or one eliminates the noncontrolled variables from the preference function by means of the constraints after which this function is maximized unconditionally with respect to the instruments. Both approaches are valuable for our purposes; the former will be carried out here, the latter in 2.1.4.

Consider the Lagrangean expression

$$(1.13)\quad w(x,y)-\lambda'(y-Rx-s) = a'x+b'y+\tfrac{1}{2}(x'Ax+y'By+x'Cy+y'C'x) -\lambda'(y-Rx-s),$$

where λ is a column vector of n Lagrangean multipliers. Differentiating (1.13) with respect to x while keeping y and λ fixed and putting the result equal to a zero vector gives[1]

$$(1.14)\qquad \frac{\partial w}{\partial x}+R'\lambda = a+Ax+Cy+R'\lambda = \mathbf{0}.$$

Similarly, if we differentiate (1.13) with respect to y while keeping x and λ constant, we obtain

$$(1.15)\qquad \frac{\partial w}{\partial y}-\lambda = b+By+C'x-\lambda = \mathbf{0}.$$

These two conditions, together with the constraints (1.6), can be written in the following partitioned form:

$$(1.16)\qquad \begin{bmatrix} A & C & R' \\ C' & B & -\mathbf{I} \\ R & -\mathbf{I} & \mathbf{0} \end{bmatrix} \begin{bmatrix} x \\ y \\ \lambda \end{bmatrix} = \begin{bmatrix} -a \\ -b \\ -s \end{bmatrix}.$$

These are $m+2n$ linear restrictions on $m+2n$ variables (x, y, λ), from which these variables can be solved if the symmetric matrix on the left is nonsingular. We shall denote this matrix by W:

$$(1.17)\qquad W = \begin{bmatrix} A & C & R' \\ C' & B & -\mathbf{I} \\ R & -\mathbf{I} & \mathbf{0} \end{bmatrix}.$$

The restrictions (1.16) are the *first-order* equilibrium conditions: if they are satisfied for some x^0, y^0, then these vectors correspond with a stationary point of the preference function (subject to the constraints). But this may be a minimum or a saddlepoint instead of a maximum. In order to be sure that we have a maximum, we should consider the *second-order* equilibrium conditions, which can be explained as follows. Consider

[1] The derivative of a scalar (like w) with respect to a column vector (like x) is defined as the column vector of first-order derivatives of this scalar with respect to each of the elements of this vector. The following rules are easily verified: $\partial(a'x)/\partial x = a$ and $\partial(x'Ax)/\partial x = 2Ax$, where a is a column vector and A a symmetric matrix of appropriate order (both independent of x).

the square matrix on the left of (1.16), and in particular its submatrix

$$\begin{bmatrix} A & C \\ C' & B \end{bmatrix},$$

which is the matrix of all second-order derivatives of the preference function: $\partial^2 w/\partial x_h \partial x_k = a_{hk}$, $\partial^2 w/\partial x_h \partial y_i = c_{hi}$, etc. Let us take an arbitrary principal minor of order $n+1$ (the number of constraints plus one) in this matrix; for example, take the determinant corresponding with the last $n+1$ rows and columns:

$$\begin{vmatrix} a_{mm} & c_{m1} & c_{m2} & \cdots & c_{mn} \\ c_{m1} & b_{11} & b_{12} & \cdots & b_{1n} \\ c_{m2} & b_{21} & b_{22} & \cdots & b_{2n} \\ \vdots & \vdots & \vdots & & \vdots \\ c_{mn} & b_{n1} & b_{n2} & \cdots & b_{nn} \end{vmatrix},$$

and border this determinant on the right and below with the corresponding elements of the last n rows and columns of W. The result is a principal minor of order $2n+1$ of this matrix:

$$\begin{vmatrix} a_{mm} & c_{m1} & c_{m2} & \cdots & c_{mn} & r_{1m} & r_{2m} & \cdots & r_{nm} \\ c_{m1} & b_{11} & b_{12} & \cdots & b_{1n} & -1 & 0 & \cdots & 0 \\ c_{m2} & b_{21} & b_{22} & \cdots & b_{2n} & 0 & -1 & \cdots & 0 \\ \vdots & \vdots & \vdots & & \vdots & \vdots & \vdots & & \vdots \\ c_{mn} & b_{n1} & b_{n2} & \cdots & b_{nn} & 0 & 0 & \cdots & -1 \\ r_{1m} & -1 & 0 & \cdots & 0 & 0 & 0 & \cdots & 0 \\ r_{2m} & 0 & -1 & \cdots & 0 & 0 & 0 & \cdots & 0 \\ \vdots & \vdots & \vdots & & \vdots & \vdots & \vdots & & \vdots \\ r_{nm} & 0 & 0 & \cdots & -1 & 0 & 0 & \cdots & 0 \end{vmatrix}.$$

This minor should have the sign of $(-)^{n+1}$, i.e., it should be negative if n is even in order that the stationary point be a maximum, and it should be positive if n is odd. Furthermore, when we border such a minor by another row and column of W such that a principal minor of order $2n+2$ results, this should have opposite sign; and so on, up to the determinant of W itself. For more details we refer to the Appendix of this chapter (Section 2.A).

Summarizing our results, we have:

THEOREM 2.1. *Suppose that Assumptions* 2.1 *and* 2.2 *are satisfied. Then, in order that the preference function* (1.5) *be stationary subject to the constraints* (1.6) *in* $\mathbf{x}^0$, $\mathbf{y}^0$, *it is necessary and sufficient that these vectors satisfy* (1.16) *for some vector* $\boldsymbol{\lambda}$ *of n components. In order that this station-*

ary value be a maximum, it is sufficient that the principal minors of order $n+1, \ldots, n+m$ *of the matrix of second-order derivatives of the preference function, bordered with the corresponding n rows and columns of the multiplicative coefficients* $[\mathsf{R} \;\; -\mathbf{I}]$ *of the constraints as in* (1.17), *have alternating signs, the first having the sign of* $(-)^{n+1}$.

Let us apply this result to the factory manager example. Starting with the second-order condition, we conclude from (1.8) and (1.9) that

$$\text{(1.18)} \qquad \mathsf{W} = \begin{bmatrix} -2c & 0 & 1 \\ 0 & -2c' & -1 \\ 1 & -1 & 0 \end{bmatrix}.$$

Since $n = 1$, the second-order condition implies only one single condition, viz., that the determinant of W should be positive; and this is equivalent to

$$\text{(1.19)} \qquad c+c' > 0.$$

From (1.16) we derive that the optimal values of the two variables are the first two elements of the vector which is obtained by postmultiplying the inverse of W by $\{b \;\; b' \;\; S-I_0\}$; see (1.8) and (1.9). So we find for the optimal production decision:

$$\text{(1.20)} \qquad P^0 = \frac{c'}{c+c'}(S-I_0) - \frac{b+b'}{2(c+c')},$$

which states that this decision is a linear function of the excess of sales over the initial inventory level. It is an increasing function if $c' > 0$, i.e., if the marginal cost of holding inventories increases with the inventory level. For the inventory level associated with this optimal decision we find in the same way:

$$\text{(1.21)} \qquad I^0 = \frac{c}{c+c'}(I_0-S) - \frac{b+b'}{2(c+c')}.$$

For the consumer example we start again with the second-order conditions, and this time W takes the form:

$$\text{(1.22)} \qquad \mathsf{W} = \begin{bmatrix} a_{11} & \cdots & a_{1m} & a_{1,m+1} & -p_1/p_{m+1} \\ \vdots & & \vdots & \vdots & \vdots \\ a_{m1} & \cdots & a_{mm} & a_{m,m+1} & -p_m/p_{m+1} \\ a_{m+1,1} & \cdots & a_{m+1,m} & a_{m+1,m+1} & -1 \\ -p_1/p_{m+1} & \cdots & -p_m/p_{m+1} & -1 & 0 \end{bmatrix}.$$

Since we are only interested in signs of principal minors of W, there is no objection to multiplying the last row and the last column by $-p_{m+1}$;

this simply implies that all principal minors of Theorem 2.1 are multiplied by p_{m+1}^2, so that their signs are not affected. Thus W is simplified to

$$\begin{bmatrix} a_{11} & \cdots & a_{1m} & a_{1,m+1} & p_1 \\ \vdots & & \vdots & \vdots & \vdots \\ a_{m1} & \cdots & a_{mm} & a_{m,m+1} & p_m \\ a_{m+1,1} & \cdots & a_{m+1,m} & a_{m+1,m+1} & p_{m+1} \\ p_1 & \cdots & p_m & p_{m+1} & 0 \end{bmatrix}.$$

Since $n = 1$, the second-order maximum conditions then take the familiar form:

$$(1.23)\qquad \begin{vmatrix} a_{11} & a_{12} & p_1 \\ a_{21} & a_{22} & p_2 \\ p_1 & p_2 & 0 \end{vmatrix} > 0, \qquad \begin{vmatrix} a_{11} & a_{12} & a_{13} & p_1 \\ a_{21} & a_{22} & a_{23} & p_2 \\ a_{31} & a_{32} & a_{33} & p_3 \\ p_1 & p_2 & p_3 & 0 \end{vmatrix} < 0, \ldots,$$

where the numbering of the commodities is immaterial. The m conditions (1.23) all involve quadratic inequality constraints on the prices; e.g., the first is equivalent to

$$a_{22}p_1^2 + a_{11}p_2^2 - 2a_{12}p_1p_2 < 0.$$

The explicit expression for the x^0's is directly obtained by inverting the W of (1.22) in accordance with (1.16).

2.1.4. Derivation of the Maximum by Elimination of the Noncontrolled Variables

The maximum conditions of Theorem 2.1 are applicable under even more general conditions than those which we introduced here.[1] On the other hand, granted that we are using the restrictive conditions of quadratic preferences and linear constraints, it is appropriate to use them efficiently. This can be done as follows.

If we substitute (1.6) into (1.5), we obtain the preference level which is attained if any vector x is applied. This can be written in the form

$$(1.24)\qquad w(x, Rx+s) = k_0 + k'x + \tfrac{1}{2}x'Kx,$$

where k_0 is a scalar, k a column vector of m components, and K a symmetric matrix of order $m \times m$:

$$k_0 = b's + \tfrac{1}{2}s'Bs;$$

$$(1.25)\qquad k = a + R'b + (C+R'B)s = [\mathbf{I} \quad R'] \begin{bmatrix} a & C \\ b & B \end{bmatrix} \begin{bmatrix} 1 \\ s \end{bmatrix};$$

$$K = A + R'BR + CR + R'C' = [\mathbf{I} \quad R'] \begin{bmatrix} A & C \\ C' & B \end{bmatrix} \begin{bmatrix} \mathbf{I} \\ R \end{bmatrix},$$

[1] See H. Theil, *Economic Forecasts and Policy*, Second Revised Edition, p. 428.

the three unit matrices in the partitioned expressions being all of order $m \times m$.

It is easy to see that the right-hand side of (1.24) can be written as

$$k_0 + k'x + \tfrac{1}{2}x'Kx = k_0 - \tfrac{1}{2}k'K^{-1}k + \tfrac{1}{2}(x + K^{-1}k)'K(x + K^{-1}k), \tag{1.26}$$

provided that K is nonsingular. The derivatives of the right-hand function with respect to the instruments are all zero at

$$x^0 = -K^{-1}k, \tag{1.27}$$

which means that this is a stationary point. Further, since the matrix of the quadratic form on the right of (1.26) is $\frac{1}{2}K$, a sufficient condition for this point to be a maximum is that K be negative-definite. To summarize:

THEOREM 2.2. *Suppose that Assumptions* 2.1 *and* 2.2 *are satisfied. Then, in order that the preference function* (1.5) *be stationary subject to the constraints* (1.6), *it is necessary and sufficient that the instrument vector takes the value* x^0 *as defined in* (1.27), *where* K *and* k *are defined in* (1.25). *In order that this stationary value be a maximum, it is sufficient that* K *be negative definite.*

The conditions of Theorems 2.1 and 2.2 are of course equivalent as will be shown below (Theorem 2.3 in 2.1.5). Here, we confine ourselves to stating that in the factory manager example, k and K are given by

$$k = [1 \quad 1]\begin{bmatrix} -b & 0 \\ -b' & -2c' \end{bmatrix}\begin{bmatrix} 1 \\ I_0 - S \end{bmatrix} = [2c'(S - I_0) - b - b'];$$

$$K = [1 \quad 1]\begin{bmatrix} -2c & 0 \\ 0 & -2c' \end{bmatrix}\begin{bmatrix} 1 \\ 1 \end{bmatrix} = [-2c - 2c'],$$

from which it follows immediately that the optimal decision $-K^{-1}k$ is identical with P^0 as defined in (1.20).

2.1.5. The Equivalence of the Maximum Conditions of Theorems 2.1 and 2.2

Let us reconsider the bordered matrix of second-order derivatives of the preference function introduced in (1.17):

$$W = \begin{bmatrix} A & C & R' \\ C' & B & -\mathbf{I} \\ R & -\mathbf{I} & \mathbf{0} \end{bmatrix}.$$

According to (1.16), this matrix has to be inverted if we want to derive the optimal values of the vectors x, y, λ. Since W is partitioned into nine submatrices (of order $m \times m$, $m \times n$, $n \times m$, and $n \times n$), it seems rather obvious to partition the inverse conformably. Thus, we introduce

$$W^{-1} = \begin{bmatrix} (xx) & (xy) & (x\cdot) \\ (yx) & (yy) & (y\cdot) \\ (\cdot x) & (\cdot y) & (\cdot\cdot) \end{bmatrix}, \tag{1.28}$$

where the leading submatrix (xx) is of order $m \times m$, (xy) and $(x\cdot)$ of order $m \times n$, and so on. This notation is chosen because (xx) stands in W^{-1} in the same place as A in W, and A is the matrix of the second-order derivatives of the preference function with respect to all possible pairs of instruments; similarly, C in W represents the cross-derivatives with respect to instruments and noncontrolled variables, hence (xy) in W^{-1} in the same place, etc. Obviously, W^{-1} is symmetric because W is, hence $(xy) = (yx)'$, etc.

If we postmultiply W^{-1} by W, we should obtain the unit matrix of order $m+2n$:

$$\begin{bmatrix} (xx) & (xy) & (x\cdot) \\ (yx) & (yy) & (y\cdot) \\ (\cdot x) & (\cdot y) & (\cdot\cdot) \end{bmatrix} \begin{bmatrix} A & C & R' \\ C' & B & -\mathbf{I} \\ R & -\mathbf{I} & \mathbf{0} \end{bmatrix} = \begin{bmatrix} \mathbf{I} & \mathbf{0} & \mathbf{0} \\ \mathbf{0} & \mathbf{I} & \mathbf{0} \\ \mathbf{0} & \mathbf{0} & \mathbf{I} \end{bmatrix},$$

which enables us to express the submatrices of W^{-1} in those of W. Thus, if we multiply the first m rows of W^{-1} into the last n columns of W, we obtain $(xx)R' - (xy) = \mathbf{0}$ and hence $(xy) = (xx)R'$. If we then multiply the first m rows of W^{-1} into the columns numbered $m+1$ through $m+n$ of W, we find $(xx)C + (xy)B - (x\cdot) = \mathbf{0}$, hence $(x\cdot) = (xx)(C+R'B)$. Multiplying the first m rows of W^{-1} into the first m columns of W gives

$$(xx)A + (xy)C' + (x\cdot)R = (xx)(A + R'C' + CR + R'BR) = \mathbf{I}$$

and hence:

$$(xx) = (A + R'BR + CR + R'C')^{-1} = K^{-1}. \tag{1.29}$$

When proceeding in this way, we obtain all submatrices of W^{-1}. They can be expressed conveniently in (xx):

$$W^{-1} = \begin{bmatrix} (xx) & (xx)R' & (xx)(C+R'B) \\ R(xx) & R(xx)R' & R(xx)(C+R'B) - \mathbf{I} \\ (C+R'B)'(xx) & (C+R'B)'(xx)R' - \mathbf{I} & (C+R'B)'(xx)(C+R'B) - B \end{bmatrix}. \tag{1.30}$$

If we multiply this matrix into the right-hand column of (1.16), we obtain the optimal values of x, y and λ. For the first vector the result is

$$\begin{aligned} x^0 &= -[(xx)a + (xx)R'b + (xx)(C+R'B)s] \\ &= -(xx)[a + R'b + (C+R'B)s], \end{aligned} \tag{1.31}$$

which proves the equivalence with the x^0 of Theorem 2.2. Multiplying the rows $m+1$ through $m+n$ of W^{-1} into the right-hand column vector of (1.16) gives the vector y^0 associated with the optimal decision x^0:

$$y^0 = -R(xx)[a+R'b+(C+R'B)s]+s = Rx^0+s, \tag{1.32}$$

which is as it should be. Finally, multiplying the last n rows of W^{-1} into the same column gives the vector of Lagrangean multipliers associated with x^0 and y^0:

$$\begin{aligned} \lambda^0 &= -(C+R'B)'(xx)[a+R'b+(C+R'B)s]+b+Bs \\ &= (C'+BR)x^0+b+Bs = b+C'x^0+By^0, \end{aligned} \tag{1.33}$$

from which it is seen that λ^0 is equal to the vector of derivatives of the preference function (1.5) with respect to the noncontrolled variables, evaluated at x^0, y^0.[1] Our results can be summarized as follows:

THEOREM 2.3. *Suppose that Assumptions* 2.1 *and* 2.2 *are satisfied. Then the stationarity conditions of Theorems* 2.1 *and* 2.2 *are equivalent, and the same applies to their second-order maximum conditions. If the latter conditions are satisfied, the preference function* (1.5) *has one single maximum subject to the constraints* (1.6).

The last sentence of Theorem 2.3 follows immediately from the fact that the preference function—after elimination of the noncontrolled variables—can be written in the form (1.26), K being negative definite. For the equivalence of the second-order maximum conditions we refer to the Appendix (Section 2.A).

2.1.6. The Optimal Reaction Functions

The Lagrangean procedure of 2.1.3 is certainly less straightforward than the direct elimination approach of 2.1.4. But its usefulness will soon become clear.

Suppose that for some reason beyond the control of the decision maker, the parameters of his constraints are changed. For example, take the consumer's case and suppose that there are changes in prices and in his income. This will affect his optimal decisions, which clearly are dependent on prices and income. Hence:

$$\begin{aligned} x_1^0 &= f_1(M, p_1, p_2, \ldots) \\ x_2^0 &= f_2(M, p_1, p_2, \ldots) \\ &\ldots\ldots\ldots\ldots\ldots, \end{aligned} \tag{1.34}$$

[1] Note that this is in accordance with (1.15).

which are the familiar demand functions of classical consumption theory. More generally, we shall be interested here in the effect of changes of the parameter matrices R and s of the constraints (1.6), and we shall analyze this effect by means of the so-called *optimal reaction functions*,

$$x^0 = x(R, s) \quad \text{and} \quad y^0 = y(R, s), \tag{1.35}$$

which specify the vectors x^0, y^0 which maximize the preference function (1.5) subject to the constraints (1.6) for any values of R and s. Naturally, the existence of such a maximum presupposes that the variations in R should be such that K remains negative definite; see (1.25) and Theorem 2.2.

One could say that the dependence of x^0 and y^0 is completely described by (1.31) and (1.32), respectively, so that there is no need for an additional analysis. The first statement is correct, but its conclusion is not fully justified since we shall be able to prove certain interesting results for the effects of infinitesimal changes in the arguments of the optimal reaction functions. Let us go back to the stationarity condition (1.16) and suppose that R and s change by dR and ds respectively. In the new situation the stationarity condition becomes

$$\begin{bmatrix} A & C & (R+dR)' \\ C' & B & -\mathbf{I} \\ R+dR & -\mathbf{I} & \mathbf{0} \end{bmatrix} \begin{bmatrix} x^0+dx \\ y^0+dy \\ \lambda^0+d\lambda \end{bmatrix} = \begin{bmatrix} -a \\ -b \\ -(s+ds) \end{bmatrix}, \tag{1.36}$$

where x^0, y^0, λ^0 are the vectors of the original optimum and dx, dy, $d\lambda$ the changes induced by dR, ds. On subtracting (1.16) from (1.36) we obtain

$$\begin{bmatrix} \mathbf{0} & \mathbf{0} & (dR)' \\ \mathbf{0} & \mathbf{0} & \mathbf{0} \\ dR & \mathbf{0} & \mathbf{0} \end{bmatrix} \begin{bmatrix} x^0 \\ y^0 \\ \lambda^0 \end{bmatrix} + \begin{bmatrix} A & C & R' \\ C' & B & -\mathbf{I} \\ R & -\mathbf{I} & \mathbf{0} \end{bmatrix} \begin{bmatrix} dx \\ dy \\ d\lambda \end{bmatrix} = \begin{bmatrix} \mathbf{0} \\ \mathbf{0} \\ -ds \end{bmatrix},$$

products of differentials being disregarded. The second square matrix on the left is W; hence, applying (1.28), we obtain the following solution for dx, dy, $d\lambda$:

$$\begin{bmatrix} dx \\ dy \\ d\lambda \end{bmatrix} = \begin{bmatrix} (xx) & (xy) & (x\cdot) \\ (yx) & (yy) & (y\cdot) \\ (\cdot x) & (\cdot y) & (\cdot\cdot) \end{bmatrix} \begin{bmatrix} -(dR)'\lambda^0 \\ \mathbf{0} \\ -(dR)x^0 - ds \end{bmatrix}.$$

The result for the optimal reaction functions can be summarized as follows:

THEOREM 2.4. *Suppose that Assumptions* 2.1 *and* 2.2 *are satisfied;*

suppose also that the second-order maximum condition formulated in Theorem 2.2 *is satisfied, both when the coefficient matrix* R *of the constraints* (1.6) *is as it is and when it takes the value* $\mathsf{R}+d\mathsf{R}$, *where* $d\mathsf{R}$ *is a matrix of infinitesimal changes. Then the change in* x^0 *and* y^0 *according to the optimal reaction functions* (1.35), *caused by* $d\mathsf{R}$ *and by a vector* $d\mathsf{s}$ *of infinitesimal changes in the coefficient vector* s *of the constraints* (1.6), *is given by*

$$\begin{bmatrix} dx \\ dy \end{bmatrix} = -\begin{bmatrix} (x\cdot) \\ (y\cdot) \end{bmatrix}[(dR)x^0+ds]-\begin{bmatrix} (xx) \\ (yx) \end{bmatrix}(dR)'\lambda^0, \tag{1.37}$$

where $(x\cdot)$, $(y\cdot)$, (xx), (yx) *are defined in* (1.28)–(1.30), *and* x^0 *and* λ^0 *in* (1.31) *and* (1.33), *respectively.*

The partial derivatives of the optimal reaction functions follow immediately from (1.37). For the derivatives with respect to the additive structure we have:

$$\frac{\partial x_h}{\partial s_j} = -(x\cdot)_{hj} \quad \text{and} \quad \frac{\partial y_i}{\partial s_j} = -(y\cdot)_{ij} \tag{1.38}$$

and for those with respect to the multiplicative structure:

$$\begin{aligned} \frac{\partial x_h}{\partial r_{jk}} &= -x_k^0(x\cdot)_{hj}-\lambda_j^0(xx)_{hk} \\ \frac{\partial y_i}{\partial r_{jk}} &= -x_k^0(y\cdot)_{ij}-\lambda_j^0(yx)_{ik}\,. \end{aligned} \tag{1.39}$$

2.1.7. Substitution, Complementarity, and Tinbergen Surfaces

The matrices $(x\cdot)$, (xx), ... played an important role in the theorem which we just derived; and since they will continue to be important in the further analysis, it is worthwhile to pay somewhat more attention to their interpretation.

It follows from (1.37) that the effect of dR, ds on the optimal values of x and y consists of two parts, and that dR plays a role in both but ds in only one of them. To consider these two effects in more detail, it is useful to separate them. Consider then the second:

$$-\begin{bmatrix} (xx) \\ (yx) \end{bmatrix}(dR)'\lambda^0,$$

which is the only effect that occurs if it is true that

$$ds = -(dR)x^0, \tag{1.40}$$

for the first part of (1.37) will then necessarily vanish. Now ds as defined in (1.40) is called a *compensating change* in s, given dR. It is compensating in the following sense. Suppose again that the original constraints are $y = Rx+s$ and that they are changed to $y = (R+dR)x+s$. The original optimal decision x^0 implied a value Rx^0+s for the noncontrolled variables in the original situation, but in the new situation this becomes $(R+dR)x^0+s$, i.e., the new noncontrolled vector exceeds the original one by $(dR)x^0$. It will be observed that in the new situation the original optimal decision x^0 is no longer optimal, but this is irrelevant for the present argument; we just stick to the old x^0. Now suppose that not only R is changed by dR but also s by ds, and that $ds = -(dR)x^0$ as in (1.40). Then the noncontrolled vector implied by x^0 in this situation becomes

$$y = (R+dR)x^0+(s+ds) = Rx^0+s,$$

i.e., we obtain the noncontrolled vector of the original situation. In other words: if there is any change dR in the multiplicative structure of the constraints, and if there is a compensating change ds in the additive structure satisfying (1.40), then this can be interpreted in the sense that the decision maker is able to attain the original vectors x^0, y^0 in spite of these changes in the constraints. We shall illustrate this by means of the consumer example. Going back to the end of 2.1.2 and interpreting the price of savings (p_{m+1}) as 1 for the sake of convenience, we can write the budget constraint as

$$x_{m+1} = -p_1x_1- \dots -p_mx_m+M.$$

A change in the multiplicative structure means now a change in prices, and a change in the additive structure is an income change. The procedure just described is then equivalent to price changes which are accompanied by a compensating income change in such a way that the consumer is able to choose the original expenditure pattern. Thus his "real income" in unaffected and the changes in the price ratios are the only things that are relevant for him.

It was noted that even if the decision maker is able to arrive at the vectors x^0, y^0 due to the compensating change in s, it is no longer true that these vectors are optimal in the new situation. In fact, the second term on the right of (1.37) measures precisely the shift in the optimum due to a compensated change dR [which will be our abbreviated expression for "a change dR accompanied by a change ds which satisfies (1.40)"]. This term is called the *substitution effect* of a change dR and will be considered in more detail in the next paragraph. The first term on the right of (1.37) is the *constant-term effect.*[1] Thus, a change ds in the vector of constant terms of the constraints leads to a change $(-x\cdot)ds$ in the optimal instrument values and a change $-(y\cdot)ds$ in the corresponding noncontrolled values, and these are the only effects of ds; there is no substitution effect because ds does not occur in the second term of (1.37). But dR has two effects, one of which is the constant-term effect: $-(x\cdot)(dR)x^0$ for the x's, $-(y\cdot)(dR)x^0$ for the y's. This is because a change dR is partly equivalent to a change in the additive structure of the constraints as has been argued in the preceding paragraph.

The substitution effect of dR deals with the other part and is thus concerned with changes in the effectiveness of the various instruments with respect to the various noncontrolled variables after a correction has been made such that the decision maker could stay in his original position x^0, y^0 if he chose to do so. The analysis of this effect will be simplified if we agree to measure our variables such that the marginal utilities in x^0, y^0 are all nonnegative:

$$\begin{bmatrix} \partial w/\partial x \\ \partial w/\partial y \end{bmatrix}_{\substack{x=x^0 \\ y=y^0}} = \begin{bmatrix} a \\ b \end{bmatrix} + \begin{bmatrix} A & C \\ C' & B \end{bmatrix} \begin{bmatrix} x^0 \\ y^0 \end{bmatrix} \geqq \mathbf{0}. \tag{1.41}$$

This is always possible by replacing any variable by minus itself, and it has the important advantage that it facilitates our definitions. Suppose then that there is a compensated increase in one multiplicative coefficient r_{jk}; i.e., the effectiveness of the instrument x_k with respect to the noncontrolled variable y_j increases by $dr_{jk} > 0$, and this is compensated as indicated above. The effect of this change on any instrument x_h is $-\lambda_j^0(xx)_{hk}dr_{jk}$ as follows from (1.39). Suppose $\lambda_j^0 > 0$, $(xx)_{hk} > 0$; then the increased effectiveness of x_k with respect to y_j leads to a reduction of x_h, which will be indicated by saying that x_h is *a substitute of x_k with respect to the constraint for y_j*. Suppose now $\lambda_j^0 > 0$, $(xx)_{hk} < 0$; then the increased effectiveness leads to an increase of x_h, in which case it is said that x_h is *complementary with x_k with respect to the constraint for y_j*. This covers the possibilities for $\lambda_j^0 > 0$; but it should be remembered that we adjusted the problem such that $\lambda_j^0 \geqq 0$ for any j. This follows from the fact that $\boldsymbol{\lambda}^0$ is equal to the vector of derivatives of the preference function with respect to the noncontrolled variables evaluated at x^0, y^0,

---

[1] The original term was source effect (analogous to the income effect of consumption theory), see *Economic Forecasts and Policy*, Second Revised Edition, p. 433; but the present terminology is preferred because it can be translated more easily into other languages.

see (1.33); and this vector is taken as nonnegative according to (1.41).[1] It follows that if x_h is a substitute of x_k with respect to some constraint, it is complementary with x_k with respect to no constraint, and vice versa; hence we can speak about substitution and complementarity relations without reference to a particular constraint, and we shall indicate from now on (xx) as the *substitution matrix of the instruments*. The following statements are now easily verified. First, substitution and complementarity are symmetric relations (if x_h is a substitute of x_k, then x_k is a substitute of x_h, and similarly for complementarity); this holds because (xx) is symmetric. Second, any instrument is complementary with itself: a compensated increase dr_{jk} for any j implies a positive dx_k (except when $\lambda_j = 0$). This is because (xx), being the inverse of the negative definite K [see (1.29)], is negative definite and hence has negative elements in the main diagonal. Third, there are similar relations of substitution and complementarity for any instrument on the one hand and any noncontrolled variable on the other hand. This, too, follows from (1.39), which shows that the effect on y_i of a compensated increase dr_{jk} is $-\lambda_j^0(yx)_{ik}dr_{jk}$. Hence, if $(yx)_{ik} > 0$, an increased effectiveness of x_k with respect to y_j leads to a reduction of y_i. In that case it is said that y_i is a substitute of x_k with respect to the constraint for y_j; and we may delete this constraint for the same reasons as those given above for inter-instrumental substitution relations. Conversely, if $(yx)_{ik} = (xy)_{ki} < 0$, an increased effectiveness of x_k leads to an increase of y_i, which is the case of complementarity. We shall accordingly indicate (xy) as the *mixed substitution matrix* of instruments and noncontrolled variables. It is possible to proceed in the same way for (yy) as the substitution matrix of the noncontrolled variables,[2] but this matrix plays no role in the further analysis.

To summarize, we have interpreted the effect of changes $d\mathsf{R}$ and $d\mathsf{s}$ on the optimal values of x and y as consisting of a constant-term effect and a substitution effect, the latter of which gave rise to the distinction between substitution and complementarity relations based on the signs of the elements of (xx) and (xy). The former effect gives a complete description of the consequences of s-changes. Any change ds_j leads to a

[1] In fact, the only part of (1.41) which we need here is $\partial w/\partial y_i = \lambda_i \geqq 0$ for all i in the equilibrium point $(\mathsf{x}^0, \mathsf{y}^0)$. But it has some advantages to impose $\partial w/\partial x_h \geqq 0$ as well. The reason is that we consider the effect of a compensated increase of r_{ih}, so that the sign of this coefficient should be well-defined. (If we replace x_h by $-x_h$, the increase of r_{ih} would become a decrease.)

[2] See *Economic Forecasts and Policy* (Second Edition), pp. 432–434.

change $-(x\cdot)_{hj}ds_j$ in x_h and a change $-(y\cdot)_{ij}ds_j$ in y_i; and hence, since the elements of $(x\cdot)$ and $(y\cdot)$ are independent of s [see (1.28)–(1.30)], the optimal reaction functions are linear in s. Geometrically, if we take R as given and describe the dependence of the optimal value of any of our $m+n$ variables on the n elements of s, we obtain a hyperplane in an $(n+1)$-dimensional space. These hyperplanes are called *Tinbergen surfaces* and are n-dimensional (flat) planes under quadratic preference assumptions; [1] their slopes are the elements of $-(x\cdot)$ and $-(y\cdot)$. Thus, we have:

THEOREM 2.5. *Suppose that the assumptions of Theorem* 2.4 *are satisfied. Then*:

(i) *The effect on* x^0 *and* y^0 *of infinitesimal changes* dR, ds *in the parameter matrices of the constraints* (1.6) *consists of a constant-term effect and a substitution effect, but the substitution effect of* ds *is identically zero.*

(ii) *The Tinbergen surfaces describing the dependence of* x^0 *and* y^0 *on* s *for given* R *are n-dimensional planes, and their slope matrices are* $-(x\cdot)$ *and* $-(y\cdot)$ *as defined in* (1.28)–(1.30).

(iii) *If an instrument is a substitute of* (*complementary with*) *another instrument or a noncontrolled variable with respect to some constraint, it is complementary with* (*a substitute of*) *this variable with respect to no constraint. Substitution and complementarity are symmetric relations*; *complementarity is also a reflexive relation.*

2.1.8. Extension of the Optimal Reaction Functions

It might be argued that for a case like that of the factory manager, it is much more interesting to analyze the implications of changes in the parameters of the preference function than those of changes in R, for R is simply [1], see (1.9). It is indeed more interesting to analyze changes in the parameters of the cost function, which may be due to such reasons as factor price changes or changes in labour conditions, etc. Doing so, we shall find that the R-analysis of the preceding pages is far from superfluous even for those cases in which R-changes must be condemned as unrealistic.

If we admit the possibility of changes in the preference coefficients, the optimal reaction functions must be written in the form

$$x^0 = x(R, s; a, b, A, B, C) \tag{1.42}$$

[1] In the consumer example the Tinbergen surfaces are the wellknown Engel curves, which are straight lines under quadratic utility conditions.

instead of (1.35). We shall confine ourselves to the instrumental optimal reaction functions, because those of the noncontrolled variables will play no role in the further analysis. Further, we shall confine ourselves to first-order differentials, so that we have to consider expressions of the type

$$dx_h = \sum_j \sum_k \frac{\partial x_h}{\partial r_{jk}} dr_{jk} + \ldots + \sum_k \sum_j \frac{\partial x_h}{\partial c_{kj}} dc_{kj} .$$

This leads to a sum of seven sets of terms, of which the first two are in dR and ds, so that they need not be considered here because they are covered by Theorem 2.4. The others are in da, db, dA, ..., and they are derived in exactly the same way. We consider again the linear system (1.16) and compare it now with

$$\begin{bmatrix} A+dA & C+dC & (R+dR)' \\ (C+dC)' & B+dB & -\mathbf{I} \\ R+dR & -\mathbf{I} & \mathbf{0} \end{bmatrix} \begin{bmatrix} x^0+dx \\ y^0+dy \\ \lambda^0+d\lambda \end{bmatrix} = - \begin{bmatrix} a+da \\ b+db \\ s+ds \end{bmatrix},$$

which is similar to (1.36) except that there are now infinitesimal changes in a, b, . . . as well. As in that case we subtract (1.16) and solve, neglecting products of differentials. The result is:

$$\begin{bmatrix} dx \\ dy \\ d\lambda \end{bmatrix} = - \begin{bmatrix} (xx) & (xy) & (x\cdot) \\ (yx) & (yy) & (y\cdot) \\ (\cdot x) & (\cdot y) & (\cdot\cdot) \end{bmatrix} \begin{bmatrix} (dA)x^0+(dC)y^0+(dR)'\lambda^0+da \\ (dC)'x^0+(dB)y^0+db \\ (dR)x^0+ds \end{bmatrix},$$

from which we see that changes in the coefficients of the preference function have no constant-term effect on x^0 but only a substitution effect. For example:

$$\frac{\partial x_h}{\partial a_k} = -(xx)_{hk} \quad \text{and} \quad \frac{\partial x_h}{\partial b_j} = -(xy)_{hj} .$$

Our results can be summarized as follows:

THEOREM 2.6. *Suppose that Assumptions* 2.1 *and* 2.2 *are satisfied; suppose also that the second-order maximum condition formulated in Theorem* 2.2 *is satisfied, both when the coefficient matrix* R *of the constraints* (1.6) *and the matrices* A, B *and* C *of the preference function* (1.5) *are as they are and when they take the values*

$$R+dR, \quad A+dA, \quad B+dB, \quad C+dC,$$

respectively, where dR, dA, dB *and* dC *are matrices of infinitesimal changes,* dA *and* dB *being symmetric. Then the change in* x^0 *according to the optimal reaction functions in the generalized form* (1.42), *caused by these changes and by the vectors* ds, da *and* db *of infinitesimal changes in the coefficient vectors* s, a *and* b *of the constraints* (1.6) *and the preference function* (1.5), *is given by*:

$$(1.43)\quad dx = -(x\cdot)[(dR)x^0+ds]-(xx)(dR)'\lambda^0 - (xx)[da+(dA)x^0+(dC)y^0]-(xy)[db+(dC)'x^0+(dB)y^0],$$

where $(x\cdot)$, (xx), (xy) *are defined in* (1.28)–(1.30), *and* x^0, y^0, λ^0 *in* (1.31)–(1.33), *respectively. The optimal value* x^0 *is a linear function of the vectors* s, a *and* b, *and a nonlinear function of* R, A, B *and* C.

The last sentence of this theorem follows directly from (1.31).

2.1.9. Summary

The results of this section can be summarized as follows:[1]

(1, 2) We consider a decision maker who maximizes a quadratic preference function subject to linear constraints. The arguments of the preference function are partly controlled variables (instruments), partly noncontrolled variables. The constraints express each of the noncontrolled variables linearly in the instruments. No uncertainty is assumed in this section. Further, the attention is confined to static decision-making, which implies that a single numerical choice is to be made for each of the instruments.

(3) The conditional maximization problem can be solved by means of the Lagrangean technique, which leads to a number of linear relations from which the optimal values of the instruments and the corresponding values of the noncontrolled variables can be determined. The number of equations of this system is equal to the number of instruments plus twice the number of noncontrolled variables. The system supplies the first-order maximum condition (stationarity condition); the second-order maximum condition can be formulated in terms of alternating signs of appropriate principal minors of the matrix of the system. The elements of this matrix include the second-order derivatives of the preference function (which are constants under the quadratic assumption) as well as the multiplicative coefficients of the constraints.

(4, 5) An alternative but equivalent method of deriving the optimum consists of using the constraints to eliminate the noncontrolled variables from the preference function and then maximizing this function unconditionally with respect to the instruments. This leads directly to explicit expressions for the optimal instrument values, for the corresponding

---

[1] The summary is arranged by subsections. Thus, the paragraph headed by (1, 2) summarizes 2.1.1 and 2.1.2, and similarly (3) for 2.1.3, and so on.

noncontrolled values, and for the associated values of the Lagrangean multipliers that are used in the approach under (3). If the second-order maximum condition is fulfilled (which is assumed), then the maximum is unique.

(6, 8) The remainder of the section is devoted to an analysis of the dependence of the optimal instrument values on the coefficients of the preference function and of the constraints (the optimal reaction functions). The coefficients of the linear part of the preference function and the additive coefficients ("constant terms") of the constraints affect the optimal instrument values linearly. This is not true for the other coefficients (those of the quadratic part of the preference function and the multiplicative coefficients of the constraints); for these coefficients only the first-order or linearized effect is analyzed, which is done by differentiating the equation system mentioned under (3).

(7) It appears that changes along the optimal reaction functions can be described conveniently in terms of the matrix of the system mentioned under (3), in particular by certain submatrices of the inverse of that matrix. Thus the linear dependence of the optimal instrument values on the constant terms of the constraints (described geometrically as the Tinbergen surfaces of the instruments) is characterized by a coefficient matrix which is identical with such a submatrix apart from sign; similarly, the linear dependence on the coefficients of the linear part of the preference function is characterized by a coefficient matrix which is identical with another submatrix except for its sign. This is used to make a distinction between the constant-term effect and the substitution effect of changes in the determining coefficients; the former effect applies to changes in the constant terms of the constraints, the latter to changes in the preference coefficients. Changes in the multiplicative coefficients of the constraints have both a substitution and a constant-term effect. The submatrices mentioned above, particularly the substitution matrix of the instruments, will play an important role in the further analysis.

2.2. UNCERTAINTY AND CERTAINTY EQUIVALENCE

2.2.1. Introductory; Types of Uncertainty

There are many cases in which a decision problem can be formulated in terms of linear constraints and a quadratic preference function, or at least approximately so, but it is then not necessarily true that there is certainty with respect to the determining factors. These factors are the coefficients of the preference function and of the constraints, and accordingly it is convenient to discuss the implications of uncertainty under the following four headings:

(i) There may be uncertainty as to the elements of the vector s, which describes the additive structure of the constraints. For example, in the case of the factory manager's decision problem as outlined in 2.1.1, s consists of one single element: $I_0 - S$ [see (1.9)]; and since next month's shipments (S) are generally unknown at the beginning of the month when the decision has to be made, there is then uncertainty as to the additive structure of the constraints.

(ii) We may be uncertain about some or all of the elements of R, i.e., about the multiplicative structure of the constraints. In the factory manager's example this will not be the case, since it is known that R consists of a single unit element; see (1.9). However, when it is realized that in the general theory any element of R, say r_{ih}, describes the effectiveness of the instrument x_h with respect to the noncontrolled variable y_i, it is not difficult to see that there should be many cases in which there is only limited knowledge of the precise value of this effectiveness.

(iii) There may be uncertainty as to the elements of a and b, which are the coefficients of the linear part of the preference function. To put it slightly differently: if we differentiate the preference function with respect to instruments and noncontrolled variables, so that we obtain the marginal utilities of these variables of which the a and b-elements are the constant terms, then uncertainty as to these elements is equivalent to uncertainty of the levels of the marginal utilities. If we consider the factory manager's case again, it is easily seen that uncertainty of this kind may well be realistic; for the coefficients discussed here are parameters of the cost function [viz., $-b$ and $-b'$, see (1.8)]. Such parameters must in general be estimated from engineering and statistical data and will therefore be subject to errors of estimation.

(iv) Finally, we may have uncertainty as to the elements of A, B and C; or, what amounts to the same, uncertainty as to the way in which the marginal utilities are affected by changes in controlled and noncontrolled variables. This, too, can be illustrated conveniently by means of the factory manager's example; we refer to the parameters $-2c$ and $-2c'$ of the cost function, see (1.8).

In this book it will be assumed that the uncertainty is of the probabilistic type. The simplest case occurs when the coefficient about which the decision maker feels uncertain is subject to a probability distribution with a known mean value. But there is also the more difficult case when the mean of the distribution is unknown and must be replaced by an estimate. The simple case will be elaborated in 2.2.2, the more complicated ones in 2.2.3.

2.2.2. Second Set of Assumptions; Certainty Equivalence

We shall start by assuming that the only type of uncertainty is that of the additive structure of the constraints. As a matter of fact, it is not difficult to see that it is not unreasonable to give a prominent role to this type of uncertainty, given the importance of additive disturbances in econometric models and similar equation systems.

Suppose then that the uncertainty as to s can be formalized by stating that its elements are subject to a joint distribution with finite variances. In the factory manager's case this amounts to assuming that next month's shipments are subject to a distribution with finite variance; we make here the convenient assumption that the initial inventory level (I_0) is known, see (1.9), and we also assume that the coefficients of the cost function are known. Then the optimal production decision is a random variable, just as next month's shipments, see (1.20). Hence, whether any particular production decision is optimal or not depends on the outcome of a chance mechanism. Clearly, this does not carry us very far. We therefore have to change our criterion, which will be done by assuming that the decision maker, when facing probabilistic uncertainty, behaves as if he maximizes the expectation of the preference function. More precisely:

ASSUMPTION 2.3. *Assumption* 2.1 *is satisfied. Moreover, if the vector of noncontrolled variables contains stochastic elements, the decision maker behaves as if his preferences are measured by the expectation of the function* (1.5), $\mathscr{E}w(\mathsf{x}, \mathsf{y})$.

The counterpart at the constraint level is Assumption 2.4, in which it is also assumed that the expectations, variances and covariances of the s-elements are independent of the instruments (for reasons that will be apparent immediately).

ASSUMPTION 2.4. *Assumption* 2.2 *is satisfied, except that the elements of the vector* s *of* (1.6) *are subject to a joint distribution with finite variances. The means, variances and covariances of these elements do not depend on the instrument vector* x.

The problem is thus shifted from the maximization of w subject to the nonstochastic constraints $\mathsf{y} = \mathsf{R}\mathsf{x}+\mathsf{s}$ to the maximization of $\mathscr{E}w$ subject to the same constraints but interpreted stochastically. It is solved conveniently by applying the procedure of 2.1.4, i.e., by eliminating the noncontrolled variables from the preference function. In accordance with (1.24), this gives

$$w(x, Rx+s) = k_0+k'x+\tfrac{1}{2}x'Kx,$$

where k_0, k and K are defined in (1.25). We are interested in the mean value of the preference function for any given x, which is

$$\mathscr{E}w(x, Rx+s) = \mathscr{E}k_0+(\mathscr{E}k)'x+\tfrac{1}{2}x'Kx, \tag{2.1}$$

where use is made of the fact that K is independent of s and hence non-stochastic. Now let us compare the expected preference level (2.1), for any given x, with the preference level which is attained when the same x is applied but under the condition that the random vector s coincides with its expectation, $\mathscr{E}s$. Then (1.24) is still applicable except that k_0 is to be interpreted as $b'\mathscr{E}s+\frac{1}{2}(\mathscr{E}s)'B\mathscr{E}s$ and, similarly, k such that the s on the right of its equation in (1.25) is replaced by $\mathscr{E}s$; K is not affected. It is easily seen that if s is replaced by $\mathscr{E}s$ in the equation for k, we obtain $\mathscr{E}k$ (since k is a linear function of s). Hence the preference level attained under the condition $s = \mathscr{E}s$ is

$$w(x, Rx+\mathscr{E}s) = b'\mathscr{E}s+\tfrac{1}{2}(\mathscr{E}s)'B\mathscr{E}s+(\mathscr{E}k)'x+\tfrac{1}{2}x'Kx. \tag{2.2}$$

On comparing this with (2.1), we see that the expected preference level corresponding with x differs from the preference level corresponding with the same x under the condition $s = \mathscr{E}s$ by a quantity which is a constant with respect to x:

$$\begin{aligned}
&\mathscr{E}w(x, Rx+s)-w(x, Rx+\mathscr{E}s)\\
&\quad= \mathscr{E}(b's+\tfrac{1}{2}s'Bs)-b'\mathscr{E}s-\tfrac{1}{2}(\mathscr{E}s)'B\mathscr{E}s\\
&\quad= \tfrac{1}{2}\mathscr{E}(s'Bs)-\tfrac{1}{2}(\mathscr{E}s)'B\mathscr{E}s = \tfrac{1}{2}\sum_i\sum_j b_{ij}\operatorname{cov}(s_i, s_j),
\end{aligned}$$

where the last expression is indeed constant because the variances and covariances of the s-elements are assumed to be independent of x in Assumption 2.4. It follows that the expected preference level (which we wish to maximize) is obtained from the preference level under the condition $s = \mathscr{E}s$ by adding a constant, and hence that the two functions (2.1) and (2.2) must reach their maximum for the same x. But it follows from (1.27) and (1.31) that (2.2) is maximized by

$$\begin{aligned}
\hat{x} = -K^{-1}\mathscr{E}k &= -(xx)[a+R'b+(C+R'B)\mathscr{E}s]\\
&= -(A+R'BR+CR+R'C')^{-1}[a+R'b+(C+R'B)\mathscr{E}s],
\end{aligned} \tag{2.3}$$

so that this must be the vector which maximizes the mean value of the preference function subject to the stochastic constraints. It is also easily seen that $\hat{x}$ is the expectation of the optimal decision x^0, the expectation being taken over all possible values of the random vector s. Thus, we have proved:

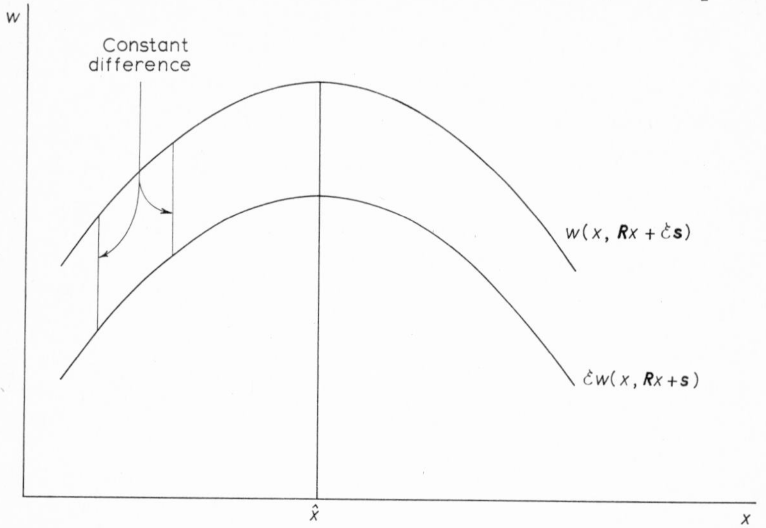

Figure 2.1. Illustration of the proof of the (static) certainty equivalence theorem for the case of one instrument

THEOREM 2.7. *Suppose that Assumptions* 2.3 *and* 2.4 *are satisfied. Then the instrument vector which maximizes the mean value of the preference function* (1.5) *subject to the stochastic constraints* (1.6) *is identical with the vector which maximizes* (1.5) *subject to* (1.6) *under the restriction that the vector* s *coincides with its expectation, and this instrument vector is* $\hat{x}$ *as specified in* (2.3)—*provided that these maxima exist. This proviso is fulfilled if the second-order maximum condition formulated in Theorem* 2.2 *is fulfilled.*

This is the theorem of (static) certainty equivalence; it can be interpreted in the sense that the expectation of s is a certainty equivalent for s, i.e., that by acting as if the uncertain s is equal to its expectation the decision maker maximizes the expected preference level. In the factory manager's example, e.g., this implies a $\hat{P}$ which depends on the mean value of next month's shipments in the same way as P^0 depends on the actual shipments. Note that $\hat{P}$ is not "truly optimal" in the sense that it minimizes costs. P^0 minimizes cost, and $\hat{P}$ is a "surrogate" for P^0; the use of a surrogate is necessary because lack of perfect foresight forces the retreat to a "second-best" criterion, viz., the minimization of expected costs. Note further the condition involving the independence of the covariance matrix of s. In the example this condition is not particularly serious, since there is little reason to expect that changes in the rate of production affect the variance of sales. But there may be cases in which the situation is different; for example, when particular instrument changes force certain noncontrolled variables in the direction of a ceiling where their variance is reduced.

2.2.3. Extension of Certainty Equivalence; Two Kinds of Randomness and a Bayesian Approach

Theorem 2.7 can be easily extended to the case in which there is also uncertainty as to the coefficients of the linear part of the preference function. For suppose that a and b are random with means $\mathscr{E}a$ and $\mathscr{E}b$, respectively, and that these means as well as all variances and covariances in which these vectors enter are independent of x. The expected value of the preference function is then given by (2.1) as before, but $\mathscr{E}k_0$ and $\mathscr{E}k$ should now be interpreted as

$$\mathscr{E}(b's)+\tfrac{1}{2}\mathscr{E}(s'Bs) \quad \text{and} \quad \mathscr{E}a+R'\mathscr{E}b+(C+R'B)\mathscr{E}s,$$

respectively. If we compare this variant of (2.1) with the preference level attained under the condition that a, b and s are all equal to their expectations, we find that the linear and the quadratic parts are the same, whereas the constant terms are different. The constant term of the expected preference level is $\mathscr{E}(b's)+\frac{1}{2}\mathscr{E}(s'Bs)$, and that of the certainty equivalence procedure $(\mathscr{E}b)'\mathscr{E}s+\frac{1}{2}(\mathscr{E}s)'B\mathscr{E}s$. Hence the difference is

$$\begin{aligned}(2.4)\qquad & \mathscr{E}(b's)-(\mathscr{E}b)'\mathscr{E}s+\tfrac{1}{2}\mathscr{E}(s'Bs)-\tfrac{1}{2}(\mathscr{E}s)'B\mathscr{E}s \\ & = \sum_i \operatorname{cov}(b_i, s_i)+\tfrac{1}{2}\sum_i\sum_j b_{ij}\operatorname{cov}(s_i, s_j),\end{aligned}$$

which is a constant with respect to x under the conditions stated above.

This result can be used to handle random fluctuations of the levels of the marginal utilities. Suppose, e.g., that in the factory manager's case the marginal production costs shift upward or downward depending on the quality of certain raw materials. If successive shipments of raw materials are random with respect to quality, the same will apply to b which is the coefficient measuring the level of the marginal cost of production; see (1.8). In such a case b is to be replaced by its expectation if the manager wishes to minimize expected costs.

It is of some interest to consider the following alternative assumption.

Suppose that the coefficient b is fixed rather than random, but that the manager does not know this fixed value and estimates it by means of some statistical procedure. In that case he will commit sampling errors in general. Or let us consider a combination of this case and that of the preceding paragraph: b is random and its expectation is $\mathscr{E}b$, but the manager does not know $\mathscr{E}b$ and estimates it. In such a case we face two distinct kinds of randomness: one is the random variability of the true b around its own expectation, and the other is the random variability of the estimator of this expectation around the value which it serves to estimate. It will be noted that this "double randomness" is not necessarily confined to coefficients of the linear part of the preference function. For example, next month's shipments S may be distributed around an unknown expectation μ, which is estimated by m. In general, S, μ and m are pairwise different; which implies that s, its expectation, and the estimate of this expectation are also pairwise different, see (1.9). The question arises whether the same certainty equivalence result applies to such estimates if they are unbiased. In other words, is it true that the factory manager minimizes expected costs by replacing S by m if $\mathscr{E}m = \mu$? The answer is yes and no. It is no if the problem is considered from the traditional ("non-Bayesian") statistical point of view, since it turns out that the decision which minimizes expected costs will then depend both on the true μ and on the variance of m around μ. The problem of finding the maximizing decision which does not involve unknown parameters is unsolved and it seems that the procedure of a simple replacement of S by m, although it is perhaps not optimal, cannot be easily surpassed.[1] On the other hand, the answer is yes if we adopt the following Bayesian point of view. We measure the factory manager's uncertainty about next month's shipments by a subjective probability distribution and postulate that the mean of this distribution is m. Then m can be regarded as the conditional expectation of S, given the information which is available to the factory manager. Under this interpretation Theorem 2.7 is applicable in the sense that m serves as a certainty equivalent for S in the minimization of the conditional expectation of costs, given the available information. The extension of this result to estimators of $\mathscr{E}\mathsf{a}$, $\mathscr{E}\mathsf{b}$ and $\mathscr{E}\mathsf{s}$ will be obvious.

---

[1] See P. J. M. VAN DEN BOGAARD, "On the Static Theory of Certainty Equivalence," Report 6010 of the Econometric Institute of the Netherlands School of Economics; also an unpublished paper by J. DURBIN quoted in this article. For the Bayesian approach, see e.g. R. SCHLAIFER, *Probability and Statistics for Business Decisions* (1959).

The extension to the matrices A, B, C and R is not that simple. In fact, the only thing which can be derived fairly easily is that—under appropriate assumptions—replacing these matrices by their expectations is characterized by a first-order certainty equivalence. We refer to Appendix 2.B for a more detailed elaboration.

2.2.4. *Summary*

(1) Four types of uncertainty are considered, concerning (i) the additive structure of the constraints, (ii) their multiplicative structure, (iii) the coefficients of the linear part of the preference function, and (iv) the coefficients of the quadratic part of this function.

(2) Assuming that the uncertainty is of the probabilistic variety, we shift the criterion of maximizing the preference function to that of maximizing its expectation. It is shown that if the uncertainty is confined to the additive structure of the constraints, the decision that maximizes expected utility is identical with the decision that maximizes the preference function under the condition that these random coefficients are equal to their expectations (certainty equivalence). This result presupposes that the variances and covariances of these coefficients are finite and independent of the instruments.

(3) The certainty equivalence result can be extended in a straightforward fashion to random fluctuations of the coefficients of the linear part of the preference function: replacing them by their expectations maximizes expected utility. It can also be extended to the case in which only estimates of such expectations are available; in that case, under the appropriate Bayesian interpretation, the conditional expectation of the preference function is maximized, given the available information at the moment when the decision has to be made. For random specification errors in the multiplicative structure of the constraints and in the quadratic part of the preference function there is no certainty equivalence result in the strict sense; but if such errors have zero expectation, there is a first-order certainty equivalence (see Appendix 2.B).

2.3. LOSSES DUE TO SUBOPTIMAL DECISIONS AND TO IMPERFECT SPECIFICATIONS OF CONSTRAINTS AND PREFERENCE FUNCTION

2.3.1. *The Loss Concept; The Loss Due to a Suboptimal Decision*

We return to the optimal decision x^0 which maximizes the preference function (1.5) subject to the constraints (1.6); see (1.27) and (1.31).

In many cases there will be imperfections which cause another x to be selected. For example, if s is stochastic with expectation $\mathscr{E}s$ and if the decision maker maximizes expected utility, then the selection is $x = \hat{x}$ as specified in (2.3). There are many other possibilities of a behaviour which deviates from the optimal decision, and they have all the following feature in common; they depress the utility level attained below the attainable maximum. This utility reduction is called the *loss* associated with the suboptimal decision; or, more generally, the loss associated either with such a decision or with the cause of its suboptimality such as an error in specifying the vector s. Here, in 2.3.1, we shall consider only suboptimal decisions without going back to the reason of the suboptimal character. In 2.3.2 and 2.3.3 it will be assumed that an incorrect specification of s is the cause, after which this assumption is extended to the other coefficient matrices of the preference function and the constraints.

We shall write w^0 for the maximal preference level attainable. Upon combining (1.24), (1.26) and (1.27), we find that w^0 is given by

$$w^0 = k_0 - \tfrac{1}{2}k'K^{-1}k = k_0 - \tfrac{1}{2}x^{0\prime}Kx^0. \tag{3.1}$$

Further, we shall write w_x for the preference level which is attained if the decision x is selected, where x is any vector of m real-valued elements. Then (1.24) specifies

$$w_x = k_0 + k'x + \tfrac{1}{2}x'Kx. \tag{3.2}$$

The loss associated with the decision x is then defined as the difference between (3.1) and (3.2):

$$w^0 - w_x = -\tfrac{1}{2}(x^{0\prime}Kx^0 + 2k'x + x'Kx);$$

or, taking account of $k = -Kx^0$ [see (1.27)] and applying some minor rearrangements:

$$w^0 - w_x = -\tfrac{1}{2}(x - x^0)'K(x - x^0) = -\tfrac{1}{2}(x - x^0)'(xx)^{-1}(x - x^0), \tag{3.3}$$

where use has been made of (1.29). Hence the loss associated with x is a quadratic form in the *decision error* $x - x^0$, and the matrix of this form is $-\frac{1}{2}$ times the inverse of the substitution matrix of the instruments. This matrix is positive definite, since (xx) and $(xx)^{-1} = K$ are negative definite according to the second-order condition formulated in Theorem 2.2.—Thus we have:

THEOREM 2.8. *Suppose that Assumptions* 2.1 *and* 2.2 *are satisfied; suppose also that the second-order maximum condition formulated in Theorem* 2.2 *is satisfied. Then the loss associated with any decision* x *is the positive definite quadratic form* (3.3) *in the decision error* $\mathbf{x}-\mathbf{x}^0$, *where* $\mathbf{x}^0$ *is the optimal decision as specified in* (1.27) *and* (1.31), $(\mathbf{xx})$ *the substitution matrix of the instruments as specified in* (1.29), *and* $\mathbf{K}$ *is given in* (1.25).

In the static variant of the factory manager example we have only one instrument (P), so that the loss consists of one single quadratic term, viz., $(c+c')(P-P^0)^2$; see (1.8)–(1.9). The loss (in this case: the additional costs above the minimum attainable) due to a given decision error in production is therefore larger when the "total curvilinearity" of the production and inventory cost functions (measured by the sum of the coefficients c and c') is larger; and, given c and c', the loss varies with the square of the decision error and is therefore very small if the error is small, while it becomes quite substantial for large errors. This holds more generally: a decision error which is of the first order of smallness leads to a loss which is small of the second order. In plain English this means that it is not really necessary to "hit" the optimum exactly; it is sufficient to get close to it, and once one has succeeded in this any additional efforts to approach the optimum still closer meet sharply decreasing returns.

The static factory manager example is not very interesting in this context because there is only one instrument. When there are two, say, we need the inverse of their 2×2 substitution matrix:

$$(\mathbf{xx})^{-1} = \frac{1}{(xx)_{11}(xx)_{22}-\{(xx)_{12}\}^2}\begin{bmatrix}(xx)_{22} & -(xx)_{12}\\ -(xx)_{21} & (xx)_{11}\end{bmatrix},$$

so that the loss as specified in (3.3) consists of two weighted squares:

$$-\tfrac{1}{2}\frac{(xx)_{22}}{(xx)_{11}(xx)_{22}-\{(xx)_{12}\}^2}(x_1-x_1^0)^2$$

$$-\tfrac{1}{2}\frac{(xx)_{11}}{(xx)_{11}(xx)_{22}-\{(xx)_{12}\}^2}(x_2-x_2^0)^2,$$

plus a weighted product:

$$\frac{(xx)_{12}}{(xx)_{11}(xx)_{22}-\{(xx)_{12}\}^2}(x_1-x_1^0)(x_2-x_2^0).$$

This shows that errors of opposite sign tend to compensate each other if $(xx)_{12} > 0$, i.e., if the instruments are substitutes; and that they reinforce each other if the instruments are complementary. It is also seen that a given decision error in x_1, say, is more serious when its "own" substitution term, $(xx)_{11}$, is closer to zero.

2.3.2. *The Loss Due to an Imperfect Prediction of the Additive Structure of the Constraints*

It was argued at the beginning of 2.2.2 that as far as uncertainty and lack of complete knowledge are concerned the additive structure of the constraints plays a dominating role. Accordingly, it is appropriate to start with the assumption that an imperfectly specified s is the cause of the suboptimal x.

The argument is as follows. Suppose that the decision maker stands at the beginning of the period to which the constraints $y = Rx+s$ apply; e.g., the factory manager who stands at the beginning of the month during which his optimal production is P^0 as specified in (1.20). Suppose also that he has a forecast s_e of the additive structure at his disposal, so that the prediction error is the vector $s_e - s$; e.g., his forecast may be the unbiased prediction $\mathscr{E}s$, in which case he maximizes expected utility according to Theorem 2.7 if he behaves as if $s = \mathscr{E}s$. Suppose finally that it is indeed true that the decision maker behaves as if $s = s_e$; i.e., that the actual decision which he makes is the x which maximizes the preference function subject to the constraints with the understanding that the vector s of the constraints is replaced by s_e. It follows immediately that the decision error $x - x^0$ is then identical with the change in the instrument values according to the optimal reaction functions if the constraints would change such that s is replaced by s_e. Since the optimal reaction functions are linear in s (Theorem 2.6), this implies

$$x - x^0 = -(x\cdot)(s_e - s) \tag{3.4}$$

according to (1.43). But the decision error $x - x^0$ leads to the loss (3.3); hence the prediction error $s_e - s$ leads, *via* its impact on the decision made, to the loss

$$-\tfrac{1}{2}(s_e - s)'F(s_e - s), \tag{3.5}$$

where F—called the *failure matrix* for reasons to be given in 2.3.3—is the symmetric matrix

$$F = (x\cdot)'(xx)^{-1}(x\cdot) = (\cdot x)(xx)^{-1}(x\cdot) = (C+R'B)'(xx)(C+R'B), \tag{3.6}$$

see (1.30). This result is summarized in the first part of

THEOREM 2.9. *Suppose that Assumptions* 2.1 *and* 2.2 *are satisfied; suppose also that the second-order maximum condition formulated in Theorem* 2.2 *is satisfied. Then the decision error implied by behaving as if the forecast* s_e *of the additive structure of the constraints* (1.6) *is identical with the true additive structure is equal to* (3.4), *where* x^0 *is the optimal decision as specified in* (1.27) *and* (1.31), *and* $-(x\cdot)$ *the slope matrix of the Tinbergen surfaces of the instruments as specified in* (1.28)–(1.30); *further, the loss associated with this forecast is the positive semi-definite or positive definite quadratic form* (3.5) *where* $F = [f_{ij}]$ *is defined in* (3.6). *If, in addition, Assumptions* 2.3 *and* 2.4 *are satisfied, then*

$$(3.7) \qquad -\tfrac{1}{2}\mathscr{E}[(s-\mathscr{E}s)'F(s-\mathscr{E}s)] = -\tfrac{1}{2}\sum_i\sum_j f_{ij}\operatorname{cov}(s_i, s_j)$$

is the expected loss associated with maximizing expected utility in accordance with Theorem 2.7.

It will be noted that the failure matrix is described as being either negative semi-definite or negative definite. The former possibility applies if we take $m < n$ (fewer instruments than noncontrolled variables), for F is then of order $n \times n$ while its rank cannot exceed m [the rank of the product $(\cdot x)(xx)^{-1}(x\cdot)$ is necessarily equal to the rank of $(x\cdot)$]. For example, take the case $m = 1$, $n = 2$; and suppose that the optimal reaction function for the (single) instrument, given the other coefficient matrices except s, is $x^0 = 3+2s_1+s_2$. Then any prediction errors in s_1 and s_2 with ratio 1 : (−2) lead to a zero loss because they do not affect the decision. This holds more generally: if F is not negative definite, there exist particular combinations of s-errors which leave the optimal decision unchanged and hence lead to a zero loss. On the other hand, most s-errors do not fall under this category and imply a positive loss. This loss is a quadratic form (as in the case of decision errors); it is therefore small of the second order if the prediction errors are small of the first order.

The second part of Theorem 2.9 deals with the loss due to the application of the certainty equivalence procedure of Theorem 2.7. This loss is found by substituting $\mathscr{E}s$ for s_e in (3.5); and it is stochastic, due to the fact that the s-elements are random under Assumption 2.4. The mean value of the stochastic loss is specified in (3.7); it shows that, given the failure matrix, the consequences of replacing the maximization of utility by maximizing expected utility depend on the covariance matrix of the vector s.

2.3.3. Success and Failure of a Forecast

Sometimes the unit in which a loss is measured is so obvious and concrete that it is not worthwhile to dwell on it in any detail. For example, in the factory manager's case losses are expressed in dollars per month. However, this is not true in all cases. In the consumer's example we have a rather abstract utility unit; and, similarly, when we shall maximize a social preference function for an economy as a whole, any losses will be expressed in social utility units. In such a case we may prefer a more convenient unit.

Let us write $w(s_e|s)$ for the preference level attained if the decision maker behaves as if s_e is the additive structure of the constraints whereas s is the true additive structure. Then $w(s|s) = w^0$ and the loss associated with s_e is

$$w^0 - w(s_e|s) = -\tfrac{1}{2}(s_e - s)'F(s_e - s), \tag{3.8}$$

see (3.5). Now the additive structure is in general determined by past as well as future factors. For example, in the factory manager's case of 2.1.1 (static variant) the constraint for the period immediately ahead is $I_1 = P_1 + (I_0 - S_1)$, so that $s = [I_0 - S_1]$; I_0 is the initial inventory level and is therefore completely determined by the past, while S_1 stands for the shipments from now until the end of the first period and is thus future. It is obvious that the factory manager is always in a position to use S_0 as a predictor of S_1, i.e., to take shipments of the most recent period (provided he is sufficiently rapidly informed). This means that he uses $s_0 = [I_0 - S_0]$ instead of the "true" $s = [I_0 - S_1]$; in words, he replaces the "future" part of the additive structure by the corresponding most recent observations.

More generally, the additive structure will always be a function of certain events that will take place in the period under consideration (q_1) and of events which took place in a certain number of previous periods ($q_0, q_{-1}, q_{-2}, \ldots$). The "extrapolated" additive structure is the same function but the q_1-arguments are replaced by their immediate predecessors:

$$\begin{aligned} s &= f(q_1, q_0, q_{-1}, \ldots) \\ s_0 &= f(q_0, q_0, q_{-1}, \ldots). \end{aligned} \tag{3.9}$$

Now it will be clear that by applying this no-change extrapolation the decision maker is able to attain the preference level $w(s_0|s)$ and the corresponding loss is then

$$w^0 - w(s_0|s) = -\tfrac{1}{2}(s_0 - s)'F(s_0 - s).$$

This is frequently a useful unit in which the loss due to an imperfect prediction s_e can be measured. The result is called the *failure* of the forecast s_e:

$$\text{fail } s_e = \frac{w^0 - w(s_e|s)}{w^0 - w(s_0|s)} = \frac{(s_e - s)'F(s_e - s)}{(s_0 - s)'F(s_0 - s)}. \tag{3.10}$$

Hence the failure of s_e is the ratio of two quadratic forms, both of them being characterized by the same matrix F (hence the term failure matrix). The failure is zero if the prediction is perfect ($s_e = s$).[1] It is 1 if the forecast is the no-change extrapolation and, more generally, if the forecast leads to the same loss as the no-change extrapolation. The failure has no finite upper bound, which means that it is possible to do considerably worse than extrapolating on a simple no-change basis. Furthermore, it is frequently also useful to introduce the *success* of a forecast s_e, which is defined as the excess of the preference level attained by adopting s_e over the level corresponding with s_0, and which is measured in the same units:

$$\text{suc } s_e = 1 - \text{fail } s_e = \frac{w(s_e|s) - w(s_0|s)}{w^0 - w(s_0|s)} = \frac{(s_0 - s_e)'F(s_0 + s_e - 2s)}{(s_0 - s)'F(s_0 - s)}. \tag{3.11}$$

In the same way as the decision maker can reduce the failure to 1 (viz., by no-change extrapolation) he can enforce a nonnegative success.

We shall also use success and failure concepts in a statistical population. They will be indicated by Suc and Fail respectively, and defined as the corresponding ratios of expected values. Summarizing, we have:

THEOREM 2.10. *Suppose that Assumptions* 2.1 *and* 2.2 *are satisfied; suppose also that the second-order maximum condition formulated in Theorem* 2.2 *is satisfied. Then the failure of the forecast* s_e *of the additive structure of the constraints* (1.6) *is the ratio of two positive semi-definite quadratic forms* (3.10) *with the understanding that the denominator (involving the extrapolated additive structure* s_0*) is supposed not to vanish. If, in addition, Assumptions* 2.3 *and* 2.4 *are satisfied, then*

$$\text{Fail } \mathscr{E}s = \frac{\mathscr{E}[(s - \mathscr{E}s)'F(s - \mathscr{E}s)]}{\mathscr{E}[(s_0 - s)'F(s_0 - s)]} \tag{3.12}$$

is the parent failure of the procedure of maximizing expected utility of Theorem 2.7, *again with the understanding that the denominator is supposed not to vanish.*

The proviso that the denominator should not vanish is rather obvious. It will be noted that it is not sufficient to assume $s_0 \neq s$, since F may be semi-definite and not definite.

[1] It may also be zero for imperfect forecasts because F may be semi-definite and not definite; see 2.3.2.

2.3.4. *The Loss Due to Specification Errors in All Coefficient Matrices*

We will now assume that there are errors in a and b as well as in s. Thus, we suppose that the decision maker behaves as if these vectors are a_e, b_e, s_e, respectively. Applying Theorem 2.6, we find that the resulting decision error is

$$x-x^0 = -(xx)(a_e-a)-(xy)(b_e-b)-(x\cdot)(s_e-s), \tag{3.13}$$

and the corresponding loss can be derived by applying (3.3).

The situation is more complicated when there are specification errors in the matrices A, B, C, R. The reason is that their effect on the decision taken is nonlinear, the optimal reaction functions being linear in the vectors a, b, s but nonlinear in the matrices A, B, C, R. However, if the errors in these matrices are sufficiently small, a satisfactory approximation to the decision error is obtained if we replace the curvilinear reaction functions by their tangent planes in the optimal decision. In that case we can apply Theorem 2.6 as before, so that

$$x-x^0 \approx -(x\cdot)[(dR)x^0+ds]-(xx)[(dR)'\lambda^0+dw], \tag{3.14}$$

where $\approx$ indicates that terms of the second order of smallness are neglected, while dR stands for the specification error in R and ds for that in s, and

$$\begin{aligned} dw &= da+(dA)x^0+(dC)y^0+(xx)^{-1}(xy)[db+(dC)'x^0+(dB)y^0] \\ &= da+(dA)x^0+(dC)y^0+R'[db+(dC)'x^0+(dB)y^0] \end{aligned} \tag{3.15}$$

stands for the relevant linear combination of the errors in the coefficients of the preference function; note that $(xx)^{-1}(xy) = R'$ follows from (1.30). Now the first term on the right of (3.14) is the constant-term effect of the specification errors, the second the substitution effect. Consequently, when we apply the quadratic form (3.3) to find the loss associated with this array of errors, we can distinguish three components: a *constant-term component* which is a quadratic form in the constant-term effect, a *substitution component* which is a quadratic form in the substitution effect, and a *mixed component* which is a bilinear form in the two effects jointly. This is elaborated in

THEOREM 2.11. *Suppose that Assumptions* 2.1 *and* 2.2 *are satisfied. Then the decision error implied by behaving as if* $R+dR$, $s+ds$ *are the coefficient matrices of the constraints* (1.6) *and as if*

$$a+da,\ b+db,\ A+dA,\ B+dB,\ C+dC\ (dA,\ dB \text{ symmetric})$$

are the coefficient matrices of the preference function (1.5) *is given by*

(3.14), *provided that* (i) *squares and products of the elements of the error matrices* $dR, \ldots, dC$ *can be neglected, and* (ii) *the second-order maximum condition as formulated in Theorem* 2.6 *is satisfied. Under Assumptions* 2.1 *and* 2.2 *and proviso* (ii) *the loss associated with these errors is the sum of three components (apart from products of three and more error matrices), viz.: the constant-term component, which is a positive definite or semi-definite quadratic form in the errors of the coefficient matrices of the constraints*:

$$L_o = -\tfrac{1}{2}[(dR)x^0+ds]'F[(dR)x^0+ds]; \tag{3.16}$$

the substitution component, which is a positive definite quadratic form in the errors of the multiplicative structure of the constraints and of the coefficient matrices of the preference function:

$$L_u = -\tfrac{1}{2}[(dR)'\lambda^0+dw]'(xx)[(dR)'\lambda^0+dw]; \tag{3.17}$$

and the mixed component, which is a bilinear form involving all error matrices of constraints and preference function:

$$L_m = -[(dR)'\lambda^0+dw]'(x\cdot)[(dR)x^0+ds]. \tag{3.18}$$

These three components satisfy the inequalities

$$L_o \geqq 0; \qquad L_u \geqq 0; \qquad L_m^2 \leqq 4L_oL_u. \tag{3.19}$$

Only the last inequality requires an explicit proof, which is however simple. If we write p^* for the constant-term effect and q^* for the substitution effect, so that $x-x^0 = p^*+q^*$ (apart from terms of higher order of smallness), then the loss is

$$-\tfrac{1}{2}(p^*+q^*)'(xx)^{-1}(p^*+q^*).$$

Since $-\tfrac{1}{2}(xx)^{-1}$ is a positive definite matrix, it can be written $Q'Q$ where Q is an $m \times m$ matrix of full rank. Hence, if $p = Qp^*$ and $q = Qq^*$, the loss takes the form

$$(p+q)'(p+q) = p'p+q'q+2p'q,$$

where $p'p$ is the constant-term component, $q'q$ the substitution component, and $2p'q$ the mixed component. But $(p'q)^2 \leqq p'p \times q'q$ according to Schwartz' inequality, hence $L_m^2 \leqq 4L_oL_u$.

2.3.5. Summary

(1) If a decision x is made which deviates from the optimal decision x^0, the preference level attained is below the attainable maximum. This utility difference is called the loss due to the decision error $x-x^0$. It is equal to a positive definite quadratic form in the decision error, the matrix

being (apart from a factor $-\frac{1}{2}$) the inverse of the substitution matrix of the instruments.

(2) If the decision maker behaves as if some forecast of the additive structure of the constraints coincides with the true additive structure, then he commits a decision error which is a homogeneous linear combination of the prediction errors; the coefficient matrix of this linear combination is the slope matrix of the Tinbergen surfaces of the instruments. The loss which is due to such prediction errors (*via* their effect on the decision made) is a positive definite or semi-definite quadratic form in these errors. The matrix of this form is (apart from a factor $-\frac{1}{2}$) the failure matrix, which is determined by the slope matrix just mentioned and by the substitution matrix of the instruments. The expected loss due to maximizing expected utility in the certainty-equivalent manner of Theorem 2.7 is determined by the failure matrix and the covariance matrix of the additive structure of the constraints.

(3) A convenient way to measure the loss due to a prediction error in the additive structure of the constraints is that of the failure of this prediction, which is defined as the ratio of this loss to the loss that would be incurred if the decision maker extrapolates the additive structure. The failure is the ratio of two positive definite or semi-definite quadratic forms and varies from 0 to ∞, the lower limit being reached if the prediction is perfect and the value 1 if the forecast implies the same loss as no-change extrapolation. The success of a forecast of the additive structure of the constraints is defined as 1 minus the failure; it varies from $-\infty$ to 1.

(4) Decision errors are linear in the specification errors as long as the latter refer to the coefficients of the additive structure of the constraints and to those of the linear part of the preference function. They are nonlinear in the specification errors of all other coefficients; but we can approximate such relations linearly as long as these specification errors are not too large. This approximation expresses the decision error as the sum of two effects, viz., a constant-term effect (involving errors in the coefficients of the constraints) and a substitution effect (involving errors in the multiplicative structure of the constraints and in the coefficients of the preference function). The corresponding loss, a quadratic form in the decision error, is the sum of three components: the constant-term component and the substitution component (both being quadratic forms in the corresponding effects just mentioned) and the mixed component (a bilinear form in the two effects).

Appendix to Chapter 2

2.A. SECOND-ORDER MAXIMUM CONDITIONS

The second-order maximum conditions of Theorems 2.1 and 2.2 differ to the extent that one of them deals with an unconditional maximum while the other is concerned with a constrained maximum, the constraint consisting of a number of linear equations. There are several places in the literature in which these maximum conditions are considered; [1] we shall confine ourselves here to the case of three variables for which the analysis is simple and straightforward.

Let us write z_1, z_2, z_3 for these variables and let us start by considering the unconstrained maximum. This is the case of 2.1.4 and it implies that the z's should all be interpreted as instruments. The function to be maximized can then be written in the form

$$\varphi(z_1, z_2, z_3) = \sum_{1}^{3}\sum_{1}^{3} \alpha_{rs}(z_r - z_r^0)(z_s - z_s^0), \tag{A.1}$$

which can be regarded as equivalent with (1.26)—after the irrelevant constant term $k_0 - \frac{1}{2}k'K^{-1}k$ is deleted—, provided that we identify x with the z's, $-K^{-1}k$ with the z^0's, and $\frac{1}{2}K$ with the matrix $[\alpha_{rs}]$ which we take as symmetric. For notational simplicity, we write ζ_r for $z_r - z_r^0$; then after some algebraic rearrangements we find that φ can be written as the sum of three terms:

$$\alpha_{11}\left(\zeta_1 + \frac{\alpha_{12}}{\alpha_{11}}\zeta_2 + \frac{\alpha_{13}}{\alpha_{11}}\zeta_3\right)^2,$$

$$\frac{\alpha_{11}\alpha_{22} - \alpha_{12}^2}{\alpha_{11}}\left(\zeta_2 - \frac{\alpha_{12}\alpha_{13} - \alpha_{11}\alpha_{23}}{\alpha_{11}\alpha_{22} - \alpha_{12}^2}\zeta_3\right)^2,$$

$$\frac{\alpha_{11}\alpha_{22}\alpha_{33} + 2\alpha_{12}\alpha_{13}\alpha_{23} - \alpha_{11}\alpha_{23}^2 - \alpha_{13}^2\alpha_{22} - \alpha_{12}^2\alpha_{33}}{\alpha_{11}\alpha_{22} - \alpha_{12}^2}\zeta_3^2.$$

---

[1] See in particular G. Debreu, "Definite and Semidefinite Quadratic Forms," *Econometrica*, Vol. 20 (1952), pp. 295–300. Also P. A. Samuelson, *Foundations of Economic Analysis* (Cambridge, Mass., 1953), pp. 357–379; E. Burger, "On Extrema with Side Conditions," *Econometrica*, Vol. 23 (1955), pp. 451–452. The present simplified analysis follows closely the arguments given by J. R. Hicks in *Value and Capital* (Oxford, 2nd ed., 1946), Appendix.

Each of these terms is a square, multiplied by a constant; and the successive constants can all be written in terms of determinants:

$$\alpha_{11}, \quad \frac{\begin{vmatrix} \alpha_{11} & \alpha_{12} \\ \alpha_{21} & \alpha_{22} \end{vmatrix}}{\alpha_{11}}, \quad \frac{\begin{vmatrix} \alpha_{11} & \alpha_{12} & \alpha_{13} \\ \alpha_{21} & \alpha_{22} & \alpha_{23} \\ \alpha_{31} & \alpha_{32} & \alpha_{33} \end{vmatrix}}{\begin{vmatrix} \alpha_{11} & \alpha_{12} \\ \alpha_{21} & \alpha_{22} \end{vmatrix}}.$$

If φ is to have a maximum in z_r^0, $r = 1, 2, 3$, then it should be negative everywhere except in this maximum; and this implies that all three squares should be multiplied by negative constants. For the first square this means $\alpha_{11} < 0$; for the second (and given $\alpha_{11} < 0$) that

$$\begin{vmatrix} \alpha_{11} & \alpha_{12} \\ \alpha_{21} & \alpha_{22} \end{vmatrix} > 0,$$

and so on. In other words, the leading principal minors of $[\alpha_{rs}]$ should have alternating signs, the first (α_{11}) being negative. This is a necessary and sufficient condition in order that $[\alpha_{rs}]$ be negative definite.

Suppose now that $\varphi = \sum\sum \alpha_{rs}\zeta_r\zeta_s$ is to be maximized subject to one linear constraint:

$$\sum_{r=1}^{3} \beta_r \zeta_r = 0. \tag{A.2}$$

This is to be identified with the case of two instruments and one noncontrolled variable. Obviously, we can reduce the present constrained maximum problem to the unconstrained case by using (A.2) to eliminate one of the variables, say ζ_1 (the noncontrolled variable). We then obtain:

$$\varphi = \sum_{2}^{3}\sum_{2}^{3} \gamma_{rs}\zeta_r\zeta_s, \tag{A.3}$$

where

$$\gamma_{rs} = \alpha_{rs} - \frac{\alpha_{r1}\beta_s + \alpha_{1s}\beta_r}{\beta_1} + \frac{\alpha_{11}\beta_r\beta_s}{\beta_1^2} \qquad (r, s = 2, 3). \tag{A.4}$$

On applying the rules of the preceding paragraph, we see that the maximum requires

$$\gamma_{22} < 0; \quad \begin{vmatrix} \gamma_{22} & \gamma_{23} \\ \gamma_{32} & \gamma_{33} \end{vmatrix} > 0. \tag{A.5}$$

These two inequalities are necessary and sufficient for the negative definiteness of $[\gamma_{rs}]$, which can be identified with K. We shall now show that they are equivalent to the sign rule for the bordered principal minors. We start by observing that the first inequality is equivalent to $\beta_1^2\gamma_{22} < 0$ and hence [see (A.4)]:

$$\alpha_{22}\beta_1^2-\alpha_{21}\beta_1\beta_2-\alpha_{12}\beta_1\beta_2+\alpha_{11}\beta_2^2 < 0,$$

which in turn is equivalent to

$$\text{(A.6)} \qquad \begin{vmatrix} \alpha_{11} & \alpha_{12} & \beta_1 \\ \alpha_{21} & \alpha_{22} & \beta_2 \\ \beta_1 & \beta_2 & 0 \end{vmatrix} > 0,$$

that is, the 2×2 determinant of α's bordered by the corresponding β's should be positive. The second inequality of (A.5) can be written in the form

$$\begin{vmatrix} \alpha_{11} & 0 & 0 & \beta_1 \\ \alpha_{21} & \gamma_{22} & \gamma_{23} & \beta_2 \\ \alpha_{31} & \gamma_{32} & \gamma_{33} & \beta_3 \\ \beta_1 & 0 & 0 & 0 \end{vmatrix} < 0,$$

as is easily verified by expanding the determinant according to the elements of the last row and then according to those of the first row. On multiplying the first column by β_2/β_1 and the last by $\alpha_{12}/\beta_1-\alpha_{11}\beta_2/\beta_1^2$ and adding the result to the second column, we obtain

$$\begin{vmatrix} \alpha_{11} & \alpha_{12} & 0 & \beta_1 \\ \alpha_{21} & \alpha_{22} & \gamma_{23} & \beta_2 \\ \alpha_{31} & \alpha_{32} & \gamma_{33} & \beta_3 \\ \beta_1 & \beta_2 & 0 & 0 \end{vmatrix} < 0.$$

A similar operation applied to the third column leads to

$$\text{(A.7)} \qquad \begin{vmatrix} \alpha_{11} & \alpha_{12} & \alpha_{13} & \beta_1 \\ \alpha_{21} & \alpha_{22} & \alpha_{23} & \beta_2 \\ \alpha_{31} & \alpha_{32} & \alpha_{33} & \beta_3 \\ \beta_1 & \beta_2 & \beta_3 & 0 \end{vmatrix} < 0,$$

which, when combined with (A.6), shows that the bordered principal minors should have alternating signs in order that we have a constrained maximum, the first being positive. The order of the first determinant in such a series becomes larger when there are more constraints [it is $(n+1)\times(n+1)$ disregarding the bordering rows and columns when there are n constraints]; and its sign oscillates: $(-)^{n+1}$ for n constraints. Evidently, the matrix from which principal minors should be taken in our case is W as defined in (1.17).

2.B. FIRST-ORDER CERTAINTY EQUIVALENCE

Supposing that all coefficient matrices

$$a, b, A, B, C, R, s$$

are random (with finite moments of any required order), we have for the expected value of the preference function after elimination of the noncontrolled variables:

$$\mathscr{E}w_x = \mathscr{E}k_0 + (\mathscr{E}k)'x + \tfrac{1}{2}x'\mathscr{E}Kx, \tag{B.1}$$

where

$$\begin{aligned} \mathscr{E}k_0 &= \mathscr{E}(b's) + \tfrac{1}{2}\mathscr{E}(s'Bs) \\ \mathscr{E}k &= \mathscr{E}a + \mathscr{E}(R'b) + \mathscr{E}[(C+R'B)s] \\ \mathscr{E}K &= \mathscr{E}A + \mathscr{E}(R'BR) + \mathscr{E}(CR) + \mathscr{E}(R'C'). \end{aligned} \tag{B.2}$$

This will be compared with the preference level (for the same x) in case all coefficient matrices are replaced by their expectations:

$$\begin{aligned} &(\mathscr{E}b)'\mathscr{E}s + \tfrac{1}{2}(\mathscr{E}s)'\mathscr{E}B\mathscr{E}s + (\mathscr{E}a + (\mathscr{E}R)'\mathscr{E}b + [\mathscr{E}C + (\mathscr{E}R)'\mathscr{E}B]\mathscr{E}s)'x \\ &\quad + \tfrac{1}{2}x'[\mathscr{E}A + (\mathscr{E}R)'\mathscr{E}B\mathscr{E}R + \mathscr{E}C\mathscr{E}R + (\mathscr{E}R)'(\mathscr{E}C)']x, \end{aligned}$$

which can also be written in the form

$$(\mathscr{E}k_0 - g_0) + (\mathscr{E}k - g)'x + \tfrac{1}{2}x'(\mathscr{E}K - G)x, \tag{B.3}$$

where g_0 is a scalar:

$$g_0 = \sum_i \operatorname{cov}(b_i, s_i) + \tfrac{1}{2}\sum_i\sum_j \{\mathscr{E}(b_{ij}s_is_j) - \mathscr{E}b_{ij}\mathscr{E}s_i\mathscr{E}s_j\}; \tag{B.4}$$

g an m-element column vector of which the hth element is

$$\begin{aligned} g_h = &\sum_i \operatorname{cov}(r_{ih}, b_i) + \sum_i \operatorname{cov}(c_{hi}, s_i) \\ &+ \sum_i\sum_j \{\mathscr{E}(r_{ih}b_{ij}s_j) - \mathscr{E}r_{ih}\mathscr{E}b_{ij}\mathscr{E}s_j\}; \end{aligned} \tag{B.5}$$

and G an $m \times m$ matrix whose $(h, k)^{\text{th}}$ element is

$$\begin{aligned} g_{hk} = \sum_i\sum_j \{\mathscr{E}(r_{ih}b_{ij}r_{jk}) - \mathscr{E}r_{ih}\mathscr{E}b_{ij}\mathscr{E}r_{jk}\} &+ \sum_i \operatorname{cov}(c_{hi}, r_{ik}) \\ &+ \sum_i \operatorname{cov}(r_{ih}, c_{ki}). \end{aligned} \tag{B.6}$$

If the joint distribution of the elements of the coefficient matrices is independent of x, then g_0, g and G consist of constant elements; also,

g_0 is then irrelevant for purposes of maximization. Furthermore, if the five matrices B, C, R, b and s are distributed independently, then g is a zero vector while G is simplified such that its $(h, k)^{\text{th}}$ element becomes

(B.7) $$g_{hk} = \sum_i \sum_j \mathscr{E} b_{ij} \operatorname{cov}(r_{ih}, r_{jk}).$$

We shall consider this special case first. It implies that (B.1) and (B.3) are maximized by

(B.8) $$x_1 = -(\mathscr{E}K)^{-1}\mathscr{E}k \quad \text{and} \quad x_2 = -(\mathscr{E}K-G)^{-1}\mathscr{E}k,$$

respectively. Hence the discrepancy between these two vectors is

(B.9) $$\Delta x = x_2 - x_1 = -[(\mathscr{E}K-G)^{-1} - (\mathscr{E}K)^{-1}]\mathscr{E}k,$$

which means that we have to evaluate the difference between the two inverses. It is then useful to write K in the form

(B.10) $$K = P'QP,$$

where

(B.11) $$P = \begin{bmatrix} I \\ R \end{bmatrix}; \qquad Q = \begin{bmatrix} A & C \\ C' & B \end{bmatrix},$$

see (1.25). Then $(\mathscr{E}K)^{-1} = [\mathscr{E}(P'QP)]^{-1}$ and $(\mathscr{E}K-G)^{-1} = [(\mathscr{E}P)'\mathscr{E}Q\mathscr{E}P]^{-1}$; the last equation follows from the fact that in $\mathscr{E}K-G$, all coefficient matrices are replaced by their expectations. Let us also write $\Delta P = P - \mathscr{E}P$, $\Delta Q = Q - \mathscr{E}Q$, then

$$\mathscr{E}(P'QP) = (\mathscr{E}P)'\mathscr{E}Q\mathscr{E}P + (\mathscr{E}P)'\mathscr{E}(\Delta Q \Delta P) + \mathscr{E}[(\Delta P)'\mathscr{E}Q\Delta P] + \mathscr{E}[(\Delta P)'\Delta Q]\mathscr{E}P + \mathscr{E}[(\Delta P)'\Delta Q \Delta P],$$

of which the second and fourth matrix on the right are zero if R is distributed independently of B and C. We also neglect the last matrix because it is of a higher order of smallness than the third. Hence:

$$\mathscr{E}(P'QP) \approx (\mathscr{E}P)'\mathscr{E}Q\mathscr{E}P + \mathscr{E}[(\Delta P)'\mathscr{E}Q\Delta P],$$

and by taking the inverse:

(B.12) $$[\mathscr{E}(P'QP)]^{-1} \approx [(\mathscr{E}P)'\mathscr{E}Q\mathscr{E}P]^{-1} - [(\mathscr{E}P)'\mathscr{E}Q\mathscr{E}P]^{-1}\mathscr{E}[(\Delta P)'\mathscr{E}Q\Delta P][(\mathscr{E}P)'\mathscr{E}Q\mathscr{E}P]^{-1}$$

under appropriate convergence conditions. On combining (B.9) and (B.12) we obtain

(B.13) $$\Delta x \approx -[(\mathscr{E}P)'\mathscr{E}Q\mathscr{E}P]^{-1}\mathscr{E}[(\Delta P)'\mathscr{E}Q\Delta P][(\mathscr{E}P)'\mathscr{E}Q\mathscr{E}P]^{-1}\mathscr{E}k = [(\mathscr{E}P)'\mathscr{E}Q\mathscr{E}P]^{-1}\mathscr{E}[(\Delta P)'\mathscr{E}Q\Delta P]x_2,$$

see (B.8).

To interpret this result, let us write

$$(\overline{xx}) = [(\mathscr{E}P)'\mathscr{E}Q\mathscr{E}P]^{-1}, \tag{B.14}$$

which is the substitution matrix of the instruments in case all coefficient matrices are replaced by their expectations. Furthermore, we note that there are no sampling errors in P as far as its unit submatrix is concerned, which means that

$$\mathscr{E}[(\Delta P)'\mathscr{E}Q\Delta P] = \mathscr{E}[(\Delta R)'\mathscr{E}B\Delta R], \tag{B.15}$$

where $\Delta R = R - \mathscr{E}R$; see (B.7). Hence, from (B.13)–(B.15),

$$\Delta x \approx (\overline{xx})\mathscr{E}[(\Delta R)'\mathscr{E}B\Delta R]x_2, \tag{B.16}$$

in words: the discrepancy between the decision made by maximizing expected utility and the one made by maximizing utility in case all coefficient matrices are replaced by their expectations is in first approximation derived as follows: take the latter decision and premultiply it by (B.15), which is a square matrix whose elements are linear combinations of the variances and covariances of the multiplicative structure of the constraints, the weights of these combinations being the expected values of the coefficients of pairs of noncontrolled variables in the quadratic part of the preference function; and premultiply this by the substitution matrix of the instruments after all coefficient matrices are replaced by their expectations.

It will be observed that Δx vanishes to our order of approximation in case the sampling errors are confined to matrices other than R. This suggests that sampling errors in R are the most "dangerous" ones in case the decision maker acts as if all random coefficient matrices coincide with their expectations. But this applies only in case B, C, R, b and s are distributed independently. If this is not true, then — as easily follows from (B.5) and (B.6) — moments involving these other matrices enter also into the picture.

Let us indicate the order of magnitude of the sampling errors ΔR in (B.16) by ε; then it follows from (B.16) that Δx is of order ε^2, which may be interpreted in the sense that there is a first-order certainty equivalence for the decision made under the assumption that R coincides with its expectation. The same argument applies in case there are errors in all coefficient matrices which do not satisfy the independence condition discussed above; this follows immediately from the fact that g and G as specified in (B.5)–(B.6) involve moments about the means of the second and higher order.

CHAPTER 3

Applications of the Static Theory

3.1. A SIMPLE ANTI-DEPRESSION POLICY FOR THE UNITED STATES IN THE NINETEEN-THIRTIES [1]

3.1.1. Introduction; Constraints in the Form of an Econometric Model

The purpose of this chapter is primarily to interrupt the flow of theoretical results before the presentation of the dynamic generalizations. Here, we shall consider a simple macroeconomic application which is to be regarded as a pilot study; it will be followed (in Section 3.2) by a microeconomic application dealing with production and work force scheduling. In both cases we shall start by presenting the problem in dynamic form, after which it will be reduced to the static case. This is of course a roundabout procedure, but it is convenient to the extent that it is then unnecessary to present a dynamic reformulation later on when the appropriate generalization will be treated, while moreover it serves to illustrate that the dynamic problems are the really interesting ones.

Let us go back to the beginning of 1933, when President Roosevelt started his first administration. At that time there was a considerable unemployment in the United States, a low per capita consumption level, and a negative net investment level. We shall assume that the macroeconomic decision maker, being interested in bringing the depression to an end, formulates a quadratic social preference function which he wishes to maximize subject to the constraints under which the American economy operates. In accordance with the set-up of Chapter 2, the arguments of the preference function will be partly controlled, partly noncontrolled, while the same arguments will also enter as variables into the constraints.

---

[1] This section and also Section 6.1 of Chapter 6 are partly based on P. J. M. VAN DEN BOGAARD and H. THEIL, "Macrodynamic Policy-Making: An Application of Strategy and Certainty Equivalence Concepts to the Economy of the United States, 1933–1936," *Metroeconomica*, Vol. 11 (1959), pp. 149–167.

The discussion will be simplified if we start by formulating the constraints. This will be done on the basis of a simple six-equation econometric model which was formulated by L. R. KLEIN to describe the mechanism of the American economy in the interwar period;[1] it will be hereafter referred to as "Klein's Model I." Three equations of this system are behavioural relations, the first of which is a consumption function describing total real consumption (C) as a linear function of total real profits (Π), of the same variable lagged one year (Π_{-1}), and of the total real wage bill. The last variable is written as W_1+W_2, where W_1 is the wage bill paid by private industry and W_2 the government wage bill. Thus the consumption function takes the form

$$(1.1) \qquad C = \alpha_0+\alpha_1\Pi+\alpha_2\Pi_{-1}+\alpha_3(W_1+W_2)+u_C,$$

where the α's are the coefficients of the linear relation and u_C a disturbance. Such disturbances are introduced into behavioural relations to account for the fact that these relations do not hold exactly. It is usually assumed (and will also be assumed here) that each disturbance is a random drawing from a parent with zero mean. Furthermore, all variables of the model are measured in billions (10^9) of dollars of 1934 purchasing power per year, except when stated otherwise.

The second equation is an investment equation describing total real net investment (I) as a linear function of profits (Π), profits lagged one year (Π_{-1}), and the capital stock at the beginning of the year (K_{-1}, measured in billions of 1934 dollars):

$$(1.2) \qquad I = \beta_0+\beta_1\Pi+\beta_2\Pi_{-1}+\beta_3K_{-1}+u_I,$$

the β's being coefficients and u_I the disturbance of the investment equation. The third equation is an employment equation. It describes the private wage bill (W_1) as a linear function of net national income (Y) plus indirect taxes ($\overline{T}$) minus the government wage bill (W_2), of the same variable lagged one year, $(Y+\overline{T}-W_2)_{-1}$, and of time ($t$, measured in calendar years):

$$(1.3) \qquad W_1 = \gamma_0+\gamma_1(Y+\overline{T}-W_2)+\gamma_2(Y+\overline{T}-W_2)_{-1}+\gamma_3(t-1931)+u_W.$$

The last three equations are of the definitional type and therefore hold exactly without disturbance terms. The first of these states that net national income plus indirect taxes is the sum of consumption, net

[1] See L. R. KLEIN, *Economic Fluctuations in the United States, 1921–1941* (New York–London 1950), Chap. III.

investment, and government expenditure on goods and services (G);[1] the second states that net national income is the sum of profits and the wage bill; and the third that the end-of-year capital stock is the sum of net investment and the capital stock at the beginning of the year:

$$
\begin{aligned}
Y+\bar{T} &= C+I+G \\
Y &= \Pi+W_1+W_2 \\
K &= I+K_{-1}.
\end{aligned}
\tag{1.4}
$$

As a whole, this six-equation system contains 15 variables, all lagged variables such as Π_{-1} and K_{-1} being counted separately. The function of this model is to describe six of these variables (as many as the number of equations) in terms of the other nine and the disturbances. The former category is that of the jointly dependent variables of the model, the latter that of the predetermined variables, where the term "predetermined" is either used in a temporal sense (for lagged variables) or in a "logical" sense (for exogenous variables which are determined in a manner independent of the equation system).[2] There are five lagged variables (Π, K, Y, $\bar{T}$, W_2, all with -1 subscript); and there are three variables which may be considered exogenous because they are largely government-controlled (W_2, $\bar{T}$, G), while t (time) is a fourth exogenous variable for obvious reasons. These are the nine predetermined variables; the other six, viz., C (consumption), Π (profits), W_1 (private wage bill), I (net investment), K (end-of-year capital stock) and Y (net national income), are taken as jointly dependent. It will appear in 3.1.2 that the latter category supplies the noncontrolled variables and the former the instruments of the decision problem. The system (1.1)–(1.4) supplies the constraints subject to which the maximization of the preference function will take place. To handle these constraints in numerical form, we shall have to specify the values of the coefficients of the three behavioural equations (1.1)–(1.3). Such coefficients are not known in general, and

[1] The variable G actually includes the annual surplus on the balance of payments (which is rather small relative to government spending on goods and services). Note that the national account definitions are such that the government wage bill (W_2) is included in the amount of government expenditure on goods and services. Hence the instrument interpretation must be: decide on total government expenditure on goods and services, then decide on how much of this is paid to family households.

[2] For more details regarding this distinction, see e.g. T. C. Koopmans and W. C. Hood, "The Estimation of Simultaneous Linear Economic Relationships" (Chap. VI of *Studies in Econometric Method*, ed. by W. C. Hood and T. C. Koopmans; New York–London 1953), pp. 122–125.

their specification is a problem of statistical estimation. The estimates that will be used are given in Table 3.1.[1,2]

TABLE 3.1

NUMERICAL VALUES OF THE COEFFICIENTS OF KLEIN'S MODEL I

	α_i	β_i	γ_i
$i = 0$	16.786	17.784	1.599
1	0.020	0.231	0.420
2	0.225	0.546	0.164
3	0.800	−0.146	0.135

3.1.2. Dynamic Formulation of the Social Preference Function

The first problem in the formulation of the preference function is the specification of its arguments. It will be clear that the use of such a highly aggregative equation system as Klein's Model I does not enable us to attain a considerable refinement in this respect. We shall therefore introduce only three instruments and three noncontrolled variables, the former group consisting of W_2 (government wage bill), $\overline{T}$ (indirect taxes), and G (government expenditure on goods and services). It will be noted that $\overline{T}$ is not a variable which is really controlled by the government and that it would be preferable to use tax rates instead of the deflated amount of tax received; but we shall take $\overline{T}$ as it is because this is one of the variables of Klein's Model I.[3]

Turning to the noncontrolled variables, we shall suppose that our macroeconomic decision maker wishes to bring the depression to an end in 1936 (the last year of President Roosevelt's first administration), and that he wants to specify this general goal in terms of immediate

---

[1] The estimates used are derived by means of the full-information maximum-likelihood method under the assumption that the disturbances of the three behavioural equations are uncorrelated in each year. For their numerical derivation, see H. CHERNOFF and N. DIVINSKY, "The Computation of Maximum-Likelihood Estimates of Linear Structural Equations" (Chap. X of *Studies in Econometric Method*, ed. by W. C. HOOD and T. C. KOOPMANS; New York–London 1953), pp. 237, 250, 299.

[2] The coefficients of this table (and similarly for the other tables of this chapter) are specified in three decimal places, but the actual calculations were carried out in six. This rather large number should not be regarded as an indication of accuracy, but rather as an attempt to control rounding errors.

[3] See, however, note 1 of p. 91 for an approximate procedure of "translating" statements about amounts of tax received to tax rates.

welfare for the population as a whole, of future welfare, and of a fair distribution of income. These three separate goals will be measured by consumption (C), net investment (I), and the ratio of profits to the private wage bill (Π/W_1), respectively. This ratio had fluctuated around $\frac{1}{2}$ during the nineteen-twenties, but it dropped considerably after the beginning of the depression.[1]

We now proceed to the form of the preference function, which will be specified in two steps. First, we shall formulate certain "desired values" for each of the variables—controlled and noncontrolled—in each of the four years 1933–1936; thereafter, we shall specify a quadratic form in the deviations between the actual and these desired values. The minimization of this quadratic form is then equivalent to the maximization of a quadratic social preference function.

Considering the desired level of consumption first, we shall assume that our decision maker wants to restore the 1929 level of real per capita consumption in the year 1936. But Klein's Model I contains total consumption, not per capita consumption. Since the rate of growth of the population during the four-year period 1933–1936, at the beginning of which the decision maker has to formulate his preferences, is unknown, we shall simplify this target by assuming that the annual rate of increase of the population is 1 per cent in each of the years 1929–1936. This leads to the following desired value of total real income in 1936:

$$C_{36}^{*} = C_{29} \times 1.01^{7} = 57.8 \times 1.01^{7} = 61.97$$

in billions of dollars of 1934 purchasing power per year. [$C_{29} = 57.8$ is the realized level of total consumption in 1929.] As to investment (I), it appears that this variable was of the order of 10 per cent of consumption during the nineteen-twenties, after which it decreased to a negative level. We assume that the decision maker wishes to restore the original ratio, which implies $I_{36}^{*} = 0.1 \times C_{36}^{*} = 6.20$ for the desired level of net investment in 1936. In the same way, we shall suppose that it is desired to restore the ratio of profits to the private wage bill to its original level $\frac{1}{2}$. But it is rather inconvenient to work with ratios of jointly dependent variables; we shall therefore introduce a "distribution variable,"

$$D = W_1 - 2\Pi, \tag{1.5}$$

and put its desired level in 1936 equal to zero: $D_{36}^{*} = 0$. This is, of course, equivalent to the desire $\Pi/W_1 = \frac{1}{2}$.

[1] These as well as all other numerical statements in this section are based on the data published by KLEIN, *loc. cit.*, p. 135.

So far, we have confined our attention to 1936, which is the last year we shall take into account. But we must also specify desired values for the intermediate years 1933–1935. This will be done by simple linear interpolation between the actual values in 1932 (the last year before President Roosevelt's administration) and the corresponding desired values in 1936. Hence:

$$
\left.\begin{aligned}
C^*_{32+t} &= C_{32} + \frac{t}{4}(C^*_{36} - C_{32}) \\
I^*_{32+t} &= I_{32} + \frac{t}{4}(I^*_{36} - I_{32}) \\
D^*_{32+t} &= D_{32} + \frac{t}{4}(D^*_{36} - D_{32})
\end{aligned}\right\} \quad t = 1, \ldots, 4. \tag{1.6}
$$

The numerical specification of these desired values is given in Table 3.2.

TABLE 3.2

DESIRED VALUES OF NONCONTROLLED VARIABLES, 1933–1936

(in billions of 1934 dollars per year)

	C^*	I^*	D^*
1933	49.69	−3.10	11.25
1934	53.78	0.00	7.50
1935	57.88	3.10	3.75
1936	61.97	6.20	0.00

We proceed to the instruments, which will be handled in an analogous manner. We recall that these variables too are arguments of the preference function (2.1.5), so that they affect the preference level in two ways: directly and also indirectly, viz., *via* their influence on the noncontrolled variables (as specified by the constraints). The latter effect is obvious, but the former is not to be neglected either. For example, it is not unreasonable to say that in an expanding economy like that of the United States the number of civil servants and their real income should increase gradually, quite apart from the effect which this has on the economy as a whole. Such a statement refers to the importance of an instrument *per se*, not to its purely instrumental importance with respect to noncontrolled variables. Here too, we shall formalize this by specifying desired values for each of the three instruments in each of the four years. Following the trend argument presented above for the case of the government wage bill, we shall proceed in a very simple manner; viz., by taking the least-squares regressions of these three variables on time (t) during the period 1920–1932 and by using the extrapolated values in 1933–1936 as "desired values." This leads to

$$(1.7)\qquad \left.\begin{aligned} (W_2^*)_{32+t} &= 4.823+0.215t \\ \overline{T}^*_{32+t} &= 7.157+0.239t \\ G^*_{32+t} &= 10.008+0.430t \end{aligned}\right\} \quad t = 1, \ldots, 4;$$

and the corresponding numerical values are specified in Table 3.3.

TABLE 3.3

DESIRED VALUES OF INSTRUMENTS, 1933–1936
(in billions of 1934 dollars per year)

	W_2^*	$\overline{T}^*$	G^*
1933	5.038	7.396	10.438
1934	5.254	7.635	10.868
1935	5.469	7.874	11.298
1936	5.685	8.113	11.727

Finally, there is the quadratic form in the deviations between actual and desired values which is to be minimized. We shall choose the simplest possible form, viz., the total sum of squares of these deviations. This implies that our social preference function is

$$(1.8)\quad -\sum_{t=1}^{4}\big[\{(W_2)_{32+t}-(W_2^*)_{32+t}\}^2+(\overline{T}_{32+t}-\overline{T}^*_{32+t})^2+(G_{32+t}-G^*_{32+t})^2$$
$$+(C_{32+t}-C^*_{32+t})^2+(I_{32+t}-I^*_{32+t})^2+(D_{32+t}-D^*_{32+t})^2\big].$$

This is to be maximized subject to the constraints implied by the econometric model (1.1)–(1.4).

3.1.3. Some Comments on the Assumptions Made

It is hardly necessary to stress that the assumptions introduced so far are such that criticism is very easy. But it is more important to see to what extent our restrictive assumptions are due to the usual simplifications of a pilot study, and to what extent they are inherent to the theory itself. (The advantage of a simple pilot study is of course that we can see more easily what is going on than in the case of more complicated preference functions and constraints.)

Obviously, we can replace the desired values of Tables 3.2 and 3.3

by any other values; this will affect the numerical outcomes but it does not involve any problem of principle. The same applies to the quadratic form in the deviations between actual and desired values. We can replace the unit form by a general diagonal form, which allows for the possibility of different weights corresponding to different variables and different years.[1] We can also generalize the diagonal form to a nondiagonal form, in which case the penalty put on a given deviation between an actual and a desired value is made dependent on other deviations—either corresponding to another variable or to another year or both. Thus, there is a considerable variety of cases which can be covered by a quadratic preference function. But it does have restrictive properties. This is easily seen when we go back to Table 3.2, from which it appears that the desired value of net investment in the first year is −3.1 billions. Would it not be much better to have a positive value, say 5 billions, if we believe so much in a 10 per cent investment-consumption ratio? Yet it follows from the quadratic preference function (1.8) that any negative investment below the "desire" of −3.1 billions is considered better than that positive level, provided only that this negative level differs from −3.1 billions by less than 8 billions. And what about consumption? Is it not better to apply a rule of "the more the better" by formulating a social preference function which increases continuously with consumption, rather than to specify a 50 billion level in 1933 above which everything is considered waste and worse than that?

These questions as such should of course receive an affirmative answer; but the point is that they are not relevant. A quadratic social preference function can in general claim no validity for arbitrarily large variations of its arguments, and the specifications of Tables 3.2 and 3.3 have been made, partly at least, on the basis of an idea of the actual range of variation that may reasonably be expected. This implies that our preference function does not measure "pure preferences:" it approximates these in the relevant range, and what is the relevant range is determined by the decision made. Now the decision made is the one which maximizes the

[1] Note that our unit form involves an implicit *relative* weighting. For a 1 billion dollar discrepancy between actual and desired values will occur much more easily for consumption than for the government wage bill, the former variable taking values of the order of 50 billions per year and the latter of only 5 billions. Hence—given the quadratic character of the preference function—a 1 per cent discrepancy of consumption is regarded as about 100 times more serious than a 1 per cent discrepancy of the government wage bill.

approximating preference function or its expectation subject to the constraints. Hence our quadratic preference function is indeed "impure" because it contains elements of the constraints. Also, the fact that the decision made and hence the relevant range of variation of our variables depend on the preference function implies a certain amount of circularity in the argument: the preference function chosen determines the relevant range, and this range determines the way in which this function is approximated.[1] As long as the quadratic approximation is not very sensitive to changes in this range, this is not serious; but it shows that the procedure followed is partly an art, partly a science.

The reader, if sufficiently pragmatic, may agree with all this; but he may still feel unhappy about the linear approximation that was applied to specify the desired values of the noncontrolled variables in 1933–1935. If it is considered desirable to return to the 1929 per capita consumption level and to the 10 per cent investment-consumption ratio, why should we postpone this desire to 1936 and not apply it to the earlier years? Here, too, the art of approximating enters into the picture. We could of course desire the same per capita consumption level in 1933 as that of 1929 and an investment level equal to 10 per cent of desired aggregate consumption. This would imply a C^*_{33} of almost 60 billions and an I^*_{33} of almost 6 billions; compared with the realized values in 1932, it would imply an increase in net investment by 12 billions and an increase in consumption by more than 30 per cent. Clearly, this is much more than one can reasonably expect. This as such is not particularly serious, because these increases are only desires and our quadratic form is able to handle any deviations between desired and actual development over time. However, the point is that if we impose such extravagant desires in the first year, the resulting large deviations are weighted very heavily in the quadratic preference function. In later years such as 1936 it should be possible to attain goals like the 1929 level of per capita consumption more closely, so that later-year deviations between actual and desired values are then much smaller and hence weighted much less heavily in the preference function. But if we formulate extravagant desires in the first year, we run the risk of using all our ammunition for the first one or two years and neglecting the last years.

It is appropriate to compare the arbitrariness in specifying the pref-

---

[1] See also C. C. Holt, F. Modigliani and H. Simon, "A Linear Decision Rule for Production and Employment Scheduling," *Management Science*, Vol. 2 (1955), p. 9.

erence function with a similar arbitrariness at the level of the specification of the constraints. Klein's Model I gives of course a very aggregative description of the mechanism of the American economy; we may even add that it is not completely fair to use it, because it was formulated on the basis of data for the entire interwar period, so that our macroeconomic decision maker could not have used it in 1933. But these objections are not fundamental, for we could have used a less aggregative model specified on the basis of earlier data. A restrictive property is that the constraints should be linear, see (2.1.6). This condition is met by Klein's Model I, but larger econometric models usually have at least some nonlinearities. These have to be eliminated by linear approximations in the relevant range in the way outlined in the previous paragraphs. But in addition to this, whether an econometric model is linear or partly nonlinear, its specification is subject to uncertainties. The statistical theory which underlies the estimation of the coefficients of a model proceeds under the assumption that the form of the equations is specified correctly; but it is in general unknown whether a specification is correct or not, and the usual procedure is to experiment with many alternative specifications and to choose the one which seems most satisfactory on the basis of some more or less well-defined criterion.[1] It will be clear that it makes no sense to devote considerable resources to a refined specification of the preference function as long as the specification of the constraints is in bad shape.[2]

By now, perhaps, the reader's difficulties will have increased rather than decreased. What to say about a method of making decisions whose two corner-stones—preference function and constraints—compete in the poorness of their quality? Should we have any illusions about the quality of such a decision? Again, these questions are sound as such, but not completely relevant for two reasons. For one thing, it is not unreasonable to compare the quality of this decision with the way in which similar decisions are made in practice; and it is not unreasonable either to expect that it should be possible to obtain better results. For another, the theory developed here enables us to compute the losses associated with erro-

---

[1] See e.g. H. THEIL, *Economic Forecasts and Policy*, Second Revised Edition, pp. 211–214.

[2] Particularly also because of the first-order certainty equivalence result of Section 2.B of the Appendix of Chapter 2, which suggests that errors in the multiplicative structure of the constraints should be considered more serious than errors in the coefficients of the preference function.

neous specifications of the preference function and the constraints, and such losses form a direct indication of the way in which research efforts can be spent usefully. A general theoretical result for the static theory has been obtained in Chapter 2 (Theorem 2.11), and a number of applications (in particular of the more interesting dynamic type) will be presented in later chapters; see Section 5.2 of Chapter 5 (for a paint factory), 6.1.5 of Chapter 6 (dealing with the present anti-depression policy), and 7.1.2 of Chapter 7 (concerning the optimal management of research).

3.1.4. Statement of the Static Problem

We shall now reduce the decision problem to a static one to illustrate the theoretical results of Chapter 2. We therefore assume that the macroeconomic decision maker is interested only in the first year (1933), so that we can confine ourselves to the first rows of Tables 3.2 and 3.3. The algebra will be simplified slightly if we measure our variables as deviations from the corresponding desired values; hence the vectors of instruments and of noncontrolled variables are defined as

$$x = \begin{bmatrix} W_2 - W_2^* \\ \bar{T} - \bar{T}^* \\ G - G^* \end{bmatrix}; \qquad y = \begin{bmatrix} C - C^* \\ I - I^* \\ D - D^* \end{bmatrix}, \tag{1.9}$$

where time subscripts are deleted because all variables refer now to 1933. The static variant of the quadratic preference function (1.8) can then be written in the simple form

$$w(x, y) = -\tfrac{1}{2}x'x - \tfrac{1}{2}y'y, \tag{1.10}$$

which means that the coefficient matrices of the general quadratic preference function (2.1.5) are specified as follows:

$$a = b = \mathbf{0}; \quad A = B = -\mathbf{I}; \quad C = \mathbf{0}, \tag{1.11}$$

where the first $\mathbf{0}$ is a column of three zeros, the second a 3×3 zero matrix, and $\mathbf{I}$ a 3×3 unit matrix.[1]

Proceeding to the constraints, we observe that the equation system (1.1)–(1.4) is not in the required form (2.1.6). The reason is that (2.1.6) contains its noncontrolled variables on the left while (1.1) and (1.2)

---

[1] The halves on the right of (1.10) have been introduced to ensure that A and B have -1 on the main diagonal, rather than -2 which would be slightly inconvenient. Note also that we have $a = b = \mathbf{0}$ only because our variables are taken as deviations from desired values.

contain W_1 and Π (which are the constituents of the distribution variable D) on the right. But this is remedied easily. We recall that the six-equation system (1.1)–(1.4) serves to describe the six jointly dependent variables linearly in terms of the predetermined variables and the disturbances. Hence we can solve the system for the jointly dependent variables,[1] so that we obtain another six-equation system which describes each of the jointly dependent variables explicitly in terms of the predetermined variables and the disturbances. The former system is known as the system of structural equations (because each of its equations describes a part of

TABLE 3.4

NUMERICAL VALUES OF THE REDUCED-FORM COEFFICIENTS OF KLEIN'S MODEL I

	Constant term	*Current instruments*			*Current noninstrum. exogenous:*	*Lagged instruments*	
		W_2	$\bar{T}$	G	t–1931	$(W_2)_{-1}$	$\bar{T}_{-1}$
C	41.816	0.666	−0.188	0.671	0.155	−0.189	0.189
Π	38.059	0.224	−1.281	1.119	−0.052	0.063	−0.063
W_1	30.338	−0.162	−0.204	0.811	0.195	−0.237	0.237
I	26.581	−0.052	−0.296	0.259	−0.012	0.015	−0.015
Y	68.397	0.614	−1.484	1.930	0.143	−0.174	0.174
K	26.581	−0.052	−0.296	0.259	−0.012	0.015	−0.015

	Lagged endogenous			*Structural disturbances*		
	Π_{-1}	Y_{-1}	K_{-1}	u_C	u_I	u_W
C	0.743	0.189	−0.098	1.671	0.671	1.148
Π	0.863	−0.063	−0.164	1.119	1.119	−0.386
W_1	0.626	0.237	−0.119	0.811	0.811	1.445
I	0.746	−0.015	−0.184	0.259	1.259	−0.089
Y	1.489	0.174	−0.283	1.930	1.930	1.059
K	0.746	−0.015	0.816	0.259	1.259	−0.089

the structure of the economy); the latter is the reduced form. The coefficients of the reduced form, corresponding with the structural coefficients of Table 3.1, are given in Table 3.4. A distinction is made between current instruments (viz., $W_2, \bar{T}, G$), current noninstrumental exogenous variables

[1] Provided that the square matrix of coefficients of the six jointly dependent variables in the six equations (1.1)–(1.4) is nonsingular. This proviso is fulfilled for the numerical values of Table 3.1.

(of which there is only one: time), lagged instruments [viz., $(W_2)_{-1}$ and $\bar{T}_{-1}$, the variable G_{-1} being absent], lagged endogenous variables (i.e., lagged values of the jointly dependent variables: Π_{-1}, Y_{-1}, K_{-1}), and structural disturbances (u_C, u_I, u_W).

The numerical specifications of Table 3.4 enable us to derive the constraints

$$y = Rx + s \tag{1.12}$$

in a simple manner. Considering consumption, we observe that Table 3.4 specifies

$$C = 41.816 + 0.666 W_2 - 0.188 \bar{T} + \ldots + 0.671 u_I + 1.148 u_W .$$

Taking account of the fact that we measure instruments and noncontrolled variables as deviations from their desired values, we rewrite this as

$$\begin{aligned} C - C^* = {} & (41.816 - C^* + 0.666 W_2^* - 0.188 \bar{T}^* + 0.671 G^*) \\ & + 0.666 (W_2 - W_2^*) - 0.188 (\bar{T} - \bar{T}^*) + 0.671 (G - G^*) \\ & + 0.155 (t - 1931) + \ldots + 1.148 u_W . \end{aligned}$$

The expression in parentheses on the first line is a weighted sum of known numbers, because $C^*, \ldots, G^*$ can be read from the first rows of Tables 3.2 and 3.3. The coefficients in the second line form the first row of R; they measure the effectiveness of the instruments with respect to the first noncontrolled variable. For the second $(I - I^*)$ we proceed in the same manner by using the fourth row of Table 3.4 instead of the first. For the third noncontrolled variable $(D - D^*$ where $D = W_1 - 2\Pi)$ we should take the third row minus twice the second. Collecting the resulting three sets of coefficients of the instruments, we find:

$$R = \begin{bmatrix} 0.666 & -0.188 & 0.671 \\ -0.052 & -0.296 & 0.259 \\ 0.285 & 2.358 & -1.427 \end{bmatrix} \begin{matrix} (C) \\ (I) \\ (D) \end{matrix} \qquad \text{columns: } (W_2) \; (\bar{T}) \; (G) \tag{1.13}$$

which implies that the instrument W_2 is positively effective with respect to C and D but negatively with respect to I, see the first column;[1] and

[1] It might be considered strange that W_2 is negatively effective with respect to investment, but it is not really strange. Raising W_2 while keeping G constant implies that government expenditure on material goods is reduced (see footnote 1 on p. 77). If government expenditure on goods remains unchanged, an increase in W_2 must be accompanied by the same increase in G, which leads to an increase and not to a decrease in investment.

similarly, that $\bar{T}$ is positively effective with respect to D but negatively with respect to C and I, while the converse holds for the G-instrument.

It follows from (1.12) that the additive structure s comprises the remainder of the constraints. Returning to the equation for $C-C^*$, we see that the first component of s must then be equal to

$$\begin{aligned}&(41.816-C^*+0.666W_2^*-0.188\bar{T}^*+0.671G^*)\\&+0.155(t-1931)-0.189(W_2)_{-1}+0.189\bar{T}_{-1}+0.743\Pi_{-1}\\&+0.189Y_{-1}-0.098K_{-1}+(1.671u_C+0.671u_I+1.148u_W).\end{aligned}$$

As stated above, the term in brackets in the first line is known numerically. The same applies to the t-term because $t = 1933$. The five lagged variables which follow refer to 1932, and these numerical values will be supposed to be known at the beginning of 1933. They are:

$$W_2 : 5.3; \quad \bar{T} : 8.3; \quad \Pi : 7.0; \quad Y : 41.3; \quad K : 207.1. \tag{1.14}$$

Combining all numerical terms, we find $s_1 = -5.393$ plus the linear combination of the three disturbances. We proceed in the same way for the other two components of s, which gives

$$s = \begin{bmatrix}-5.393\\-3.704\\-0.729\end{bmatrix} + S\begin{bmatrix}u_C\\u_I\\u_W\end{bmatrix}, \tag{1.15}$$

where

$$S = \begin{array}{c} \\ \left[\begin{array}{rrr}1.671 & 0.671 & 1.148\\0.259 & 1.259 & -0.089\\-1.427 & -1.427 & 2.217\end{array}\right] \end{array}\begin{array}{l}(C)\\(I)\\(D)\end{array} \qquad \text{columns: } (u_C)\ (u_I)\ (u_W) \tag{1.16}$$

The optimal decision x^0 can now be formulated as the vector which maximizes the social preference function (1.10) subject to the constraints (1.12), the coefficients of which are specified in (1.13), (1.15) and (1.16). A complete numerical specification of this vector requires knowledge of the 1933-values of the disturbances u_C, u_I, u_W; these are:

$$u_C : 0.63; \quad u_I : 1.04; \quad u_W : 0.40. \tag{1.17}$$

Generally, we should expect that a decision maker who stands at the beginning of 1933 does not know these values and interprets the u's as random variables with zero means. The "next best" decision is then x which maximizes the expectation of the preference function subject to the contraints, the latter being interpreted stochastically.

3.1.5. Three Decisions and Their Losses; Substitution and Complementarity

For the derivation of x^0 we need the matrix K defined in (2.1.25), which in view of (1.11) takes the simple form

$$(1.18)\qquad K = -(\mathbf{I}+R'R) = \begin{array}{c} \begin{matrix} (W_2) & (\bar{T}) & (G) \end{matrix} \\ \begin{bmatrix} -1.527 & -0.563 & -0.026 \\ -0.563 & -6.684 & 3.568 \\ -0.026 & 3.568 & -3.553 \end{bmatrix} \end{array} \begin{matrix} (W_2) \\ (\bar{T}) \\ (G) \end{matrix}$$

Also, we need the vector k defined in (2.1.25), which is here

$$(1.19)\quad k = -R's = -R' \begin{bmatrix} -5.393 \\ -3.704 \\ -0.729 \end{bmatrix} - R'S \begin{bmatrix} u_C \\ u_I \\ u_W \end{bmatrix} = \begin{bmatrix} 2.637 \\ 3.976 \\ -0.453 \end{bmatrix},$$

where use has been made of the numerical specification (1.17). The vector x^0 is then found by applying (2.1.27):

$$(1.20)\qquad x^0 = -K^{-1}k = \begin{bmatrix} 1.393 \\ 0.871 \\ 0.737 \end{bmatrix} \begin{matrix} (W_2) \\ (\bar{T}) \\ (G) \end{matrix}$$

and the corresponding vector of noncontrolled variables is

$$(1.21)\qquad y^0 = Rx^0 + s = \begin{bmatrix} -1.926 \\ -2.407 \\ -0.825 \end{bmatrix} \begin{matrix} (C) \\ (I) \\ (D) \end{matrix}$$

To find $\hat{x}$ we apply the theorem of certainty equivalence by replacing the disturbances by their expectations.[1] So we delete the last vector before the third equation sign in (1.19), which gives

$$(1.22)\qquad \mathscr{E}k = -R' \begin{bmatrix} -5.393 \\ -3.704 \\ -0.729 \end{bmatrix} = \begin{bmatrix} 3.608 \\ -0.393 \\ 3.536 \end{bmatrix}.$$

---

[1] Note that we need the conditional expectations of the 1933 disturbances, given the available information at the beginning of that year. If there are nonzero lagged correlations among the disturbances, the certainty equivalence procedure does *not* amount to replacing the 1933 disturbances by zero. For example, if u_C is subject to a Markov scheme $u_C = \rho_1(u_C)_{-1} + \rho_2(u_I)_{-1} + \varepsilon$, ε being a random variable with zero mean and independent over time, then the conditional expectation of the 1933 disturbance of the consumption function is ρ_1 times the 1932 disturbance of that function plus ρ_2 times the 1932 disturbance of the investment function; at least, when these 1932 disturbances are known at the beginning of 1933. If this proviso is not fulfilled but estimates are available, then these can be used instead, the argument being analogous to that of 2.2.3. Here, it is assumed that all lagged correlations vanish.

The instrument vector $\hat{x}$ and the corresponding vector of noncontrolled variables are then

$$(1.23)\qquad \hat{x} = -K^{-1}\mathscr{E}k = \begin{bmatrix} 2.107 \\ 0.618 \\ 1.600 \end{bmatrix}; \qquad R\hat{x}+s = \begin{bmatrix} -0.824 \\ -2.146 \\ -2.450 \end{bmatrix}.$$

These results, together with the actual values that were realized in the first year of President Roosevelt's administration, are summarized in Table 3.5. Contrary to the specifications (1.20)–(1.23), the figures of this table refer to the original levels of the variables $W_2, \overline{T}, \ldots, D$ rather than to deviations from desired values; e.g., the leading element of the table is 6.43, which is the top element of x^0 (1.393) plus the desired value

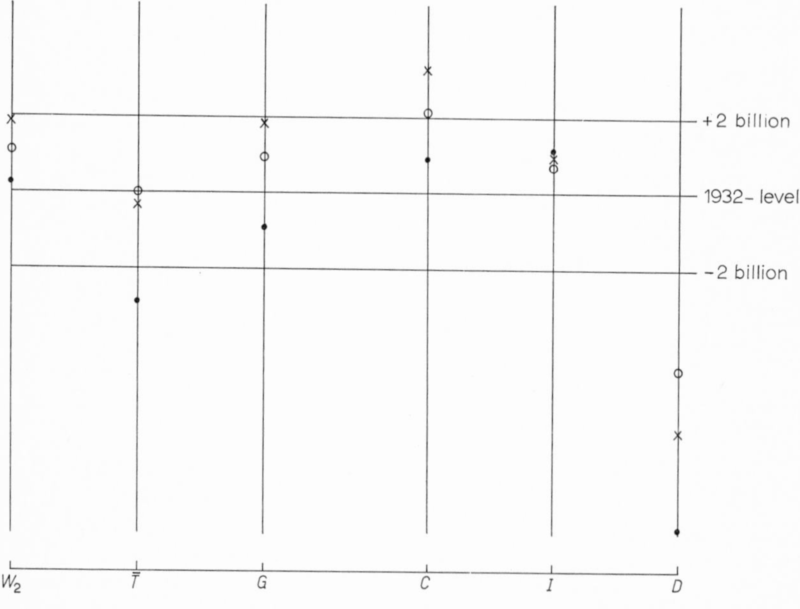

Figure 3.1. The 1933 values of instruments and noncontrolled variables (x^0—circle, $\hat{x}$—cross, actual—dot) measured as deviations from the 1932 level in billions of 1934 dollars

of W_2(5.038). It is seen that $\hat{x}$ has slightly higher W_2 and G-values than the optimal decision and that its $\overline{T}$-value is slightly lower. The decision obtained by maximizing expected utility is hence more of the deficit type than the one obtained by maximizing the social preference function itself: it stresses government spending on goods and services (G) and accepts a lower level of indirect taxes ($\overline{T}$). The policy that was actually followed in 1933 differs much more from x^0. It is characterized by much lower values of the expenditure variables W_2 and G, but also by a much lower level of indirect taxes.[1] The consequences for the noncontrolled variables are specified in the right-hand part of the table. They do not show much difference as to investment, but a 5 per cent higher consumption value for $\hat{x}$ compared with the actual figure, while the distribution variable D takes much smaller values than desired in two cases out of three, especially for the realized variant. The last feature is due to the low $\bar{T}$-value of the actual policy followed, which is much more favourable for profits than for the private wage bill (see Table 3.4) and thus reduces D.

TABLE 3.5

THREE ALTERNATIVE DECISIONS AND THEIR CONSEQUENCES FOR THE NONCONTROLLED VARIABLES

(in billions of 1934 dollars per year)

	Instruments			*Noncontrolled variables*		
	W_2	$\bar{T}$	G	C	I	D
x^0	6.43	8.27	11.17	47.76	−5.51	10.42
$\hat{x}$	7.15	8.01	12.04	48.87	−5.25	8.80
actual values	5.6	5.4	9.3	46.5	−5.1	6.1
desired values	5.04	7.40	10.44	49.69	−3.10	11.25

A step-by-step comparison of the numerical values of the individual variables is certainly instructive, but an adequate evaluation of a decision as a whole is obtained only by computing its loss. The loss of x^0 is zero by definition; that of $\hat{x}$ is given by (2.3.3) where K is as specified in (1.18), which gives 2.62.[2] The loss associated with the actual decision made in

[1] These statements refer to the volume of indirect taxes received (see also note 3 of p. 78). The following procedure shows how they can be transformed into statements concerning tax rates. From (1.4) we see that net national income plus indirect taxes ($Y+\bar{T}$) is equal to $C+I+G$, which can be read from Table 3.5: 53.42 for x^0, 55.66 for $\hat{x}$, and 50.7 for the actual 1933 situation. On comparing this with the corresponding $\bar{T}$-figures, we find that $\bar{T}$ as a percentage of $Y+\bar{T}$ is 15.5, 14.4 and 10.7, respectively. The corresponding percentage in 1932 was 16.7, hence the first two decisions involve minor tax rate reductions and the last a major one. It is of course impossible to compute such 1933 percentages at the beginning of 1933, but one can estimate C and I, given the decision made, by replacing the disturbances by zero.

[2] Since the loss is the sum of squares of a number of variables which are all expressed in billions of dollars per year, its dimension is that of the square of billions of dollars per year.

1933 is derived in the same way; it is 16.45, which is more than six times as large. It is of course not completely fair to impose "our" preferences on decisions made in 1933, but this is only a minor point in the present illustrative exposition.

It is instructive to decompose these losses into parts which are to be ascribed to the separate components of the decision error and to their interaction. For the loss associated with a decision error $\mathbf{\Delta x} = \mathbf{x}-\mathbf{x}^0$ is of the form $-\frac{1}{2}(\mathbf{\Delta x})'\mathbf{K}(\mathbf{\Delta x})$, so that $-\frac{1}{2}k_{11}(\Delta x_1)^2$ refers to the first component of $\mathbf{\Delta x}$, $-k_{12}\Delta x_1 \Delta x_2$ to the interaction of this component with the second, and so on. This decomposition is presented in Table 3.6, both for $\hat{\mathbf{x}}$ and for the actual decision made in 1933. It is seen that the loss of $\hat{\mathbf{x}}$ is largely due to its G-error and to the interaction of this and the $\overline{T}$-error, whereas the loss associated with the actual decision made is essentially due to both the G and the $\overline{T}$-errors and to their interaction. The latter interaction is favourable in the sense that it affects the loss negatively; things would have been much worse if the G and $\overline{T}$-errors had opposite sign. There is a similar negative component in the loss of $\hat{\mathbf{x}}$ (the W_2, $\overline{T}$-interaction), but this is of minor importance numerically.

TABLE 3.6

DECOMPOSITION OF TWO LOSSES*

	W_2	$\overline{T}$	G	W_2	$\overline{T}$	G
	Decision $\hat{\mathbf{x}}$			Actual decision in 1933		
W_2	0.39	−0.10	0.02	0.53	1.34	0.04
$\overline{T}$		0.21	0.78		27.47	−19.18
G			1.32			6.25

* The elements above the diagonal contain the total interaction effect; e.g., −0.10 in the first row is the sum of $-\frac{1}{2}k_{12}\Delta x_1\Delta x_2$ and $-\frac{1}{2}k_{21}\Delta x_2\Delta x_1$, each of which is −0.05.

The result of Table 3.6 shows that—at least for the decisions considered there—the W_2-error is rather unimportant compared with the G and the $\overline{T}$-errors. In fact, this holds more generally, because it follows from (1.18) that the leading element of $\mathbf{K}$ (which is the coefficient of the squared W_2-error in the loss, apart from the factor $-\frac{1}{2}$) is much smaller in absolute value than the other diagonal elements; and, similarly, the nondiagonal elements in the first row and column of $\mathbf{K}$ are also rather close to zero. The element in the second row and third column (corresponding with $\overline{T}$ and G) is much larger. This is also reflected in the substitution matrix of the instruments, which is the inverse of K [see (2.1.29)]:

$$(1.24)\quad (xx) = K^{-1} = -(\mathbf{I}+R'R)^{-1} = \begin{array}{c} \begin{array}{ccc} (W_2) & (\bar{T}) & (G) \end{array} \\ \begin{bmatrix} -0.707 & 0.134 & 0.140 \\ 0.134 & -0.348 & -0.350 \\ 0.140 & -0.350 & -0.634 \end{bmatrix} \end{array} \begin{array}{c} \\ (W_2) \\ (\bar{T}) \\ (G) \end{array}$$

This shows that W_2 is a substitute for $\bar{T}$ as well as for G, the corresponding substitution terms being both positive; further, that $\bar{T}$ and G are complementary. It is of some interest to see whether these relations are "strong" or "weak." This can be done conveniently by standardizing the substitution terms, i.e., by dividing them by the positive square root of the product of the corresponding diagonal elements (in the same way as second-order moments are standardized to obtain correlation coefficients):

$$(1.25)\qquad \frac{(xx)_{hk}}{\sqrt{(xx)_{hh}(xx)_{kk}}}\,.$$

These standardized substitution terms are between -1 and 1, so that they are a convenient measure for the strength of a substitution or a complementarity relation. For $(h, k) = (1, 2)$ corresponding with W_2 and $\bar{T}$, (1.25) gives 0.27; for (1, 3), 0.21; and for (2, 3), -0.75. We might therefore say that W_2 is a "weak substitute" for $\bar{T}$ and G, while the latter two instruments are "strongly complementary."

3.1.6. The Additive Structure of the Constraints and the Loss Associated with Its Forecasts; Tinbergen Surfaces and the Failure Matrix

The set-up of our problem implies that the only source of uncertainty which is recognized is that of the 1933 values of the three structural disturbances. They affect the constraints *via* its additive structure, and so we consider the matrix of slopes of the Tinbergen surfaces of the instruments. Applying (2.1.30), we find for this matrix:

$$(1.26)\quad -(x\cdot) = -(\mathbf{I}+R'R)^{-1}R' = \begin{array}{c} \begin{array}{ccc} (C) & (I) & (D) \end{array} \\ \begin{bmatrix} -0.402 & 0.033 & -0.085 \\ -0.080 & 0.005 & -0.282 \\ -0.266 & -0.068 & 0.119 \end{bmatrix} \end{array} \begin{array}{c} \\ (W_2) \\ (\bar{T}) \\ (G) \end{array}$$

It shows that an increase in s_1 affects all instruments negatively, see the first column; further, that an increase in s_2 affects W_2 and $\bar{T}$ positively but G negatively, while the converse is true for an increase in s_3. Numerically, the most important effects are those of s_1 on W_2 and G and of s_3 on $\overline{T}$. These three coefficients are all negative, which is intuitively rather easy to understand. For suppose that consumption is subject to an upward shift (a "windfall gain"); then it is no longer as necessary to raise W_2 and G and to use their positive effectiveness with respect to consumption [see (1.13)]. Similarly, if the distribution variable is subject to an upward shift, we can restrict the use of $\overline{T}$, which is positively effective with respect to D. The converse holds for G, its D-coefficient in (1.26) being positive.

The loss associated with an s-error is a quadratic form with $-\frac{1}{2}F$ as matrix, where F is the failure matrix which in this case is

$$(1.27)\quad F = (\cdot x)(xx)^{-1}(x\cdot) = -R(\mathbf{I}+R'R)^{-1}R'$$

$$= \begin{array}{c} \\ \left[\begin{array}{rrr} (C) & (I) & (D) \\ -0.431 & -0.024 & 0.076 \\ -0.024 & -0.021 & 0.119 \\ 0.076 & 0.119 & -0.859 \end{array}\right] \end{array} \begin{array}{c} \\ (C) \\ (I) \\ (D) \end{array}$$

This matrix shows that a given s_2-error is is much less important than a numerically equal s_1 or s_3-error, except that the interaction of s_2 and s_3-errors is of some secondary importance. The s_3-error (corresponding with the distribution variable) has a considerable weight. This is due to the fact that an s_3-error leads to $\overline{T}$ and G-errors of opposite sign, see (1.26); and these reinforce each other, see the appropriate nondiagonal element in (1.18).

As stated earlier, the cause of an s-error is an imperfect forecast of the structural disturbances. It follows from (1.15) that these disturbances affect the additive structure of the constraints *via* the matrix S of (1.16); and hence, their effect on the decision made is obtained by premultiplication by the matrix

$$(1.28)\quad -(x\cdot)S = -(\mathbf{I}+R'R)^{-1}R'S = \begin{array}{c} \begin{array}{ccc} (u_C) & (u_I) & (u_W) \end{array} \\ \left[\begin{array}{rrr} -0.542 & -0.107 & -0.653 \\ 0.270 & 0.356 & -0.718 \\ -0.632 & -0.433 & -0.037 \end{array}\right] \end{array} \begin{array}{c} \\ (W_2) \\ (\overline{T}) \\ (G) \end{array}$$

This result shows that an upward shift of the consumption function or of the investment function changes the optimal values of W_2 and G in a downward direction but that of $\overline{T}$ in an upward direction; for u_W (corresponding with the demand-for-labour function) the effects are all negative.

This is reflected by the difference between x^0 and $\hat{x}$ in the light of the realized disturbances (1.17). These 1933 disturbances are all positive; and the first and the third row of the matrix (1.28) consist of negative elements, while the single negative element of the second row is dominated by the two positive elements. Accordingly, the W_2 and G-components of $\hat{x}$ exceed those of x^0, whereas the converse is true for the $\overline{T}$-component.

The loss associated with a prediction error in the structural disturbances is a quadratic form in this error with matrix $-\frac{1}{2}S'FS$ and $S'FS$ is specified as

$$(1.29)\quad S'\,S = -S'R(\mathbf{I}+R'R)^{-1}R'S = \begin{array}{c} \begin{array}{ccc} (u_C) & (u_I) & (u_W) \end{array} \\ \begin{bmatrix} -3.43 & -2.81 & 2.13 \\ -2.81 & -2.59 & 2.69 \\ 2.13 & 2.69 & -4.44 \end{bmatrix} \end{array} \begin{array}{c} \\ (u_C) \\ (u_I) \\ (u_W) \end{array}$$

This shows that the elements are all of the same order of magnitude. In particular, the nondiagonal elements are far from zero, which means that the interaction of the structural disturbances is of considerable importance. This interaction would be systematic if the disturbances were correlated to a significant degree. For Klein's Model I this is hardly the case, so that the expected loss associated with the disturbances can then be written in the form:

$$(1.30)\quad -\tfrac{1}{2}\mathscr{E}(u'S'FSu) = 1.71 \text{ var } u_C + 1.30 \text{ var } u_I + 2.22 \text{ var } u_W,$$

where u stands for the column vector of the three disturbances and the figures on the right stand for the successive diagonal elements of $-\frac{1}{2}S'FS$. If we substitute the estimated values for the three variances:

$$(1.31)\qquad \text{var } u_C = 1.30;\quad \text{var } u_I = 1.42;\quad \text{var } u_W = 0.61,$$

the expected loss (1.30) becomes 5.42. This is about twice as large as the 2.62 value which we found for the loss associated with $\hat{x}$, which means that we should expect that the certainty equivalence procedure will lead to larger losses on the average than it did in 1933. On the other hand, the loss associated with the actual decision made in 1933 (which is 16.45) is still three times larger than the expected loss (1.30). Furthermore, it is interesting to observe that we can decompose this expected loss according to the three disturbances, since 1.71 var u_C is the part which is due to u_C, while 1.30 var u_I and 2.22 var u_W correspond to u_I and u_W respectively [see (1.30)]. On substituting the numerical values (1.31) we find that these three parts are: 2.23, 1.84 and 1.36. Hence, given the preference function chosen and given the mechanism of the American economy as described by Klein's Model I, we can conclude that the residual variation around the consumption function is about 20 per cent more serious than that of the investment function, and that the residual variation around the latter function is almost 40 per cent more serious than that of the demand-for-labour function. If the covariances of the structural disturbances do not vanish, the expected loss (1.30) becomes a weighted sum of variances and covariances. In that case the decomposition is of the same general type as that of Table 3.6.

Finally, we consider the failure of a forecast of the additive structure of the constraints. This implies that we should divide by the loss which is incurred by no-change extrapolation of the additive structure. An inspection of (2.3.9) and (1.15) shows that the extrapolated additive structure s_0 is equal to the numerical vector on the right of (1.15) plus S times the structural disturbances of 1932. These are (in the order u_C, u_I, u_W): -1.33, -0.59, -0.12. The extrapolation error is then $s_0 - s = -S\Delta u$ where Δu is the three-element vector of changes in structural disturbances (1933 minus 1932). Hence the loss associated with no-change extrapolation is $-\frac{1}{2}(\Delta u)'S'FS\Delta u$, which is 15.16. On comparing this with the 2.62 value for the loss of $\hat{x}$, we conclude that the certainty equivalence procedure was characterized by a failure of 0.17 in 1933, while the actual decision made has a failure value of 1.09. The parent failure of the certainty equivalence procedure, defined in (2.3.12), is in this case equal to $\frac{1}{2}$ if we assume that the structural disturbances of successive years are all uncorrelated and that they have constant variances and covariances.

3.1.7. Concluding Remarks

The preceding pages illustrate only part of the theory of Chapter 2. The following remarks, in particular from (ii) onward, serve to indicate other applications, most of which will be considered in more detail in a dynamic framework.

(i) The procedure of specifying a quadratic preference function in two steps (first desired values, then a quadratic form in their deviations from actual values) is frequently very convenient.[1] The following result has some further clarifying value. Let us write ξ and η for the vectors of desired values of the instruments and the noncontrolled variables, respec-

[1] Note also that if the matrix of this quadratic form (the Hessian of the preference function) is negative definite, the matrix K is also negative definite, so that the second-order maximum condition of Theorem 2.2 is then satisfied. The reason is that if a quadratic form is definite, it is certainly definite under constraint.

tively; then the preference function

$$w(x, y) = a'x + b'y + \tfrac{1}{2}(x'Ax + y'By + x'Cy + y'C'x)$$

can be written in the equivalent form

$$\begin{aligned} w(x, y) = {} & \tfrac{1}{2}[(x-\xi)'A(x-\xi) + (y-\eta)'B(y-\eta) \\ & + (x-\xi)'C(y-\eta) + (y-\eta)'C'(x-\xi)], \end{aligned}$$

where x and y are now measured from their original origins and not, as in the earlier part of this section, as deviations from their desired values. It is seen that the quadratic parts of the two preference functions are indeed equivalent, due to the fact that the same matrices A, B and C appear; but the equivalence of the linear part involves a linear dependence of a and b on ξ and η:

$$a + A\xi + C\eta = \mathbf{0}; \quad b + C'\xi + B\eta = \mathbf{0}. \tag{1.32}$$

We recall that the optimal decision x^0 is $-K^{-1}k$, where k is given by (2.1.25). Applying (1.32), we find that in this case k can be written as

$$k = a + R'b + (C + R'B)s = -(A + R'C')\xi - (C + R'B)(\eta - s).$$

Let us now write

$$y_\xi = R\xi + s \tag{1.33}$$

for the vector of noncontrolled variables which is realized when the instruments are put at their desired level. Then $\eta - s = \eta - y_\xi + R\xi$, so that k can be written as follows:

$$\begin{aligned} k &= -(A + R'BR + CR + R'C')\xi - (C + R'B)(\eta - y_\xi) \\ &= -K\xi + (C + R'B)(y_\xi - \eta). \end{aligned}$$

Combining this with $x^0 = -K^{-1}k$, we find $x^0 = \xi - K^{-1}(C + R'B) \times (y_\xi - \eta)$; and applying (2.1.28) and (2.1.30) we obtain finally

$$x^0 - \xi = -(x\cdot)(y_\xi - \eta), \tag{1.34}$$

in words: the deviation between the optimal decision x^0 and the desired values of the instruments (ξ) is a linear function of the deviation between the noncontrolled values that would be realized if the decision maker would act according to these desires (y_ξ) and the desired values of the noncontrolled variables themselves (η); and the coefficient matrix of the linear dependence is the matrix of slope coefficients of the Tinbergen surfaces. It will be noted that $y_\xi - \eta$ can be regarded as the "inconsistency" of the decision maker's desires: he wishes ξ for the instruments and η for the noncontrolled variables, but if he realizes the former desire he gets y_ξ for the noncontrolled variables, not η. It will also be noted that there is a similar simple result for the decision which maximizes expected utility; then x^0 on the left of (1.34) is replaced by $\hat{x}$, and $y_\xi = R\xi + s$ on the right by $R\xi + \mathscr{E}s$.

(ii) We considered the fact that the structural equations of Klein's Model I are "imperfect" in the sense that they contain nonzero disturbances and hence lead to uncertainty at the level of the additive structure of the constraints. But we did not recognize the fact that the equations used are even more imperfect because their coefficients are subject to sampling errors. The extent to which this is serious can be determined approximately as follows. Such sampling errors imply similar errors for the coefficient matrices R and s of the constraints; these, in turn, lead to decision errors which can be derived by means of Theorem 2.6 if the R-errors are not too large; and these errors, finally, lead to a certain loss. If the chain from the sampling errors in the structural coefficients to the decision errors is approximated linearly, the loss appears as a quadratic form in the sampling errors. Taking the expectation, we obtain the expected loss which is a function of the matrix of the second-order sampling moments of the estimated coefficients. This analysis gives insight into the seriousness of sampling errors and will be pursued in a dynamic context in Chapter 6 (see 6.1.5).

(iii) In the same way, one can investigate the implications of an incorrect specification of the social preference function. As long as the errors in the coefficients of the quadratic part of this function are not too large, the resulting decision errors can be approximated linearly so that the loss appears again as a quadratic form in the specification errors; see Theorem 2.6. In the present case the social preference function cannot claim to be very realistic, hence there is no particular reason for assuming that the coefficients of its quadratic part are subject to small errors. But we shall consider a more realistic case in the paint factory context (see Section 5.2 of Chapter 5).

(iv) In 3.1.1–3.1.3 we formulated the decision problem dynamically in terms of a four-year horizon. This period is not unreasonable in the present case, because it is the time span of an American Presidential administration; nevertheless, it is of some interest to consider the implications of alternative horizons after the dynamic approach has been formulated. This too will take place in Chapter 5 (see 5.1.2).

3.1.8. Summary

(2) The social preference function which is chosen for the American economy in the nineteen-thirties depends on three instruments and three noncontrolled variables. The instruments are: the government wage bill, the volume of indirect taxes, and government expenditure on goods and services (all in real terms); the noncontrolled variables: total consumption, net investment, and a distribution variable which effectively measures the ratio of profits to the private wage bill. The preference function is formulated for the four-year period 1933–1936 with a view of restoring per capita consumption at the end of that period to the 1929 level, the investment-consumption ratio to the 10 per cent level, and the ratio of profits to the private wage bill to the 50 per cent level. This is done by specifying a desired development over time for each of the arguments of the preference function and by minimizing the sum of squares of the deviations between the actual and the desired values. This minimization of the sum of squares is equivalent to the maximization of the corresponding quadratic preference function.

(1, 3, 4) The preference function is maximized subject to the constraints of the American economy such as these are described by Klein's Model I. The estimated coefficients of its equations are taken for the corresponding "true" coefficients. A reduced-form transformation is applied to this model in order to bring the constraints within the theoretical framework of Chapter 2. The decision process is confined to the first year (1933) in order to reduce the problem to the static case.

(5) The optimal policy, based on these constraints and this preference function, implies higher values for each of the three instruments than the decision which was actually made in 1933. Insofar as this refers to the government wage bill and government expenditure on goods and services, this leads to a larger government deficit; but the larger amount of taxes works in opposite direction. The decision which maximizes expected utility (obtained by replacing the 1933 structural disturbances of Klein's Model I by their expectations, as the theorem on certainty equivalence permits) is slightly more of the deficit type than the optimal decision; but the difference between these two is smaller than the difference between the optimal decision and the decision that was actually made, the loss of

the latter decision being more than six times larger than that of the decision which maximizes expected utility. The latter loss is largely due to the decision error concerning the government expenditure on goods and services and to the interaction of this error with that of indirect taxes; in the former loss a very important role is also played by the last-mentioned error, quite apart from its interaction with the decision errors of other instruments. These components of the total loss are obtained by dividing its quadratic form into parts; the matrix of this form is $-\frac{1}{2}$ times the inverse of the substitution matrix of the instruments, and it turns out that the government wage bill is a weak substitute for indirect taxes and for government expenditure on goods and services, whereas the latter two instruments are strongly complementary.

(6) An evaluation of the slope matrix of the Tinbergen surfaces enables us to derive the effects of additive shifts of the constraints on the optimal values of the instruments. An upward shift of the consumption function and of the investment function of Klein's Model I affects indirect taxes positively but the government wage bill and government expenditure on goods and services negatively; an upward shift of the demand-for-labour function affects the optimal values of all three instruments negatively. The expected loss associated with the certainty equivalence procedure is larger than the loss to which this procedure led in 1933, which is due to the relatively small values of the disturbances in that year. Assuming that the disturbances of the three structural equations are uncorrelated, and applying the constraints and the preference function that have been used here, we find that the largest part of the expected loss of the certainty equivalence procedure is due to the disturbances of the consumption function; the disturbances of the investment function are second in this respect and those of the demand-for-labour function third.

(7) If a quadratic preference function is formulated in terms of desired values of instruments and noncontrolled variables such that a quadratic form in the deviations between the actual and these desired values is minimized, then the optimal decision taken as a deviation from the desired values of the instruments is a linear function of the difference between the noncontrolled values implied by these desires and the desired values of the noncontrolled variables themselves; the coefficient matrix of this function is the slope matrix of the Tinbergen surfaces. Further possible applications are indicated (on specification errors of the preference function and the constraints and on alternative horizons), which are postponed till later chapters.

3.2. A CASE OF PRODUCTION AND EMPLOYMENT SCHEDULING

3.2.1. Introduction; The Cost Function to Be Minimized

In this section we shall present another illustration of the theory of Chapter 2, which is partly based on the work of HOLT, MODIGLIANI, SIMON and MUTH dealing with production and work force decisions of a paint factory.[1] We shall also draw freely on results obtained by VAN DE PANNE and others in the same field.[2]

The present subject is evidently of a much more microeconomic character than that of Section 3.1; but it is not micro to the extreme, since we shall deal with such variables as production, inventory and work force without making distinctions as to qualities and grades. The object of the analysis is to minimize the total costs associated with production and work force decisions, these two variables representing the instruments of the decision problem; the inventory level is considered as noncontrolled. We shall be interested in minimizing costs over time, which means that we shall introduce a horizon of T elementary periods (months in the present case) such that total costs for this complete period is the sum of the costs connected with the separate periods. In addition to summation over time, we shall also need summation over cost categories, because the following four groups will be considered:

---

[1] C. C. HOLT, F. MODIGLIANI and H. SIMON, "A Linear Decision Rule for Production and Employment Scheduling," *Management Science*, Vol. 2 (1955), pp. 1–30; C. C. HOLT, F. MODIGLIANI and J. F. MUTH, "Derivation of a Linear Decision Rule for Production and Employment," *ibidem*, Vol. 2 (1956), pp. 159–177; C. C. HOLT, F. MODIGLIANI, J. F. MUTH and H. A. SIMON, *Planning Production, Inventories, and Work Force* (1960). Reference is also made to other applications mentioned by E. H. BOWMAN in "Consistency and Optimality in Managerial Decision Making," *Management Science*, Vol. 9 (1963), pp. 310–321.

[2] C. VAN DE PANNE and G. J. AEYELTS AVERINK, "Imperfect Management Decisions and Predictions and Their Financial Implications in Dynamic Quadratic Cost Minimization," *Statistica Neerlandica*, Vol. 15 (1961), pp. 293–318. Also P. J. M. VAN DEN BOGAARD, A. MONREAL LUQUE et C. VAN DE PANNE, "Etude sur les implications des horizons alternatifs dans la programmation quadratique dynamique," *Revue de la Société Française de Recherche Opérationnelle*, Vol. 6 (1962), pp. 163–183; and C. VAN DE PANNE and P. BOSJE, "Sensitivity Analysis of Cost Coefficient Estimates: The Case of Linear Decision Rules for Employment and Production," *Management Science*, Vol. 9 (1962), pp. 82–107.

1. Regular payroll costs
2. Hiring and layoff costs
3. Overtime costs
4. Inventory connected costs.

Each of these groups will be approximated by linear or quadratic functions of production rates, inventory levels, and the number of employees. In what follows we shall indicate production in month t by p_t (measured in gallons [1] per month), the inventory level at the end of month t by y_t (measured in gallons), and the number of employees by q_t. Costs are measured in dollars per month.

Regular payroll costs are approximated by a linear function of the number of employees. The constant term of this relation is irrelevant for the purpose of minimizing costs, hence we use

$$\text{Regular payroll costs} = c_1 q_t, \tag{2.1}$$

where, of course, the left-hand side should be interpreted as the regular payroll costs for month t.

Hiring and layoff costs are described as a function of the number of workers hired or laid off, i.e., as a function of $q_t - q_{t-1}$. When workers are hired ($q_t > q_{t-1}$), it is necessary to spend money on interviews, selection, training, etc.; when they are laid off ($q_t < q_{t-1}$) they receive terminal pay and may necessitate a reorganization, etc. In addition, there may be intangible penalties associated with layoff. The following quadratic approximation is used:

$$\text{Hiring and layoff costs} = c_2(q_t - q_{t-1} - c_{10})^2, \tag{2.2}$$

which is asymmetric with respect to no-change in the work force ($q_t = q_{t-1}$) as soon as $c_{10} \neq 0$. For example, if c_{10} is positive, (2.2) describes the costs associated with hiring a given number of workers as below the costs associated with a layoff of the same number. It will be clear that (as in the macroeconomic application of Section 3.1) such a quadratic approximation is subject to errors and can claim validity for a limited range only.

Overtime costs (and idle-time costs) depend primarily on production relative to the work force. If we write c_4 for the maximum output of one man, then overtime costs are incurred if $p_t - c_4 q_t$ is positive and idle time costs if it is negative. This cost category is approximated by the

[1] Actually pseudo-gallons (introduced in order to disguise the company's cost data).

square of this expression, to which two linear terms and a cross-product term are added in order to improve the approximation:

(2.3) $$\text{Overtime costs} = c_3(p_t - c_4 q_t)^2 + c_5 p_t - c_6 q_t + c_{11} p_t q_t.$$

Finally, we have the group of inventory, back order, and machine setup costs. It is assumed that the optimal net inventory (net inventory being defined as physical inventory less backlog) can be approximated adequately by a linear function of sales: $c_8 + c_9 v_t$, where v_t is the rate of orders in month t. When the actual net inventory level is smaller, there will be an increase in backorders and in the number of machine setups; when it is larger, it leads to higher inventory costs. This effect is again approximated by a quadratic expression:

(2.4) $$\text{Inventory connected costs} = c_7[y_t - (c_8 + c_9 v_t)]^2,$$

y_t being the actual net inventory level.

By adding (2.1)–(2.4) and summing over t we obtain total costs over the T-month horizon:

(2.5) $$\text{Total costs} = \sum_{t=1}^{T} \{(c_1 - c_6)q_t + c_2(q_t - q_{t-1} - c_{10})^2 + c_3(p_t - c_4 q_t)^2 + c_5 p_t + c_{11} p_t q_t + c_7[y_t - (c_8 + c_9 v_t)]^2\}.$$

The numerical part of this section will be based on the following specifications made by Holt and his co-authors:

(2.6) $$\begin{array}{llll} c_1 = 340 & c_4 = 5.67 & c_7 = 0.0825 & c_{10} = 0 \\ c_2 = 64.3 & c_5 = 51.2 & c_8 = 320 & c_{11} = 0. \\ c_3 = 0.20 & c_6 = 281 & c_9 = 0 & \end{array}$$

The dimensions of these c's follow immediately from the dimensions of the variables to which they belong; see above, the end of the second paragraph. It is seen that the three zero values for c_9, c_{10} and c_{11} imply several simplifications: the optimal net inventory level is now taken as fixed rather than as dependent on sales; hiring and layoff costs are made symmetric; and the cross-product term in the overtime cost function is neglected.

3.2.2. The Optimal Static Behaviour for a Six-Month Horizon

Our objective is to minimize total costs subject to the obvious constraint

(2.7) $$y_t - y_{t-1} = p_t - v_t \qquad (t = 1, \ldots, T),$$

that is, the change in the net inventory level equals the excess of production over sales. Such a constrained minimization problem has necessarily the nature of an optimal compromise with respect to the various cost components. For we can reduce hiring and layoff costs to the zero level by keeping the work force constant (apart from normal replacement changes due to retirement, etc.), and we can reduce the inventory connected costs to a minimum by scheduling such that y_t equals $c_8+c_9v_t$ (or approximately so), but in that case there will be substantial costs of overtime and idle time. Similarly, we can try to minimize hiring and layoff costs and overtime costs, which will lead to substantial inventory connected costs; or we can concentrate on overtime and inventory costs, in which case the hiring and layoff costs will be large. Obviously, the best thing that can be done is to minimize total costs, which is indeed our objective according to (2.5).[1]

It will be clear that this objective is a dynamic one, since it deals with a series of decisions in T successive months. Hence the problem is in fact beyond the scope of the present chapter. But we shall reduce it to a static problem by postulating that all decisions have to be made at the beginning of the first month. Such a procedure has the additional advantage of illustrating the gain obtained in case no such static constraint is imposed; this will be analyzed further in the dynamic application (see Chapter 5, in particular 5.1.4 and 5.1.5). The numerical analysis of this section [starting with eq. (2.15) below] will be based on a six-month horizon ($T = 6$).

The present application can be regarded as dealing with $2T$ instruments, viz., the production and work force variables in each of the T months. Furthermore, when considering the total cost function (2.5) and observing that $c_9 = 0$ according to the specification (2.6), we see that the inventory levels are the only other variables of the preference function. They are obviously noncontrolled in the sense of Chapter 2, hence there are T noncontrolled variables. We thus have:

$$x = \begin{bmatrix} p \\ q \end{bmatrix}, \quad p = \begin{bmatrix} p_1 \\ \vdots \\ p_T \end{bmatrix}, \quad q = \begin{bmatrix} q_1 \\ \vdots \\ q_T \end{bmatrix}, \quad y = \begin{bmatrix} y_1 \\ \vdots \\ y_T \end{bmatrix}. \tag{2.8}$$

---

[1] There is one aspect which is neglected when this objective is pursued, viz., the value of the change in inventories during the T-period horizon, $y_T - y_0$ (valued at some appropriate price). However, the dynamic analysis of Chapter 5 will deal primarily with the infinite-horizon case in which this aspect is no longer relevant.

We proceed to write the preference function and the constraints in the forms (2.1.5) and (2.1.6), respectively; for simplicity's sake, we shall delete throughout the coefficients c_9, c_{10} and c_{11} which are zero according to (2.6). Starting with the preference function [and adding a minus sign to (2.5) to make it a function which is to be maximized], we find for the coefficient matrices involving noncontrolled variables:

$$b = 2c_7 c_8 \begin{bmatrix} 1 \\ 1 \\ \vdots \\ 1 \end{bmatrix}, \quad B = -2c_7 \mathbf{I}, \quad C = \mathbf{0}, \tag{2.9}$$

the orders being $T \times 1$, $T \times T$ and $2T \times T$, respectively. It is convenient to partition a and A according to the production and work force variables:

$$a = \begin{bmatrix} a_p \\ a_q \end{bmatrix}, \quad A = \begin{bmatrix} A_{pp} & A_{pq} \\ A_{qp} & A_{qq} \end{bmatrix}, \tag{2.10}$$

where

$$a_p = -c_5 \begin{bmatrix} 1 \\ 1 \\ \vdots \\ 1 \end{bmatrix}, \quad a_q = -(c_1 - c_6) \begin{bmatrix} 1 \\ 1 \\ \vdots \\ 1 \end{bmatrix} + 2c_2 q_0 \begin{bmatrix} 1 \\ 0 \\ \vdots \\ 0 \end{bmatrix},$$

$$A_{pp} = -2c_3 \mathbf{I}, \quad A_{pq} = A_{qp} = 2c_3 c_4 \mathbf{I}, \tag{2.11}$$

$$A_{qq} = -2 \begin{bmatrix} 2c_2 + c_3 c_4^2 & -c_2 & \cdots & 0 & 0 \\ -c_2 & 2c_2 + c_3 c_4^2 & \cdots & 0 & 0 \\ \vdots & \vdots & & \vdots & \vdots \\ 0 & 0 & \cdots & 2c_2 + c_3 c_4^2 & -c_2 \\ 0 & 0 & \cdots & -c_2 & c_2 + c_3 c_4^2 \end{bmatrix},$$

q_0 being the initial work force (which is taken as given). The vectors of (2.11) are T-element column vectors, the matrices all $T \times T$.

The constraints (2.7) are not in the required form $y = Rx + s$ since they contain the noncontrolled variables y_{t-1} in addition to y_t. But the former can be eliminated successively:

$$\begin{aligned} y_1 &= p_1 - (v_1 - y_0) \\ y_2 &= p_1 + p_2 - (v_1 + v_2 - y_0) \\ &\vdots \end{aligned}$$

where y_0 is the initial inventory level (which is taken as given). Hence we have

$$(2.12)\qquad R = [R_p\ \mathbf{0}],\ R_p = \begin{bmatrix} 1 & 0 & 0 & \dots & 0 \\ 1 & 1 & 0 & \dots & 0 \\ \vdots & \vdots & \vdots & & \vdots \\ 1 & 1 & 1 & \dots & 1 \end{bmatrix},\quad s = -\begin{bmatrix} v_1 - y_0 \\ v_1 + v_2 - y_0 \\ \vdots \\ \sum_1^T v_t - y_0 \end{bmatrix},$$

the zero submatrix of R being of order $T \times T$.

To derive the optimal decision x^0, we need K and k, see (2.1.25) and (2.1.27). We have $K = A + R'BR$ since $C = \mathbf{0}$; and this can be partitioned as follows:

$$(2.13)\qquad K = \begin{bmatrix} -2c_3\mathbf{I} - 2c_7 R_p' R_p & 2c_3 c_4 \mathbf{I} \\ 2c_3 c_4 \mathbf{I} & A_{qq} \end{bmatrix},$$

where A_{qq} is as specified in (2.11) and

$$(2.14)\qquad R_p' R_p = \begin{bmatrix} T & T-1 & T-2 & \dots & 1 \\ T-1 & T-1 & T-2 & \dots & 1 \\ T-2 & T-2 & T-2 & \dots & 1 \\ \vdots & \vdots & \vdots & & \vdots \\ 1 & 1 & 1 & \dots & 1 \end{bmatrix},$$

that is, the $(t, t')^{\text{th}}$ element of $R_p' R_p$ is $T+1-t$ or $T+1-t'$, whichever is smaller. If we apply the specifications (2.6) and $T = 6$, we find for the leading submatrix of K:

$$(2.15)\quad -2c_3\mathbf{I} - 2c_7 R_p' R_p = -\begin{bmatrix} 1.390 & 0.825 & 0.660 & 0.495 & 0.330 & 0.165 \\ 0.825 & 1.225 & 0.660 & 0.495 & 0.330 & 0.165 \\ 0.660 & 0.660 & 1.060 & 0.495 & 0.330 & 0.165 \\ 0.495 & 0.495 & 0.495 & 0.895 & 0.330 & 0.165 \\ 0.330 & 0.330 & 0.330 & 0.330 & 0.730 & 0.165 \\ 0.165 & 0.165 & 0.165 & 0.165 & 0.165 & 0.565 \end{bmatrix}$$

and for the lower right-hand submatrix:

$$(2.16)\quad A_{qq} = -\begin{bmatrix} 270.1 & -128.6 & 0 & 0 & 0 & 0 \\ -128.6 & 270.1 & -128.6 & 0 & 0 & 0 \\ 0 & -128.6 & 270.1 & -128.6 & 0 & 0 \\ 0 & 0 & -128.6 & 270.1 & -128.6 & 0 \\ 0 & 0 & 0 & -128.6 & 270.1 & -128.6 \\ 0 & 0 & 0 & 0 & -128.6 & 141.5 \end{bmatrix},$$

while the off-diagonal block is simply $2c_3c_4\mathbf{I} = 2.268\mathbf{I}$. We shall also need the inverse of K, which is given by:

(2.17) $-1000K^{-1}$

$$
= \left[\begin{array}{cccccc|cccccc}
1390 & -633 & -358 & -204 & -124 & -94 & 7.0 & -9.8 & -16.4 & -18.3 & -18.5 & -18.3 \\
 & 1682 & -469 & -266 & -149 & -84 & 2.0 & 15.3 & 0.5 & -6.0 & -8.4 & -8.9 \\
 & & 1778 & -408 & -217 & -92 & 0.1 & 6.6 & 21.9 & 8.2 & 2.4 & 0.7 \\
 & & & 1829 & -344 & -114 & 0.3 & 4.3 & 13.3 & 30.9 & 19.3 & 15.7 \\
 & & & & 1937 & -148 & 2.2 & 6.9 & 14.9 & 28.2 & 50.4 & 43.4 \\
 & & & & & 2309 & 6.3 & 14.9 & 26.5 & 42.4 & 64.5 & 95.6 \\
\hline
 & & & & & & 5.91 & 4.51 & 3.53 & 2.90 & 2.55 & 2.42 \\
 & & & & & & & 9.65 & 7.70 & 6.41 & 5.69 & 5.41 \\
 & & & & & & & & 12.64 & 10.67 & 9.54 & 9.10 \\
 & & & & & & & & & 15.85 & 14.30 & 13.68 \\
 & & & & & & & & & & 20.15 & 19.35 \\
 & & & & & & & & & & & 26.20
\end{array}\right]
\begin{array}{l} \text{production} \\ \\ \text{work force} \end{array}
$$

(columns: production | work force)

The elements below the main diagonal are obtained by transposition.

Turning to k, we observe that it is equal to $a+R'b+R'Bs$, given that $C = \mathbf{0}$; see (2.1.25) and (2.9). For the first two terms we have:

$$
(2.18) \qquad a+R'b = \begin{bmatrix} -c_5 \\ -c_5 \\ \vdots \\ -c_5 \\ -c_1+c_6+2c_2q_0 \\ -c_1+c_6 \\ \vdots \\ -c_1+c_6 \end{bmatrix} + 2c_7c_8 \begin{bmatrix} 1 & 1 & \dots & 1 \\ 0 & 1 & \dots & 1 \\ \vdots & \vdots & & \vdots \\ 0 & 0 & \dots & 1 \\ 0 & 0 & \dots & 0 \\ 0 & 0 & \dots & 0 \\ \vdots & \vdots & & \vdots \\ 0 & 0 & \dots & 0 \end{bmatrix} \begin{bmatrix} 1 \\ 1 \\ \vdots \\ 1 \end{bmatrix}
$$

$$
= \begin{bmatrix} -c_5+2Tc_7c_8 \\ -c_5+2(T-1)c_7c_8 \\ \vdots \\ -c_5+2c_7c_8 \\ -c_1+c_6+2c_2q_0 \\ -c_1+c_6 \\ \vdots \\ -c_1+c_6 \end{bmatrix},
$$

which becomes a vector of numerical elements as soon as we apply (2.6) and $T = 6$; except, of course, that the seventh element is a linear function of the initial work force. The third term, $R'Bs$, is a homogeneous linear function of sales and initial inventory:

$$(2.19)\quad R'Bs = 2c_7 \begin{bmatrix} 1 & 1 & \dots & 1 \\ 0 & 1 & \dots & 1 \\ \vdots & \vdots & & \vdots \\ 0 & 0 & \dots & 1 \\ 0 & 0 & \dots & 0 \\ 0 & 0 & \dots & 0 \\ \vdots & \vdots & & \vdots \\ 0 & 0 & \dots & 0 \end{bmatrix} \begin{bmatrix} v_1 - y_0 \\ v_1 + v_2 - y_0 \\ \vdots \\ \sum_1^T v_t - y_0 \end{bmatrix}$$

$$= 2c_7 \begin{bmatrix} Tv_1 + (T-1)v_2 + \dots + v_T - Ty_0 \\ (T-1)v_1 + (T-1)v_2 + \dots + v_T - (T-1)y_0 \\ \vdots \\ v_1 + v_2 + \dots + v_T - y_0 \\ 0 \\ 0 \\ \vdots \\ 0 \end{bmatrix},$$

that is, apart from the factor $2c_7$, the coefficient of v_t in the t'^{th} element is $T+1-t$ or $T+1-t'$, whichever is smaller ($t, t' \leqq T$). On combining (2.18) and (2.19) for the numerical specification (2.6) and $T = 6$, we obtain

$$(2.20)\quad k = \begin{bmatrix} 265.6 + 0.165[6(v_1 - y_0) + 5v_2 + 4v_3 + 3v_4 + 2v_5 + v_6] \\ 212.8 + 0.165[5(v_1 - y_0 + v_2) + 4v_3 + 3v_4 + 2v_5 + v_6] \\ 160.0 + 0.165[4(v_1 - y_0 + v_2 + v_3) + 3v_4 + 2v_5 + v_6] \\ 107.2 + 0.165[3(v_1 - y_0 + v_2 + v_3 + v_4) + 2v_5 + v_6] \\ 54.4 + 0.165[2(v_1 - y_0 + v_2 + v_3 + v_4 + v_5) + v_6] \\ 1.6 + 0.165[v_1 - y_0 + v_2 + v_3 + v_4 + v_5 + v_6] \\ -59 + 128.6q_0 \\ -59 \\ -59 \\ -59 \\ -59 \\ -59 \end{bmatrix}.$$

By postmultiplying minus the inverse of K by this k we obtain the optimal decision x^0, which is a 12-element column vector that can be partitioned as follows:

$$(2.21)\quad x^0 = \begin{bmatrix} p^0 \\ q^0 \end{bmatrix},$$

where p^0 is the optimal production decision vector and q^0 the optimal work force decision vector. Each of these subvectors consists of six elements corresponding to the six successive months; and each of these elements is the sum of a constant term, a term in the initial work force (q_0), and six terms involving shipments of the six months (with the understanding that the initial inventory level, y_0, is subtracted from the shipments of the first month). The result is presented in Table 3.7. It specifies the first-period decision as follows:

$$(2.22)\quad \begin{aligned} p_1^0 &= 152.8+0.902q_0+0.460(v_1-y_0)+0.231v_2+0.106v_3 \\ &\qquad +0.040v_4+0.008v_5-0.004v_6 \\ q_1^0 &= 1.18+0.760q_0+0.0106(v_1-y_0)+0.0094v_2+0.0080v_3 \\ &\qquad +0.0065v_4+0.0049v_5+0.0030v_6\,. \end{aligned}$$

The influence of later-period shipments on the first-period decision decreases rapidly in the case of the production decision and much more slowly in that of the work force decision. A difference of this kind could be expected. When future shipments are uncertain, as is usually the case. then we should of course replace them by their expectations to minimize expected costs according to the certainty equivalence theorem. Regarding the later-period decisions (p_t^0, q_t^0 with $t > 1$) Table 3.7 specifies

TABLE 3.7

THE OPTIMAL STATIC PRODUCTION AND WORK FORCE BEHAVIOUR IN THE CASE OF A SIX-MONTH HORIZON

t	*Constant term*	q_0	v_1-y_0	v_2	v_3	v_4	v_5	v_6
				p_t^0				
1	152.8	0.90	0.460	0.231	0.106	0.040	0.008	−0.004
2	78.6	0.25	0.257	0.362	0.189	0.093	0.041	0.013
3	31.6	0.02	0.143	0.202	0.339	0.182	0.092	0.039
4	−3.8	0.04	0.082	0.116	0.193	0.338	0.181	0.081
5	−39.9	0.29	0.055	0.075	0.121	0.202	0.339	0.157
6	−89.1	0.81	0.052	0.068	0.097	0.142	0.205	0.293
				q_t^0				
1	1.18	0.760	0.0106	0.0094	0.0080	0.0065	0.0049	0.0030
2	0.25	0.580	0.0141	0.0158	0.0148	0.0128	0.0101	0.0063
3	−1.59	0.454	0.0146	0.0173	0.0199	0.0189	0.0157	0.0100
4	−3.68	0.373	0.0139	0.0169	0.0209	0.0236	0.0212	0.0141
5	−5.62	0.328	0.0132	0.0162	0.0207	0.0247	0.0256	0.0181
6	−6.95	0.311	0.0128	0.0158	0.0203	0.0247	0.0265	0.0212

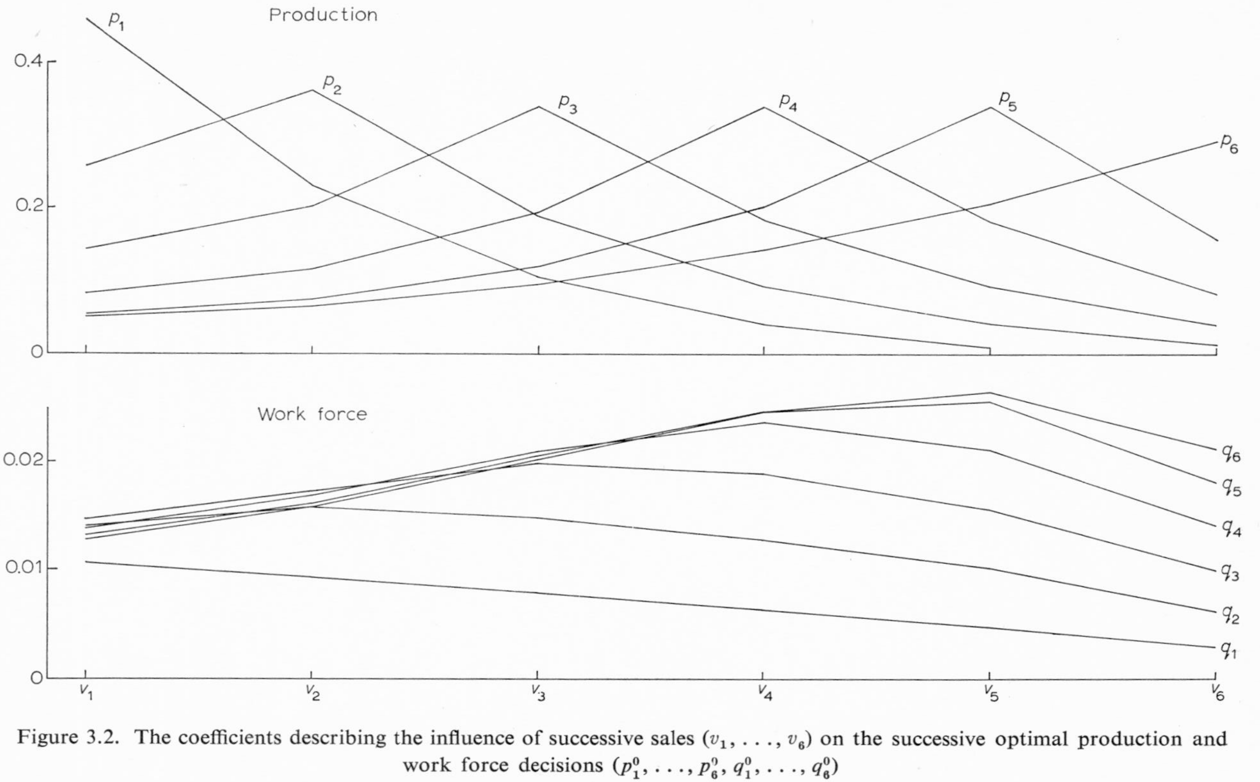

Figure 3.2. The coefficients describing the influence of successive sales ($v_1, \ldots, v_6$) on the successive optimal production and work force decisions ($p_1^0, \ldots, p_6^0, q_1^0, \ldots, q_6^0$)

that their largest v-coefficients are those of the same month t and that these coefficients become smaller and smaller when we move to the left or to the right in the same row (apart from a terminal effect for q_6^0).

3.2.3. *Losses Due to Suboptimal Decisions; Analysis of Substitution and Complementarity*

If the actual decision made deviates from the optimal one, there is a loss which can be written as a quadratic form in the decision error with $-\frac{1}{2}K$ as matrix; see (2.3.3). In the present application K has a rather simple form, which facilitates the discussion of the loss structure. Thus, if a decision error Δq_t in the work force in month t is made, the result is a loss which equals

$$(2.23) \qquad (2c_2+c_3c_4^2)(\Delta q_t)^2 = 135.0(\Delta q_t)^2;$$

i.e., a unit deviation from the optimal work force leads to a loss of \$135 per month. This follows directly from (2.11), (2.13) and (2.16), and it holds for any month t (except for a terminal effect in the last month, which is however of minor interest), The greater part of this loss is due to hiring or layoff, since $2c_2$ dominates $c_3c_4^2$; see (2.2), (2.3) and (2.6), which shows that the large coefficient c_2 refers to hiring and layoff costs, while the much smaller coefficients c_3 and c_4 belong to overtime costs. The same feature is evident when we consider a unit deviation from the optimal work force in two successive months. We then have to consider

$$(2.24) \qquad -2c_2\Delta q_t\Delta q_{t+1} = -128.6\Delta q_t\Delta q_{t+1},$$

which is the part of the loss that belongs to the joint operation of the decision errors in the work force in t and $t+1$. It is easily seen that the total loss due to a unit deviation in these two months is $2\times 135.0-128.6 = 141.5$ dollars,[1] which is only slightly more than (2.23) for a unit error in a single period. This is due to the fact that the extra costs of hiring or layoff have to be made only once.

The expressions (2.23) and (2.24) give a complete description of the loss in case there are only errors in the work force, the coefficients of $\Delta q_t\Delta q_{t+\tau}$ with $|\tau| \geqq 2$ being all zero. We proceed to consider the loss due to an error Δp_t in the production decision for t:

$$(2.25) \qquad [c_3+c_7(T+1-t)](\Delta p_t)^2 = [0.20+0.0825(7-t)](\Delta p_t)^2.$$

---

[1] The discrepancy is due to rounding errors.

Hence a unit deviation from the optimal production decision in the first month causes a loss of \$ 0.695. If such an error is made in a later month, the loss is smaller; this is due to the fact that the deviation from the optimal inventory level will then continue during a shorter period (until the end of the six-month period), as will become evident when we realize that c_7 refers to inventory connected costs. In fact, if we assume that the deviation from the optimal production decision in t is compensated by the same deviation (but with opposite sign) in $t+\tau$, then the inventory connected costs are relevant only during the τ months in between. To see this, we have to consider the term involving $\Delta p_t \Delta p_{t'} (t \neq t')$ in the total loss, which is

$$(2.26) \qquad 2c_7[T+1-\text{Max}(t, t')]\Delta p_t \Delta p_{t'} = 0.165[7-\text{Max}(t, t')]\Delta p_t \Delta p_{t'}.$$

Hence a unit deviation from the optimal production decision in t, followed by a unit deviation (in opposite direction) in $t+\tau$ $(t+\tau \leqq 6, \tau > 0)$, leads to a total loss equal to

$$\begin{aligned} &0.20+0.0825(7-t)-0.165(7-t-\tau)+0.20+0.0825(7-t-\tau) \\ &\quad = 0.40+0.0825\tau; \end{aligned}$$

that is, the total costs amount to $2c_3 = 0.40$ for the overtime costs plus $c_7\tau = 0.0825\tau$ for the inventory connected costs.

Finally, there are the losses associated with the joint operation of production and work force decision errors. The corresponding part of the K-matrix are the off-diagonal blocks $2c_3c_4\mathbf{I}$, which shows that there is a loss only if the two decision errors coincide in time, in which case it is

$$(2.27) \qquad -2c_3c_4\Delta p_t \Delta q_t = -2.268\Delta p_t \Delta q_t.$$

Hence errors of the same sign in the two decision variables tend to compensate each other. This is rather obvious; we see from (2.3) that it is due to the desirability of operating close to capacity.

This completes the discussion of losses due to suboptimal decisions in the static case. If we invert the matrix K, we obtain the substitution matrix (xx) of the instruments, which is of order 12×12 in the present case; it has been specified in (2.17), apart from the factor -1000. Taking account of this negative factor, we see that the diagonal consists of negative elements (which is as it should be) and that the off-diagonal elements in the leading submatrix are all positive. This means that production decisions in any pair of months t, t' $(t \neq t')$ are substitutes. The off-diagonal elements of the lower right-hand submatrix are all negative; hence all work force decisions are complementary with each other. As to the off-diagonal block, we see that most of its elements are negative, the exceptions being all concentrated in the first two rows. The conclusion is that as a rule production and work force decisions are complementary with each other, except that the production decisions of the first two months are substitutes for most of the later work force decisions. To ascertain the

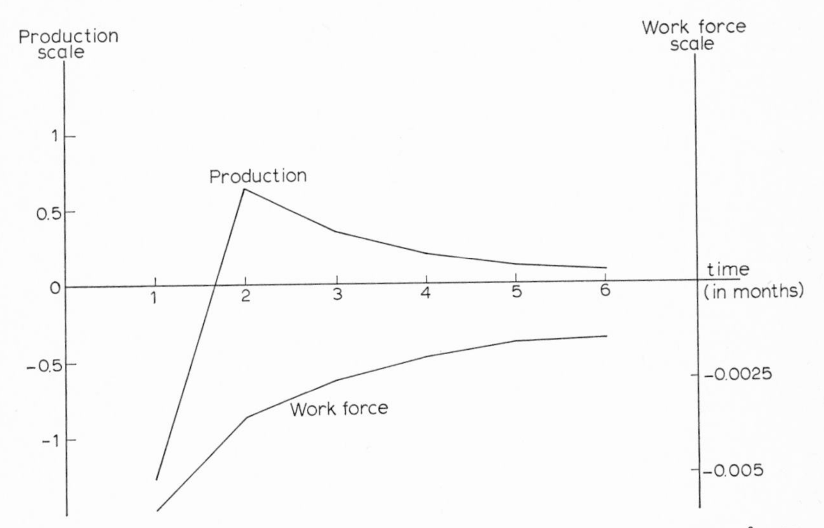

Figure 3.3. Substitution terms for the first-period instruments (connecting p_1^0 with $p_1^0, \ldots, p_6^0$ and q_1^0 with $q_1^0, \ldots, q_6^0$)

strength of these substitution and complementarity relationships, we can divide the off-diagonal elements of $(\boldsymbol{xx})$ by the geometric means of the corresponding pairs of diagonal elements; see (1.25). These standardized substitution terms are specified in Table 3.8. It shows that successive production decisions, p_t and p_{t+1}, have a weak substitution relationship when t is large, and that this relation is clearly stronger when production decisions of the first few months are considered. For successive work force decisions the relations are stronger and show a different pattern: the standardized substitution term of q_1 and q_2 is about -0.6, and this increases (apart from sign) to more than 0.8 when we go down along the diagonal. The elements which are farther from the diagonal (referring to $p_t, p_{t+\tau}$ and $q_t, q_{t+\tau}, \tau > 1$) tend to decrease. Regarding the off-diagonal block (referring to p_t, $q_{t'}$), these standardized substitution terms are small in absolute value when p_t and $q_{t'}$ both refer to the first few months, but become somewhat larger for the last months.

TABLE 3.8

STANDARDIZED SUBSTITUTION TERMS OF THE TWELVE INSTRUMENTS*

Period (in months)		Production 1	Production 2	Production 3	Production 4	Production 5	Production 6	Work force 1	Work force 2	Work force 3	Work force 4	Work force 5	Work force 6
1	Production	−1	0.41	0.23	0.13	0.08	0.05	−0.08	0.08	0.12	0.12	0.11	0.10
2	Production		−1	0.27	0.15	0.08	0.04	−0.02	−0.12	−0.00	0.04	0.05	0.04
3	Production			−1	0.23	0.12	0.05	−0.00	−0.05	−0.15	−0.05	−0.01	−0.00
4	Production				−1	0.18	0.06	−0.00	−0.03	−0.09	−0.18	−0.10	−0.07
5	Production					−1	0.07	−0.02	−0.05	−0.10	−0.16	−0.25	−0.19
6	Production						−1	−0.05	−0.10	−0.16	−0.22	−0.30	−0.39
1	Work force							−1	−0.60	−0.41	−0.30	−0.23	−0.19
2	Work force								−1	−0.70	−0.52	−0.41	−0.34
3	Work force									−1	−0.75	−0.60	−0.50
4	Work force										−1	−0.80	−0.67
5	Work force											−1	−0.84
6	Work force												−1

* Elements below the diagonal are obtained by transposition.

3.2.4. Losses Due to Imperfect Sales Forecasts

We shall now assume that the decision error is due to a prediction error in the additive structure of the constraints. It will be clear that in the present case the most important cause of such an error is that of the sales forecasts.

Let $\mathbf{\Delta}s$ be the error made in forecasting the additive structure of the constraints, then the resulting decision error is $\mathbf{\Delta}x = -(x\cdot)\mathbf{\Delta}s$ where $-(x\cdot)$ is the slope matrix of the Tinbergen surfaces; see (2.3.4). In the present case $(x\cdot) = -2c_7(xx)R'$, given that $C = \mathbf{0}$ and $B = -2c_7\mathbf{I}$, see (2.1.30) and (2.9). The loss resulting from any given error $\mathbf{\Delta}s$ is therefore [see (2.3.5)]:

$$-\tfrac{1}{2}(\mathbf{\Delta}s)'(\cdot x)(xx)^{-1}(x\cdot)\mathbf{\Delta}s = -2c_7^2(\mathbf{\Delta}s)'R(xx)R'\mathbf{\Delta}s, \tag{2.28}$$

which shows that in the present application the failure matrix is

$$F = 4c_7^2R(xx)R', \tag{2.29}$$

R being given by (2.12) and (xx) by (2.17). The zero submatrix of R implies that substitution terms involving work force variables do not affect F; we shall make use of this property in (2.32) below.

The relationship between the additive structure s and the sales variables $v_1, \ldots, v_T$ follows directly from (2.12). We have

$$s = -\begin{bmatrix} 1 & 0 & \ldots & 0 \\ 1 & 1 & \ldots & 0 \\ \vdots & \vdots & & \vdots \\ 1 & 1 & \ldots & 1 \end{bmatrix} \begin{bmatrix} v_1 \\ v_2 \\ \vdots \\ v_T \end{bmatrix} + \begin{bmatrix} y_0 \\ y_0 \\ \vdots \\ y_0 \end{bmatrix}, \tag{2.30}$$

from which we see immediately that the first vector on the right is $-R_pv$ where R_p is defined in (2.12) and v is the T-element column vector $\{v_1 \ldots v_T\}$. Hence:

$$\mathbf{\Delta}s = -R_p\mathbf{\Delta}v \tag{2.31}$$

is the relation between the forecast errors in sales and those in the additive structure of the constraints. On combining (2.31) with (2.28) we find that the loss caused by any given prediction error $\mathbf{\Delta}v$ is:

$$\begin{aligned} &-2c_7^2(\mathbf{\Delta}v)'R_p'[R_p \;\; \mathbf{0}](xx)\begin{bmatrix} R_p' \\ \mathbf{0} \end{bmatrix} R_p\mathbf{\Delta}v \\ &= -2c_7^2(\mathbf{\Delta}v)'R_p'R_p(xx)_{pp}R_p'R_p\mathbf{\Delta}v, \end{aligned} \tag{2.32}$$

where the product matrix $R_p'R_p$ is specified in (2.14), while $(xx)_{pp}$ stands for the leading $T \times T$ submatrix of the substitution matrix of the instruments. This is the substitution matrix of the production variables, which can be read for $T = 6$ from (2.17).

Evidently, the loss (2.32) is a quadratic form in the prediction errors of future sales. Its matrix is

$$(2.33) \qquad -2c_7^2 R_p' R_p (xx)_{pp} R_p' R_p$$

$$= \begin{bmatrix} 0.415 & 0.377 & 0.318 & 0.247 & 0.169 & 0.087 \\ 0.377 & 0.358 & 0.309 & 0.244 & 0.168 & 0.087 \\ 0.318 & 0.309 & 0.285 & 0.233 & 0.164 & 0.086 \\ 0.247 & 0.244 & 0.233 & 0.207 & 0.153 & 0.082 \\ 0.169 & 0.168 & 0.164 & 0.153 & 0.126 & 0.072 \\ 0.087 & 0.087 & 0.086 & 0.082 & 0.072 & 0.048 \end{bmatrix}$$

under the specification (2.6) and $T = 6$. Thus, if one single unit error is made in forecasting sales in month t ($\Delta v_t = 1$), then the resulting loss is \$ 0.415 if the forecast refers to the first month ($t = 1$), but it becomes smaller when the forecast refers to a later month. This follows from the fact that the successive elements on the diagonal decrease regularly. The off-diagonal elements are all positive and not negligible compared with the corresponding diagonal elements. This implies that errors of opposite sign in successive months tend to compensate each other. For example, if we have a positive unit error in the first month followed by a negative unit error in the second, then the total loss is

$$0.415 + 0.358 - 2 \times 0.377 = 0.019 \text{ dollars},$$

which is small compared with the isolated effect of either error. This result is very plausible, at least qualitatively. Errors of opposite sign but of the same magnitude do not imply a prediction error for the period $1, 2, \ldots, T$ as a whole; they only imply a shift from the first month to the second.

It is of some interest to consider the expected loss associated with a statistical prediction procedure, rather than the particular loss associated with a particular set of numerical predictions. To do so, we should make some probabilistic assumptions concerning this prediction procedure. Now (2.32) specifies the loss as a quadratic form in the forecast errors, hence we should consider the second moments of such errors if we want to derive the expected loss. This expectation is

$$(2.34) \qquad \sum_t \sum_{t'} m_{tt'} \mathscr{E}(\Delta v_t \Delta v_{t'}),$$

where $[m_{tt'}]$ stands for the square matrix (2.33). A simple assumption concerning the second moments, which is not entirely unrealistic, is

$$\mathscr{E}(\Delta v_t)^2 = \sigma_0^2(1+\theta)^t. \qquad (\theta > 0) \tag{2.35}$$

This makes the second moment of the forecasting error for month t an exponentially increasing funtion of t, thus specifying the plausible idea that forecasts are more uncertain when they refer to a period which is farther ahead. For the cross-moments we shall assume:

$$\begin{aligned} \mathscr{E}(\Delta v_t \Delta v_{t'}) &= \rho^{|t-t'|}\sqrt{\mathscr{E}(\Delta v_t)^2\,\mathscr{E}(\Delta v_{t'})^2} \\ &= \rho^{|t-t'|}\sigma_0^2(1+\theta)^{\frac{1}{2}(t+t')}, \qquad (-1 \leqq \rho \leqq 1) \end{aligned} \tag{2.36}$$

which is a simple assumption according to which the cross-moments

TABLE 3.9

THE EXPECTED LOSS (2.37) ASSOCIATED WITH A STATISTICAL PREDICTION PROCEDURE FOR FUTURE SHIPMENTS*

ρ	θ										
	0	0.1	0.2	0.3	0.4	0.5	0.6	0.7	0.8	0.9	1
−1	0.10	0.11	0.12	0.13	0.15	0.17	0.21	0.27	0.36	0.48	0.65
−0.9	0.19	0.23	0.27	0.32	0.40	0.49	0.62	0.78	1.00	1.27	1.62
−0.8	0.28	0.34	0.42	0.52	0.65	0.82	1.03	1.30	1.64	2.07	2.60
−0.7	0.38	0.47	0.59	0.73	0.92	1.16	1.46	1.84	2.32	2.91	3.65
−0.6	0.48	0.61	0.76	0.96	1.21	1.53	1.93	2.43	3.06	3.83	4.77
−0.5	0.60	0.76	0.96	1.22	1.54	1.94	2.45	3.08	3.87	4.83	6.01
−0.4	0.73	0.93	1.18	1.50	1.90	2.40	3.03	3.81	4.77	5.95	7.40
−0.3	0.87	1.12	1.43	1.82	2.30	2.92	3.68	4.63	5.79	7.21	8.94
−0.2	1.04	1.33	1.71	2.18	2.77	3.50	4.42	5.55	6.94	8.63	10.69
−0.1	1.22	1.58	2.02	2.59	3.29	4.17	5.26	6.60	8.25	10.25	12.68
0	1.44	1.86	2.39	3.06	3.90	4.94	6.23	7.81	9.75	12.10	14.94
0.1	1.68	2.18	2.81	3.61	4.60	5.83	7.34	9.21	11.48	14.23	17.55
0.2	1.97	2.56	3.31	4.24	5.41	6.86	8.64	10.83	13.48	16.70	20.57
0.3	2.30	3.00	3.88	4.99	6.37	8.07	10.16	12.72	15.83	19.58	24.09
0.4	2.69	3.52	4.56	5.87	7.49	9.49	11.95	14.95	18.58	22.96	28.20
0.5	3.15	4.13	5.36	6.91	8.82	11.18	14.07	17.58	21.83	26.94	33.04
0.6	3.69	4.85	6.31	8.14	10.40	13.18	16.57	20.70	25.67	31.64	38.75
0.7	4.33	5.71	7.44	9.60	12.27	15.55	19.55	24.40	30.22	37.20	45.50
0.8	5.08	6.72	8.78	11.34	14.50	18.38	23.09	28.79	35.63	43.79	53.48
0.9	5.97	7.92	10.37	13.40	17.15	21.73	27.30	34.00	42.04	51.61	62.94
1	7.03	9.34	12.25	15.86	20.30	25.72	32.29	40.19	49.64	60.86	74.13

* All figures are to be multiplied by σ_0^2.

decrease exponentially (relative to the geometric mean of the corresponding univariate second moments) when they refer to months which are farther away from each other. In the case $\mathscr{E}(\Delta v_t) = 0$ for all t, (2.35) and (2.36) specify variances and covariances, respectively, of the shipment forecast errors, and $\rho^{|t-t'|}$ is then the correlation coefficient of the prediction errors in month t and t'.

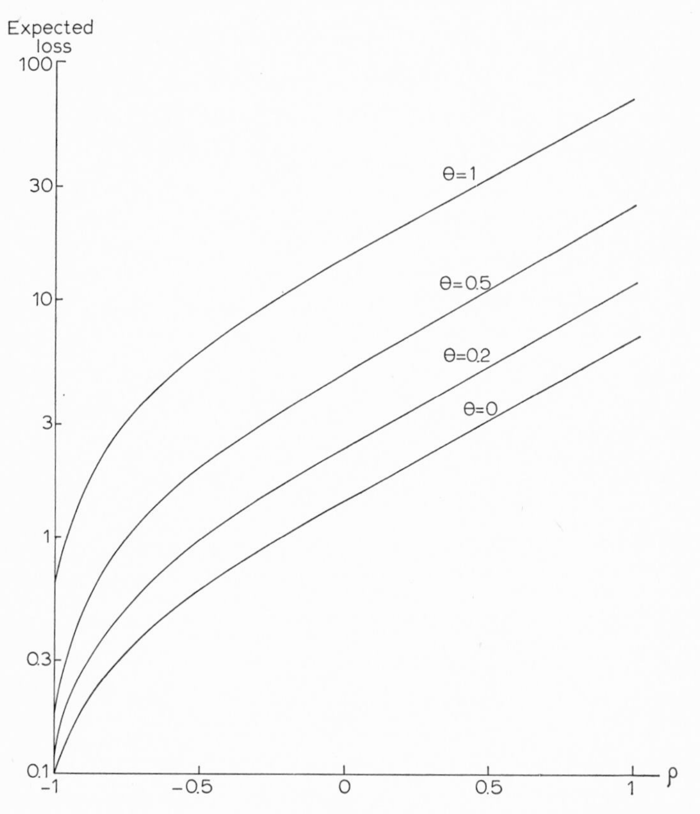

Figure 3.4. The expected loss (divided by σ_0^2) associated with a statistical forecasting procedure for future sales under conditions (2.35)–(2.36) as a function of ρ for some values of θ

On combining (2.34)–(2.36), we find that the expected loss (2.34) takes the form

$$\sigma_0^2 \sum_t \sum_{t'} m_{tt'} \rho^{|t-t'|} (1+\theta)^{\frac{1}{2}(t+t')}, \tag{2.37}$$

which can be regarded as a three-parameter family as soon as we specify

$[m_{tt'}]$ according to (2.33). It is seen that the dependence of (2.37) on σ_0^2 is of the trivial multiplicative type and that the dependence on ρ and θ is much more interesting. This is pursued further in Table 3.9 for $-1 \leqq \rho \leqq 1$ and $0 \leqq \theta \leqq 1$ with intervals of size 0.1. The table shows that given σ_0^2 and θ, the expected loss for a large positive ρ is substantially larger than in the case of a small ρ and certainly larger than in the case of a negative ρ. In fact, for most of the θ-values considered here we find that the expected loss increases about tenfold when we move from $\rho = -1$ to $\rho = -0.5$; that it increases almost threefold when we go from $\rho = -0.5$ to $\rho = 0$; that it is more than doubled at $\rho = 0.5$; and that it is again about doubled at $\rho = 1$. This illustrates the earlier proposition that successive forecast errors of opposite sign compensate each other (implying that successive errors of the same sign reinforce each other). The table shows also, as could be anticipated, a sharp rise of the expected loss with θ: for most of the ρ-values, it increases more than three times when we move from $\theta = 0$ to $\theta = 0.5$, and again three times at $\theta = 1$.

3.2.5. Summary

(1) A cost function which is to be minimized takes here the role of the preference function to be maximized. Total cost is defined as the double sum over four cost categories per unit of time (regular payroll costs, hiring and layoff costs, overtime costs, and inventory connected costs) and over T time periods, T being the horizon which the manager wishes to take into account. Each cost category is approximated by a linear or quadratic function of production and work force (which are the manager's instruments) and of the inventory level (which is noncontrolled).

(2) This T-period problem as such is a dynamic one, but it is reduced here to a static problem by proceeding under the assumption that the decisions for all successive periods are made at the beginning of the first period. Minimization of the quadratic cost function then takes place subject to the constraint that the inventory change equals the excess of production over sales in each of the T periods. This leads to a series of optimal (static) decisions of production and work force, which are linear functions of the initial work force, of the initial inventory level, and of the development of sales during the T periods. For the special case $T = 6$ months and the numerical cost coefficient data considered here, the first-period decision for production and work force depends on the sales of all six months with decreasing weights, the decrease being much sharper in the case of production than in that of the work force.

(3) The loss due to a suboptimal decision is a quadratic form whose matrix is of a fairly simple type. A unit deviation of work force from the optimal level leads to a loss which is largely determined by the hiring or layoff costs; if such a deviation lasts during two consecutive months, the total loss is only slightly larger (because no extra costs for hiring and layoff are made). A unit deviation of production from the optimal level leads to a loss which is partly determined by overtime costs, partly by inventory connected costs. There is a loss interaction of production and work force decision errors only in case these errors are made in the same month, and the corresponding loss appears to be determined by the desirability of operating close to capacity. As to substitution and complementarity relationships among the instruments, successive production decisions are moderately weak substitutes, while successive work force decisions are strongly or moderately strongly complementary. The substitution and complementarity relationships between production decisions on the one hand and work force decisions on the other are in general rather weak.

(4) Supposing that the suboptimal character of the decision made is due to prediction errors in future sales, one finds that the loss can be written as a quadratic form in these errors. The matrix of this form is such that prediction errors in the near future are more serious than numerically equal errors relating to a more distant period; also, such that errors of opposite sign in successive periods compensate each other to a large extent. The expected loss has been considered under the assumption (i) that the second moment of the forecasting errors increases exponentially with time (i.e., with the period between the moment of prediction and the beginning of the period to be predicted) and (ii) that the second-order cross-moments decrease exponentially (relative to the corresponding univariate moments) when they relate more distant forecasting errors. The stochastic dependence between prediction errors of different periods appears to be of considerable importance, positive association of successive errors leading *ceteris paribus* to a much larger expected cost than negative association.

CHAPTER 4

Dynamic Theory of Linear Decision Rules

4.1. STRATEGIES AND FIRST-PERIOD CERTAINTY EQUIVALENCE

4.1.1. Introduction; First Set of Dynamic Assumptions

Although the initial formulation of the two examples of Chapter 3 was in dynamic terms, we "reduced" them in such a way that the analysis became completely static. The purpose of this chapter is to formulate the dynamic generalization of the theory of Chapter 2. The present section is devoted to strategies and to certainty equivalence for the decision of the first period and is therefore partly an extension of Section 2.2. The further generalizations will be presented in Section 4.2.

It will prove useful to choose a notation which puts together all variables that refer to the same period. This is done by defining subvectors of instruments and noncontrolled variables for each period t:

$$(1.1) \qquad x_t = \begin{bmatrix} x_1(t) \\ \vdots \\ x_m(t) \end{bmatrix}, \qquad y_t = \begin{bmatrix} y_1(t) \\ \vdots \\ y_n(t) \end{bmatrix} \qquad (t = 1, \ldots, T),$$

where $x_h(t)$ and $y_i(t)$ are the values taken by the hth instrument and the ith noncontrolled variable, respectively, in t; such "values" are interpreted as variable, not as fixed. We then define the complete vectors of instruments and noncontrolled variables in partitioned form:

$$(1.2) \qquad \mathbf{x} = \begin{bmatrix} x_1 \\ \vdots \\ x_T \end{bmatrix}, \qquad \mathbf{y} = \begin{bmatrix} y_1 \\ \vdots \\ y_T \end{bmatrix},$$

so that in both vectors $\mathbf{x}$ and $\mathbf{y}$ the variables corresponding to the same period are indeed grouped together. It will be noted that the present notation differs from that of the production-work force example of Section 3.2: there we partitioned the instrument vector by variables, here we do so by time periods.

As in the static case, we shall assume that the preference function is quadratic; but now the total number of its arguments is $(m+n)T$. It takes the form:

$$w(\mathbf{x}, \mathbf{y}) = \mathbf{a}'\mathbf{x}+\mathbf{b}'\mathbf{y}+\tfrac{1}{2}(\mathbf{x}'\mathbf{A}\mathbf{x}+\mathbf{y}'\mathbf{B}\mathbf{y}+\mathbf{x}'\mathbf{C}\mathbf{y}+\mathbf{y}'\mathbf{C}'\mathbf{x}), \tag{1.3}$$

where **a** and **b** are columns of mT and nT elements, respectively. They can be partitioned by periods:

$$\mathbf{a} = \begin{bmatrix} a_1 \\ \vdots \\ a_T \end{bmatrix} \qquad \mathbf{b} = \begin{bmatrix} b_1 \\ \vdots \\ b_T \end{bmatrix},$$

such that a_t is the coefficient vector of x_t (and similarly for b_t and y_t). In the same way, **A** is an $mT \times mT$ matrix which can be partitioned in T^2 submatrices,

$$\mathbf{A} = \begin{bmatrix} A_{11} & A_{12} & \dots & A_{1T} \\ A_{21} & A_{22} & \dots & A_{2T} \\ \vdots & \vdots & & \vdots \\ A_{T1} & A_{T2} & \dots & A_{TT} \end{bmatrix}$$

in such a way that the submatrix $A_{tt'}$ refers to x_t and $x_{t'}$; e.g., A_{11} occurs in (1.3) in the form $x_1' A_{11} x_1$, A_{12} in the form $x_1' A_{12} x_2$, etc. The same applies to **B** and **C**; without loss of generality it can be assumed that **A** and **B** are symmetric. It will be noted that we are using two different typographical types for vectors and matrices here: one is the sanserif type which was introduced in Chapter 2 and which will continue to be used as long as the symbol refers either to one period (x_1, b_2, etc.) or to a single pair of periods (A_{12}, C_{23}, etc.); the other is the bold-face roman type which will be used for symbols referring to the set of all T periods.

Our first dynamic preference assumption, which corresponds to Assumption 2.1 of the static theory, is then:

ASSUMPTION 4.1. *All vectors* $\mathbf{x} = [x_h(t)]$, $\mathbf{y} = [y_i(t)]$ *of instruments and noncontrolled variables, respectively, in the T consecutive periods* 1, 2, . . ., *T are real-valued and ordered according to the decision maker's preference such as to allow a representation by means of the quadratic preference function* (1.3), *where* **a**, **b**, **A**, **B**, **C** *are vectors and matrices of fixed elements and of appropriate order,* **A** *and* **B** *being symmetric.*

The preference function is maximized subject to linear constraints:

$$\mathbf{y} = \mathbf{R}\mathbf{x}+\mathbf{s}, \tag{1.4}$$

where $\mathbf{R}$ is now of order $nT \times mT$ and $\mathbf{s}$ of order $nT \times 1$. We shall suppose that none of the noncontrolled variables depends on later instruments; that is, it will be assumed that the coefficient matrix by which x_t is multiplied in the part of the system (1.4) that refers to $y_{t'}$ is an $n \times m$ zero matrix as soon as $t > t'$. This is evidently a reasonable assumption [satisfied by the example of Section 3.2, see (3.2.12)], and it implies that $\mathbf{R}$ can be partitioned into T^2 submatrices, all of order $n \times m$, as follows:

$$\mathbf{R} = \begin{bmatrix} R_{11} & \mathbf{0} & \mathbf{0} & \cdots & \mathbf{0} \\ R_{21} & R_{22} & \mathbf{0} & \cdots & \mathbf{0} \\ R_{31} & R_{32} & R_{33} & \cdots & \mathbf{0} \\ \vdots & \vdots & \vdots & & \vdots \\ R_{T1} & R_{T2} & R_{T3} & \cdots & R_{TT} \end{bmatrix}. \tag{1.5}$$

The diagonal blocks $(R_{11}, R_{22}, \ldots)$ specify the effectiveness of instruments with respect to noncontrolled variables in the same period, and the submatrices below and to the left of these $(R_{21}, R_{31}, \ldots)$ specify their effectiveness with respect to later values of the noncontrolled variables. This is summarized in:

ASSUMPTION 4.2. *The vectors* $\mathbf{x}$, $\mathbf{y}$ *are connected by the linear equation system* (1.4), *where* $\mathbf{R}$ *is an* $nT \times mT$ *matrix of fixed elements which can be partitioned into* T^2 *submatrices of order* $n \times m$ *according to* (1.5), *and* $\mathbf{s}$ *is a column vector of* nT *fixed elements.*

4.1.2. A Simple Strategy Example

Assumptions 4.1 and 4.2 do not allow for uncertainty; but they will be generalized such that they cover the possibility of stochastic coefficients (in particular a stochastic $\mathbf{s}$), combined with maximization of expected utility rather than utility itself. This is completely analogous to the static theory. However, there is an important difference with respect to the domain of variation within which the maximization process takes place. In Chapter 2 we determined the numerical values of the m instruments which maximize the expectation of the preference function. Here, we should recognize the fact that it is not necessary to decide on all mT instrument values $x_h(t)$ at the same time (as we did in Section 3.2), but rather that the decision for period t has to be made only at the beginning of that period, so that it is possible to make this decision dependent on all information that becomes available prior to t. If we would have to decide on all mT instrument values right at the start, then indeed it would be true that the only thing we can do is to select these values such as to maximize expected utility, given the information available at this starting point. But this is not true, and we can arrive at a higher expected utility level by taking account of the fact that we shall have more information in later periods; more precisely, we gain by making x_t for $t > 1$ dependent on the information available before t. What we shall do, therefore, is to formulate a *strategy* or *decision rule* which specifies future decisions in terms of such information. The procedure of maximizing expected utility over time amounts then to selecting that decision rule for which expected utility reaches a maximum. In terms of the example of Section 3.2 this means that we select a rule according to which the production and work force decision for month t depends on the information available at the beginning of t; and in that case the information involves (i) the sales prior to t—assuming these to be known at the beginning of t—, and (ii) the conditional distribution of the sales in month t and later, given the manager's knowledge at that time. It will be clear that this knowledge will in general increase from month to month, so that the conditional distribution of the sales in the third month (say) on the basis of the knowledge available in the first month will be different from that which is based on the knowledge available in the second month. And it will also be clear that there is an important mathematical difference between choosing the mT values $x_h(t)$ which maximize expected utility and choosing the maximizing strategy. For a strategy is a function of a particular body of information, and choosing a maximizing function is indeed different from choosing a set of maximizing numbers.

Now it is interesting that the strategy approach has implications not only for later-period decisions, but also for the decision x_1 of the first period. A priori, one might think that this should not be the case, because this decision cannot be based on future information; this possibility is reserved for later-period decisions when the future has become past. However, although the argument is sound, the conclusion is not; the reason is that the first-period decision, which is indeed independent of the contents of later information, may nevertheless be affected by the mere fact that it is known that such knowledge will become available and that it will be possible to react to this knowledge. This probably sounds rather abstract, so that it is good to consider an example. We shall take the simplest possible case, consisting of two periods ($T = 2$), in each of which one alternative has to be chosen out of two possible decisions, while the information (available at $t = 2$, not available at $t = 1$) is also assumed to be of the dichotomy type.

Let our decision maker be the owner of a big motorcar company, who has substantial liquid funds available from previous earnings. He regards the car market as largely saturated and considers the possibility of buying an aircraft company. The difficulty is that at the end of this year there will be a Presidential Election and one of the candidates advocates a special tax on profits made on government contracts on which the aircraft company is largely dependent. An important point is therefore which candidate will win the election. Now the uncertainty created by this is reflected by the price which the car manufacturer has to pay for the aircraft company, which is indeed lower than it would have been if neither of the candidates had advocated that tax. There is no uncertainty after the election; it is supposed that the new President will act according to his promises, so that the price of the aircraft company will either increase or decrease further.

The car manufacturer's immediate ("first-period") decision is therefore either to buy the aircraft company or to stay in the car business. But we will suppose that he can also make a second-period decision after the election: if he bought, he can either sell or retain the aircraft company; if he did not buy, he can buy it now or continue to stay in the car business. That is all. It seems intuitively clear that it is advantageous to wait until after the election (because this reduces uncertainty), but the penalty is a higher price of the aircraft company in case the tax is not imposed.

Our primary concern is with the first-period decision, which will be derived by assuming that the car manufacturer wishes to maximize his expected gain under the condition that the probability that the "tax candidate" will win the election is p and under the following numerical assumptions. Let the gain be 1 (in some appropriate unit) if he stays in the car business, both in the first and in the second period, and independent of the outcome of the election. We write this in the form:

$$CtC : 1 \qquad CnC : 1,$$

where the first C indicates the first-period decision of staying in the car business, the second C the similar second-period decision, and the t and n in between that the tax is imposed or not. Further, let the gain be 5 if the car manufacturer buys the aircraft company in the first period and retains it in the second and if the tax is not imposed, but -5 if he acts in this way while the tax is imposed:

$$AtA : -5 \qquad AnA : 5,$$

where the A's indicate the decision to buy (either in the first or in the second period). Let the gain be -3 if the car manufacturer does not buy in the first period but does in the second and if the tax is imposed, but 0 if the tax is not imposed:

$$CtA : -3 \qquad CnA : 0.$$

Finally, let the gain be -4 if the aircraft company is bought in the first period and sold in the second and if the tax is imposed, but 2 if the tax is not imposed:

$$AtC : -4 \qquad AnC : 2.$$

First, we shall consider the "instrument values" of both periods combined which maximize the expected gain under the condition that they are determined before the election, so that the second-period decision is then independent of the information available at the beginning of that period. The total number of these instrument values is only four, viz., CC (staying in the car business throughout), AA (buying and retaining the aircraft company), CA (buying in the second period), and AC (buying in the first period and selling in the second). The expected gains of these alternatives are:

$$\begin{aligned} CC &: p\times 1+(1-p)1 = 1 \\ AA &: p\times(-5)+(1-p)5 = 5-10p \\ CA &: p\times(-3)+(1-p)0 = -3p \\ AC &: p\times(-4)+(1-p)2 = 2-6p. \end{aligned}$$

This result shows that CC is always better than CA, that CC is better than AA as long as $p > 0.4$ but worse when $p < 0.4$, and that CC is better than AC as long as $p > \frac{1}{6}$, but worse when $p < \frac{1}{6}$. Since AA and AC imply the same first-period decision (A), the outcome is that the car manufacturer should not buy the aircraft company before the election when the probability that the tax is imposed exceeds 0.4, and that he should buy when the probability is below 0.4.

Next, we consider strategies. They imply that the second-period decision is made dependent on whether the tax is imposed or not and are hence of the type $C(tC; nA)$, where the C before the brackets stands for the decision to stay in the car business in the first period, the tC before the semicolon for the decision to continue to do so in the second period in case the tax is imposed, and the *nA* behind the semicolon for the decision to buy the aircraft company in the second period in case the tax is not imposed. Note that decision rules of the type $C(tA; nA)$ do not make the second-period decision dependent on the available information (or at least do so only in a trivial sense); the rule just given is equivalent with *CA* and has been considered in the preceding paragraph. As a whole,

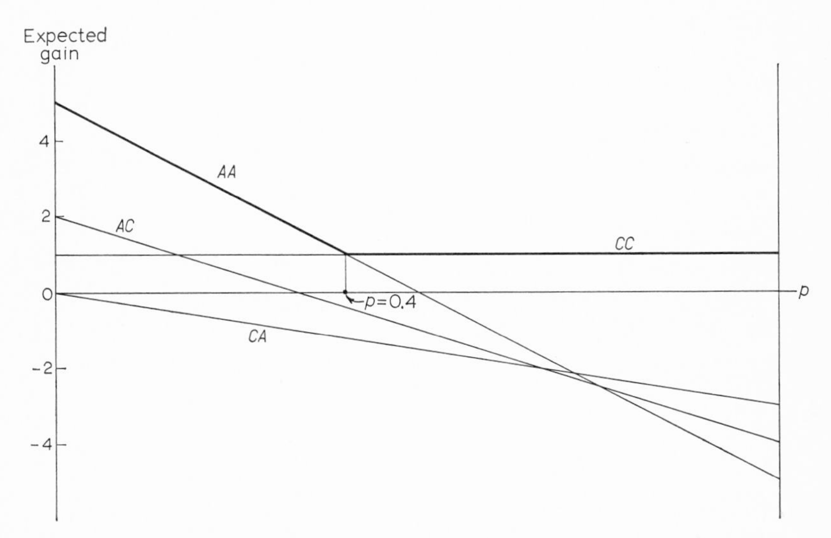

Figure 4.1. The expected gains of the decision chains *CC*, *AA*, *CA* and *AC* as functions of *p*. The heavy line segments correspond with the largest expected gain, given *p*.

there are four non-trivial strategies with the following expected gains:

$$C(tC; nA): p\times 1+(1-p)0 = p$$
$$C(tA; nC): p\times(-3)+(1-p)1 = 1-4p$$
$$A(tC; nA): p\times(-4)+(1-p)5 = 5-9p$$
$$A(tA; nC): p\times(-5)+(1-p)2 = 2-7p.$$

The first two strategies have expected gains which are below that of *CC*; evidently, if the first-period decision is to stay in the car business, the election result is irrelevant information because it is then profitable to continue this policy no matter which candidate is elected. But the situation with respect to the third strategy is different; its expected gain exceeds that of any other strategy which has A as first-period decision. In particular, this gain is larger than that of AA in which the second-period decision is not made contingent on the outcome of the election. This affects the profitability of the first-period decision. For the strategy with the highest expected gain in which A is the decision of the first period is $A(tC; nA)$, and this gain is $5-9p$; and the strategy with the highest expected gain in which C is the first-period decision is $C(tC; nC)$

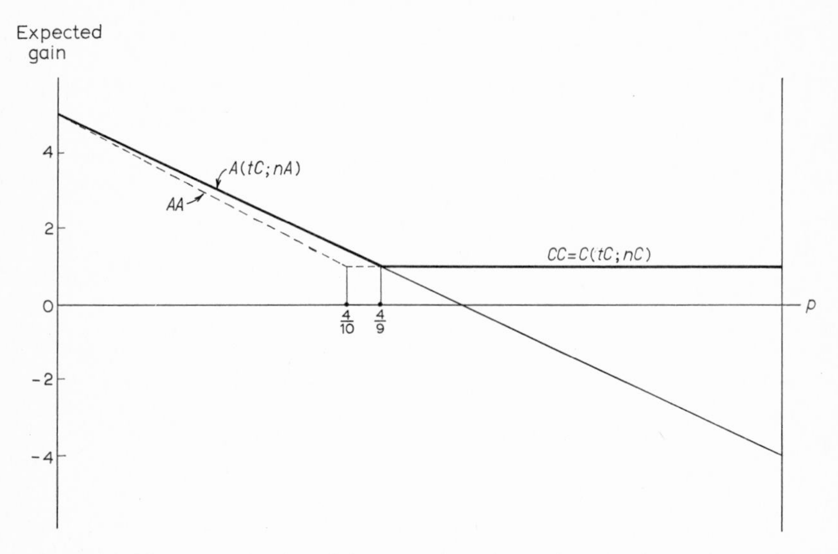

Figure 4.2. The expected gains of the strategies $A(tC; nA)$ and $C(tC; nC) = CC$ as functions of p. The broken lines correspond with the heavy line segments of Fig. 4.1 as far as these are below the present largest expected gain.

$= CC$, and this gain is 1. Consequently, A is to be selected for the first period if $p < \frac{4}{9}$, but C if $p > \frac{4}{9}$.

We thus see that the availability of information in the future and the possibility to react to this after it has become available influence the first-period decision: this raises the critical value of p from $\frac{4}{10}$ to $\frac{4}{9}$ compared with the case in which this aspect is disregarded. It is not difficult to see intuitively why this must be so. For buying the aircraft company in the first period and keeping it (AA) is very profitable if the tax is not imposed but very unprofitable if it is, and the latter feature reduces the expected gain of this policy when p takes larger values; however, there is a way to lower the loss in case the tax is imposed, viz., by selling the aircraft company. The strategy $A(tC; nA)$ uses this possibility, but

$AA = A(tA; nA)$ does not and therefore underestimates the profitability of buying the aircraft company in the first period. And the underestimation of this profitability is tantamount to an underestimation of the critical level of p below which the first-period decision should be A. So we have shown that the very knowledge that strategy decisions can be made influences the first-period decision, as we set out to do.

4.1.3. Second Set of Dynamic Assumptions

Let us return from this extremely simple example to the general quadratic preference—linear constraint set-up of Assumptions 4.1 and 4.2. It will be clear that these assumptions have to be generalized if they are to be used for deriving nontrivial strategies. For such strategies imply the use of additional information in later periods and there is no such additional information if there is no uncertainty. Hence we should generalize Assumptions 4.1 and 4.2 in such a way that they allow for uncertainty. This will be done in a manner which is very close to Assumptions 2.3 and 2.4. In fact, there is only one subtle difference, which deals with the possibility of stochastic elements of the instrument vector. In the static case the decisions concerning instrument values must all be made at one moment and hence there is no reason to interpret these values stochastically. But in the dynamic case future instrument values depend on information that will have become available in the meantime (if the decision maker decides on a strategy!), and since this information is uncertain and hence random at the present moment, the same must apply to future instrument values. We must therefore generalize our assumptions such that both instruments and noncontrolled values may be stochastic. This leads to the following preference assumption:

ASSUMPTION 4.3. *Assumption* 4.1 *is satisfied. Moreover, if the vectors of instruments and of noncontrolled variables contain stochastic elements, the decision maker behaves as if his preferences are measured by the expectation of the function* (1.3), $\mathscr{E}w(\mathbf{x}, \mathbf{y})$.

The generalization of the constraint assumption is likewise completely analogous to Assumption 2.4. We shall assume that the additive structure of the constraints ($\mathbf{s}$) is random but that the multiplicative structure ($\mathbf{R}$) is fixed and known. We shall also assume that the additive structure is independent of the instrument values, but this is to be interpreted carefully. Just as $\mathbf{x}$ can be partitioned according to time, $x_1, x_2, \ldots, x_T$, in just the same way can we partition $\mathbf{s}$: $s_1, \ldots, s_T$; s_t being that part of the additive structure that refers to the tth period. It will be clear that the decision maker is in principle in a position to know something about "past" subvectors of **s**; for according to (1.5) we have

$$y_t = \sum_{\tau=1}^{t} R_{t\tau} x_\tau + s_t, \qquad (t = 1, \ldots, T) \tag{1.6}$$

which implies that s_t can be determined from $y_t, x_1, \ldots, x_t$ and the appropriate submatrices of **R** (which are assumed to be fixed and known). Hence any "past" subvector of **s** is known as soon as the corresponding noncontrolled values (and instrument values) are known. Now this implies, in turn, that the decision maker can in principle make x_{t+1} dependent on s_t, so that there is then a stochastic dependence between **s**-subvectors and *later* **x**-subvectors. This possibility will and, in fact, must be accepted; but we shall exclude the possibility that s_t depends on $x_{t'}$ where $t \geqq t'$. More precisely:

ASSUMPTION 4.4. *Assumption* 4.2 *is satisfied, except that the elements of the vector* **s** *of* (1.4) *are subject to a joint distribution with the following properties*: (i) *the distribution of the subvector* s_t *is independent of* $x_{t'}$ *for* $t, t' = 1, \ldots, T$ *and* $t \geqq t'$, *and* (ii) *the variances of the* **s**-*elements are finite.*

4.1.4. The Structure of a Strategy

Let us consider any strategy **x**; then we can partition it according to the successive periods:

$$\mathbf{x} = \begin{bmatrix} x_1(\mathscr{I}_0) \\ x_2(\mathscr{I}_1) \\ \vdots \\ x_T(\mathscr{I}_{T-1}) \end{bmatrix}, \tag{1.7}$$

where $\mathscr{I}_t$ stands for the information which is available at the end of the tth period. Thus, working backward, the last-period decision can be made dependent on the stream of information coming in during all periods except the last (the Tth); the x_{T-1}-decision is similar in this respect except that the information during the $(T-1)^{\text{st}}$ period is not yet available, and so on, until we arrive at x_1 which can be made dependent only on information which is available prior to the whole series of T periods. The information $\mathscr{I}_t$ consists of two categories, one dealing with the past and the other with the future. The former part contains the numerical values of the subvectors $x_1, \ldots, x_t, y_1, \ldots, y_t$ as well as $s_1, \ldots, s_t$, see the discussion around (1.6); provided, of course, that there is perfect knowledge of these past values. In many cases, however, this knowledge is incomplete, so that we must retreat to probability statements: the "past" part of $\mathscr{I}_t$ will then consist of a conditional probability distribution of past vectors, given the decision maker's knowledge at the end of the tth period. [Note that these past vectors must have taken some fixed values, so that such probabilities do not refer to alternative values which they may actually take; instead, they refer to the uncertainty in the decision maker's mind as to what these fixed values actually are.] [1]

The future part of $\mathscr{I}_t$ will nearly always be concerned with uncertain events. Given the certainty which is assumed here for the coefficients of the preference function and the multiplicative structure of the constraints, our uncertain future deals with $s_{t+1}, \ldots, s_T$. Accordingly, the future part of $\mathscr{I}_t$ consists of the conditional distribution of these vectors, given the available information at the end of the tth period. Our objective will be to maximize the expectation of the preference function in the conditional sense; specifically, in the sense that at the end of every t^{th} period ($t = 0, \ldots, T-1$) account is taken of the available information at that moment, i.e., of $\mathscr{I}_t$. It will be clear that this is completely in line with the conditional static analysis which was carried out in 2.2.3 above.

Evidently, a comparison of alternative strategies to find out which one maximizes expected utility requires a considerable effort. In 4.1.2 we had two alternative first-period decisions, two alternative values which the chance element can take, and two alternative second-period decisions, hence eight combinations as a whole. Here, we are working with continuous variables which can be made dependent on previous realizations of chance elements in a fully arbitrary manner, so that the number of alternative strategies is an infinity of a high order. It would obviously be highly desirable if we could prove a certainty-equivalence result according to which, say, the maximizing strategy coincides with the decision made under the assumption that all random elements are equal to their expectations. But this hope is in vain. For the latter decision is necessarily a vector of fixed numbers, whereas the maximizing strategy is—if it is a nontrivial strategy!— such that it specifies future decisions as functions of previous information. And we cannot expect that such functions coincide with fixed numbers. However, we can do something for the first-period decision, as we shall now try to show.

[1] It will be hardly necessary to stress that the information concept used here has nothing to do with the logarithmic information measure used in information theory.

4.1.5. First-Period Certainty Equivalence

Suppose that there is a unique maximizing strategy (which will be our abbreviated expression for the strategy which maximizes expected utility). We shall denote it by $\tilde{\mathbf{x}}$ and partition it according to (1.7), so that its tth subvector is then $\tilde{x}_t(\mathscr{I}_{t-1})$. Any other strategy can be written as

$$\mathbf{x} = \tilde{\mathbf{x}} + \varepsilon\boldsymbol{\xi}, \tag{1.8}$$

where ε is a fixed scalar and $\boldsymbol{\xi}$ a vector of mT elements which can be partitioned as follows:

$$\boldsymbol{\xi} = \begin{bmatrix} \xi_1(\mathscr{I}_0) \\ \xi_2(\mathscr{I}_1) \\ \vdots \\ \xi_T(\mathscr{I}_{T-1}) \end{bmatrix}. \tag{1.9}$$

Hence $\varepsilon\boldsymbol{\xi}$ is nothing else than the difference between any given strategy $\mathbf{x}$ and the maximizing strategy $\tilde{\mathbf{x}}$. In the special case when $\mathbf{x}$ coincides with $\tilde{\mathbf{x}}$, we have of course $\varepsilon = 0$ or $\boldsymbol{\xi} = \mathbf{0}$ (or both).

Next, we consider the preference level which is attained by applying any strategy $\mathbf{x}$. This is found by substituting the constraints (1.4) into the preference function (1.3), which leads to the familiar result:

$$w_{\mathbf{x}} = w(\mathbf{x}, \mathbf{R}\mathbf{x}+\mathbf{s}) = k_0 + \mathbf{k}'\mathbf{x} + \tfrac{1}{2}\mathbf{x}'\mathbf{K}\mathbf{x}, \tag{1.10}$$

where

$$\begin{aligned} k_0 &= \mathbf{b}'\mathbf{s} + \tfrac{1}{2}\mathbf{s}'\mathbf{B}\mathbf{s} \\ \mathbf{k} &= \mathbf{a} + \mathbf{R}'\mathbf{b} + (\mathbf{C} + \mathbf{R}'\mathbf{B})\mathbf{s} \\ \mathbf{K} &= \mathbf{A} + \mathbf{R}'\mathbf{B}\mathbf{R} + \mathbf{C}\mathbf{R} + \mathbf{R}'\mathbf{C}'. \end{aligned} \tag{1.11}$$

This is, of course, nothing else than a straightforward dynamic extension of (2.1.24)–(2.1.25). We now interpret $\mathbf{x}$ of (1.10) as $\tilde{\mathbf{x}} + \varepsilon\boldsymbol{\xi}$ in accordance with (1.8) and consider the expected preference level. When separating the terms according to the various powers of ε, we obtain

$$\mathscr{E}w_{\mathbf{x}} = W_0 + \varepsilon W_1 + \tfrac{1}{2}\varepsilon^2 W_2, \tag{1.12}$$

where

$$\begin{aligned} W_0 &= \mathscr{E}k_0 + \mathscr{E}(\mathbf{k}'\tilde{\mathbf{x}}) + \tfrac{1}{2}\mathscr{E}(\tilde{\mathbf{x}}'\mathbf{K}\tilde{\mathbf{x}}) \\ W_1 &= \mathscr{E}(\mathbf{k}'\boldsymbol{\xi}) + \mathscr{E}(\tilde{\mathbf{x}}'\mathbf{K}\boldsymbol{\xi}) \\ W_2 &= \mathscr{E}(\boldsymbol{\xi}'\mathbf{K}\boldsymbol{\xi}). \end{aligned} \tag{1.13}$$

We shall now consider these expressions term by term. Regarding the first, W_0, we note that it is independent of the strategy chosen, which can be argued as follows. According to (1.13), the first part of W_0 is $\mathscr{E}k_0$, which is

$$\mathscr{E}(\mathbf{b}'\mathbf{s}+\tfrac{1}{2}\mathbf{s}'\mathbf{B}\mathbf{s}) = \mathbf{b}'\mathscr{E}\mathbf{s}+\tfrac{1}{2}\mathscr{E}(\mathbf{s}'\mathbf{B}\mathbf{s}) \tag{1.14}$$

in view of (1.11). This involves the expectations, variances and covariances of the mT elements of the random vector **s**. Now Assumption 4.4 specifies that the distribution of these elements, as far as these refer to the additive structure of the constraints in the tth period, is independent of the instrument values in the same period and before. Hence the decision maker is not in a position to affect the probability mechanism which generates s_t before it is generated, which means that the expression (1.14) is a constant from his point of view. The same applies to the second part of W_0 in (1.13), $\mathscr{E}(\mathbf{k}'\tilde{\mathbf{x}})$. For if the decision maker cannot affect the distribution of **s**, the same must apply to **k**, see (1.11). Furthermore, $\tilde{\mathbf{x}}$ cannot be affected either since it is the maximizing strategy, its successive subvectors $\tilde{x}_1, \tilde{x}_2, \ldots$ being fixed functions of relevant previous information. The same, finally, applies to the last part of W_0 in (1.13), $\tfrac{1}{2}\mathscr{E}(\tilde{\mathbf{x}}'\mathbf{K}\tilde{\mathbf{x}})$.

We have thus found that the first term in (1.12), W_0, is a constant from the decision maker's point of view, so that it can be disregarded in the maximization process. The other two terms, εW_1 and $\tfrac{1}{2}\varepsilon^2 W_2$, are not constant and do depend on the strategy chosen by the decision maker. This is so because they both involve ε and $\boldsymbol{\xi}$, which determine the strategy measured as a deviation from $\tilde{\mathbf{x}}$, see (1.8). Now it will be clear that if $\tilde{\mathbf{x}}$ really maximizes $\mathscr{E}w_{\mathbf{x}}$, then εW_1 should vanish for whatever ε and $\boldsymbol{\xi}$, and $\tfrac{1}{2}\varepsilon^2 W_2$ should be negative for whatever ε and $\boldsymbol{\xi}$ (except of course when $\varepsilon = 0$ or $\boldsymbol{\xi} = \mathbf{0}$, in which case $\tfrac{1}{2}\varepsilon^2 W_2 = 0$). For suppose that there exists an $\mathbf{x} = \tilde{\mathbf{x}}+\varepsilon\boldsymbol{\xi}$ such that εW_1 is positive. Then, by reducing ε in the direction of zero while keeping $\boldsymbol{\xi}$ constant, we can make $\tfrac{1}{2}\varepsilon^2 W_2$ negligible in absolute value compared with εW_1, so that the positive value of εW_1 implies that $\tilde{\mathbf{x}}+\varepsilon\boldsymbol{\xi}$ has a larger expected utility than $\tilde{\mathbf{x}}$ has. In the same way, when εW_1 is negative for some strategy $\tilde{\mathbf{x}}+\varepsilon\boldsymbol{\xi}$, we can attain a similar situation by reversing the sign of ε. And if $\varepsilon W_1 = 0$ for all ε and $\boldsymbol{\xi}$ but $\tfrac{1}{2}\varepsilon^2 W_2$ is positive for some $\varepsilon \neq 0$, $\boldsymbol{\xi} \neq \mathbf{0}$, then $\tilde{\mathbf{x}}+\varepsilon\boldsymbol{\xi}$ for such ε and $\boldsymbol{\xi}$ has a higher expected utility than $\tilde{\mathbf{x}}$ has.

The implications of $\varepsilon W_1 = 0$ for all ε and $\boldsymbol{\xi}$ and of $\tfrac{1}{2}\varepsilon^2 W_2 < 0$ for all $\varepsilon \neq 0$, $\boldsymbol{\xi} \neq \mathbf{0}$ are of course identical with those of $W_1 = 0$ for all $\boldsymbol{\xi}$ and $W_2 < 0$ for all $\boldsymbol{\xi} \neq \mathbf{0}$. Considering the last condition first, we note that it requires that $\mathbf{K}$ be negative definite, see (1.13). This is completely in line with the analogous condition of the static theory, see Theorem 2.2. The other condition implies

$$\mathscr{E}[(\mathbf{K}\tilde{\mathbf{x}}+\mathbf{k})'\boldsymbol{\xi}] = \mathbf{0} \text{ for all } \boldsymbol{\xi}, \tag{1.15}$$

see (1.13). Let us premultiply (1.15) by $\mathbf{K}^{-1}$:

$$\mathscr{E}[(\tilde{\mathbf{x}}+\mathbf{K}^{-1}\mathbf{k})'\boldsymbol{\xi}] = \mathscr{E}[(\tilde{\mathbf{x}}-\mathbf{x}^0)'\boldsymbol{\xi}] = \mathbf{0},$$

where $\mathbf{x}^0 = -\mathbf{K}^{-1}\mathbf{k}$ is the optimal decision (which maximizes the preference function subject to the constraints in the certainty case). It is instructive to write this result in time-partitioned form:

$$\sum_{t=1}^{T} \mathscr{E}\{[\tilde{x}_t(\mathscr{I}_{t-1})-x_t^0]'\xi_t(\mathscr{I}_{t-1})\} = \mathbf{0}, \tag{1.16}$$

where it is to be noted that x_t^0 depends on information beyond $\mathscr{I}_{t-1}$. Now (1.16) should hold for any function ξ_t of $\mathscr{I}_{t-1}$, $t = 1, 2, \ldots, T$; in particular, it should hold when all these T vector functions are identically zero except for the tth. This implies that (1.15) and (1.16) are equivalent to

$$\mathscr{E}\{[\tilde{x}_t(\mathscr{I}_{t-1})-x_t^0]'\xi_t(\mathscr{I}_{t-1})\} = \mathbf{0} \text{ for all } \xi_t(\mathscr{I}_{t-1}),\ t = 1, \ldots, T. \tag{1.17}$$

Evidently, (1.17) implies that in each period the difference between that period's decision according to the maximizing strategy and that period's optimal decision should have a zero cross-moment with any function of the information which is available at the beginning of that period. In other words, the difference $\tilde{x}_t-\tilde{x}_t^0$ should be independent of $\mathscr{I}_{t-1}$.

Another interesting result can be obtained if we consider (1.15) for all those vectors $\boldsymbol{\xi}$ which are nonstochastic. This implies that the strategy $\tilde{\mathbf{x}}+\varepsilon\boldsymbol{\xi}$ differs from the maximizing strategy by an arbitrary vector of fixed numbers. In that special case (1.15) takes the form

$$[\mathscr{E}(\mathbf{K}\tilde{\mathbf{x}}+\mathbf{k})]'\boldsymbol{\xi} = \mathbf{0} \text{ for all } \boldsymbol{\xi},$$

for which a necessary and sufficient condition is $\mathscr{E}(\mathbf{K}\tilde{\mathbf{x}}+\mathbf{k}) = \mathbf{0}$. This implies

$$\mathscr{E}\tilde{\mathbf{x}} = -\mathbf{K}^{-1}\mathscr{E}\mathbf{k}, \tag{1.18}$$

because $\mathbf{K}$ is nonstochastic. Hence the expected value of the maximizing strategy is found by postmultiplying minus the inverse of $\mathbf{K}$ by the expectation of $\mathbf{k}$. This is analogous to the decision $\hat{x}$ of (2.2.3) which maximizes expected utility in the static case, the main difference being, of course, that $\hat{x}$ is nonstochastic whereas a strategy like $\tilde{\mathbf{x}}$ contains random elements; hence the expectation sign on the left of (1.18).

Let us now consider what happens in case the decision maker decides on the instrument vector which maximizes the preference function under the condition that all random elements coincide with their expectations, i.e., under the condition that $\mathbf{s}$ is equal to $\mathscr{E}\mathbf{s}$. Then (1.10) remains valid except that we should replace k_0 by $\mathbf{b}'\mathscr{E}\mathbf{s}+\frac{1}{2}(\mathscr{E}\mathbf{s})'\mathbf{B}\mathscr{E}\mathbf{s}$ and $\mathbf{k}$ by $\mathbf{a}+\mathbf{R}'\mathbf{b}+(\mathbf{C}+\mathbf{R}'\mathbf{B})\mathscr{E}\mathbf{s}$, i.e., by $\mathscr{E}\mathbf{k}$. The change in k_0 is irrelevant because the result is a constant from the decision maker's point of view. Hence the function to be maximized is now $(\mathscr{E}\mathbf{k})'\mathbf{x}+\frac{1}{2}\mathbf{x}'\mathbf{K}\mathbf{x}$, and the maximizing vector is $-\mathbf{K}^{-1}\mathscr{E}\mathbf{k}$, which is precisely the same as $\mathscr{E}\tilde{\mathbf{x}}$, see (1.18). In other words, if in the dynamic case the uncertainty aspect is disregarded by behaving as if the random $\mathbf{s}$ coincides with its expectation, then the resulting decision vector is identical with the expectation of the maximizing strategy. But the first-period elements of this strategy are not random at all and must therefore coincide with their own expectations. This follows from the fact that for any strategy $\mathbf{x}$, the first-period subvector x_1 depends only on $\mathscr{I}_0$, i.e., on information which is available prior to the entire series of T periods which are here under consideration. It follows immediately that the first-period decision of the maximizing strategy, $\tilde{x}_1$, is equal to the first m components of the vector (1.18) and also equal to the first-period decision which is obtained when the uncertainty is disregarded.

Summarizing our results, we have:

THEOREM 4.1. *Suppose that Assumptions* 4.3 *and* 4.4 *are satisfied. Then the strategy* $\tilde{\mathbf{x}}$ *which maximizes the mean value of the preference function* (1.3) *subject to the stochastic constraints* (1.4), *if existent and unique, has the following properties*:

(i) *The difference* $\tilde{x}_t - x_t^0$ *is independent of* $\mathscr{I}_{t-1}$ *for* $t = 1, \ldots, T$, *where* $\tilde{x}_t$ *is the* t^{th} *subvector of* $\tilde{\mathbf{x}}$, x_t^0 *the* t^{th} *subvector of* $\mathbf{x}^0 = -\mathbf{K}^{-1}\mathbf{k}$ [$\mathbf{K}$ *and* $\mathbf{k}$ *being defined in* (1.11)], *and* $\mathscr{I}_t$ *is the information available at the end of the* t^{th} *period.*

(ii) *The expected value of* $\tilde{\mathbf{x}}$ *is as specified in* (1.18).

(iii) *The first-period decision of* $\tilde{\mathbf{x}}$ *is identical with the first-period subvector of the decision which maximizes* (1.3) *subject to* (1.4) *after* $\mathbf{s}$ (*the additive structure of the constraints*) *is replaced by its expectation* (*first-period certainty equivalence*); *and this first-period decision is the subvector consisting of the first* m *elements of the vector* (1.18).

A sufficient condition for the existence and uniqueness of the maximizing strategy is that **K** *as defined in* (1.11) *be negative definite.*

The existence has been proved for the first-period decision;[1] for later periods this will follow in 4.1.6 below. The uniqueness given the existence is easily proved by assuming that two different maximizing strategies exist, say **p** and **q**; then $\frac{1}{2}(\mathbf{p}+\mathbf{q})$ is another strategy but with a higher expected utility level if **K** is negative definite, thus contradicting the assumption of several maximizing strategies.

It will be noticed that since **k** is a linear function of **s**, the vector (1.18) is a linear function of the expectation of **s**. In other words, the first-period decision of the maximizing strategy turns out to be linear in the expected values of the present and future components of the additive structure of the constraints. If we apply this to the paint factory analysis of Section 3.2, this means that the first-period production and work force decisions are linear functions of expected future sales. This is repeated for the later-period decisions (see 4.1.6 below), and accordingly we speak about *linear decision rules.*[2]

4.1.6. Later-Period Decisions of the Maximizing Strategy

The result of Theorem 4.1 stands in sharp contrast to the example of 4.1.2. There, we found that if the probability of the "tax candidate" being elected is 0.42, the maximizing strategy implies that the aircraft company is to be bought in the first period, whereas a neglect of the possibility that later decisions are made dependent on relevant information implies that the aircraft company is not bought. Here we find—under appropriate assumptions!—that the first-period decisions are the same under even much stronger conditions. For if we replace **s** by its expectation, we do not merely disregard the possibility that later decisions are made dependent on information that will be available in the meantime;

---

[1] Note that (1.17) for $t = 1$ necessarily implies that $\boldsymbol{\xi}_t$ is nonstochastic, so that it can be eliminated from the expectation operator. Hence $\mathscr{E}(\tilde{\mathbf{x}}_1 - \mathbf{x}_1^0) = \mathbf{0}$ is sufficient to satisfy (1.17) for $t = 1$, which implies that $\tilde{\mathbf{x}}_1$ is uniquely defined as the first m components of $-\mathbf{K}^{-1}\mathscr{E}\mathbf{k}$.

[2] The first-period certainty equivalence theorem was originally formulated by H. A. Simon for a special case of production programming; see "Dynamic Programming under Uncertainty with a Quadratic Criterion Function," *Econometrica*, Vol. 24 (1956), pp. 74–81. It was generalized by H. Theil in "A Note on Certainty Equivalence in Dynamic Planning," *ibidem*, Vol. 25 (1957), pp. 346–349. See also Section 8.6 of *Economic Forecasts and Policy*.

we disregard all uncertainty and hence do not even look at expected utility (as the car manufacturer did when arriving at the critical p-value of 0.4). The present certainty equivalence result is completely comparable with that of the static theory, since in both cases the maximizing decisions can be computed by disregarding the uncertainty altogether; except, of course, for the difference that in the dynamic case the result applies to the first period only. It is not difficult to see that Theorem 4.1 can be generalized to incorporate uncertainty at the level of the coefficients of the linear part of the preference function (the elements of **a** and **b**), provided that the distribution of a_t, b_t is independent of $x_{t'}$ whenever $t \geqq t'$. We shall need this result very soon.

The question arises what can be said about the decisions in the second and later periods, $\tilde{x}_2, \tilde{x}_3, \ldots$ The answer is simple. There is no immediate need for computing the second-period decision since it has not to be made before the beginning of the second period, and similarly $\tilde{x}_3$ need not be made before the beginning of the third period, and so on. Now given that $\tilde{x}_1$ is the first-period decision, the problem at the beginning of the second period is essentially that of a $(T-1)$-period horizon. More specifically, let us write the preference function (1.3) in time-partitioned form:

$$w(x_1, \ldots, x_T, y_1, \ldots, y_T) = \sum_{t=1}^{T} a_t' x_t + \sum_{t=1}^{T} b_t' y_t \tag{1.19}$$

$$+\tfrac{1}{2}\left(\sum_1^T \sum_1^T x_t' A_{tt'} x_{t'} + \sum_1^T \sum_1^T y_t' B_{tt'} y_{t'} + \sum_1^T \sum_1^T x_t' C_{tt'} y_{t'} + \sum_1^T \sum_1^T y_t' C_{tt'}' x_{t'}\right).$$

Since x_1 is specified at the $\tilde{x}_1$-level at the beginning of the second period, while at the same time $y_1 = R_{11}\tilde{x}_1 + s_1$ according to (1.6), the "new" preference function has the following linear part:

$$\sum_{t=2}^{T} [a_t + (A_{t1} + C_{t1} R_{11})\tilde{x}_1 + C_{t1} s_1]' x_t \tag{1.20}$$

$$+ \sum_{t=2}^{T} [b_t + (C_{1t}' + B_{t1} R_{11})\tilde{x}_1 + B_{t1} s_1]' y_t$$

and the following quadratic part:

$$\tfrac{1}{2}\left(\sum_2^T \sum_2^T x_t' A_{tt'} x_{t'} + \sum_2^T \sum_2^T y_t' B_{tt'} y_{t'} + \sum_2^T \sum_2^T x_t' C_{tt'} y_{t'} + \sum_2^T \sum_2^T y_t' C_{tt'}' x_{t'}\right). \tag{1.21}$$

The constraints are changed in a similar manner. The y_1-part is now superfluous and at the same time x_1 is no longer subject to choice, so that $\tilde{x}_1$ should be incorporated in the additive structure of the constraints. This leads to

$$(1.22)\quad \begin{bmatrix} y_2 \\ y_3 \\ \vdots \\ y_T \end{bmatrix} = \begin{bmatrix} R_{22} & \mathbf{0} & \dots & \mathbf{0} \\ R_{32} & R_{33} & \dots & \mathbf{0} \\ \vdots & \vdots & & \vdots \\ R_{T2} & R_{T3} & \dots & R_{TT} \end{bmatrix} \begin{bmatrix} x_2 \\ x_3 \\ \vdots \\ x_T \end{bmatrix} + \begin{bmatrix} s_2 + R_{21}\tilde{x}_1 \\ s_3 + R_{31}\tilde{x}_1 \\ \vdots \\ s_T + R_{T1}\tilde{x}_1 \end{bmatrix}.$$

Summarizing, the second-period decision of the maximizing strategy, $\tilde{x}_2$, is found—given $\tilde{x}_1$ and s_1—in precisely the same first-period certainty equivalence manner as the first-period decision, it being understood that the preference function (1.3) is replaced by (1.20) plus (1.21), and the constraints (1.4) by (1.22). For the third-period decision one proceeds in the same way, and so on; this will be elaborated in 4.2.3, where a recursive formula for the successive components of the maximizing strategy will be derived. It should be noted that as far as the second-period decision is concerned, the coefficient matrices which are changed compared with the first-period problem are those of the additive structure of the constraints and of the linear part of the preference function. The former changes such that s_t is replaced by $s_t + R_{t1}\tilde{x}_1$, the latter such that a_t and b_t are replaced by the vectors in square brackets of (1.20). It should also be noted that if there is only imperfect knowledge of $s_1 = y_1 - R_{11}\tilde{x}_1$ at the end of the first period (which may readily be the case since complete information on y_1 frequently lags behind the events), there is uncertainty at the level of the coefficients of the linear part of the second-period preference function. We shall then have to use the generalized certainty equivalence result which includes random **a** and **b**-vectors (see above, the end of the first paragraph) and maximize expected utility in its conditional form, the condition on s_1 being the information available at the end of the first period.

4.1.7. Unbiased Predictions of Future Decisions and Noncontrolled Values

In the static case of decision-making under uncertainty, one can compute $\hat{x}$ but not the corresponding noncontrolled vector, because the latter is equal to $R\hat{x} + s$ and s is unknown. However, since $\mathscr{E}s$ is supposed to be known, one can predict the noncontrolled vector as $R\hat{x} + \mathscr{E}s$, and the prediction error $R\hat{x} + \mathscr{E}s - (R\hat{x} + s)$ has zero mean. It is therefore possible to formulate an unbiased prediction of the vector of values to be taken by the noncontrolled variables at the moment when the decision $\hat{x}$ is made.

In the dynamic case the scope of forecasting is extended considerably and includes future values of both instruments and noncontrolled variables. This is illustrated by (1.18), which specifies the expectation of the maximizing strategy, given the information available at the beginning of the first period ($\mathscr{I}_0$). The first-period decision $\tilde{x}_1$ coincides with its expectation, but for the later-period decisions this is not true. For these (1.18) specifies $\mathscr{E}(\tilde{x}_2|\mathscr{I}_0)$, $\mathscr{E}(\tilde{x}_3|\mathscr{I}_0), \ldots$, which are the conditional expectations of the later-period decisions of the maximizing strategy, given $\mathscr{I}_0$. We shall denote these conditional expectations simply by $\mathscr{E}_0\tilde{x}_2, \mathscr{E}_0\tilde{x}_3, \ldots$ [1] It follows from (1.18) that these vectors can be computed at the beginning of the first period and hence can be used as forecasts of the decision maker's future behaviour according to the maximizing strategy. And, as is easily seen, these forecasts are unbiased with respect to the relevant conditional distribution, since $\mathscr{E}_0(\mathscr{E}_0\tilde{x}_t - \tilde{x}_t) = \mathbf{0}$. Moreover, we can use these forecasts to obtain derived forecasts of future noncontrolled values. For the nT-element noncontrolled vector associated with the maximizing strategy is $\mathbf{R}\tilde{\mathbf{x}} + \mathbf{s}$, which—given $\mathbf{R}$—is a linear combination of random elements. By substituting $\mathscr{E}_0\tilde{\mathbf{x}}$ and $\mathscr{E}_0\mathbf{s}$ for $\mathbf{x}$ and $\mathbf{s}$, respectively, we then obtain $\mathscr{E}_0\tilde{y}_1, \mathscr{E}_0\tilde{y}_2, \ldots$, which are the conditional expectations of the noncontrolled values associated with the maximizing strategy, given $\mathscr{I}_0$. These forecasts are conditionally unbiased in the same way as $\mathscr{E}_0\tilde{x}_2, \mathscr{E}_0\tilde{x}_3, \ldots$

We thus find that the scope of prediction is indeed much greater in the dynamic theory than in the static case. But there is even more, because during the first period the information $\mathscr{I}_1$ becomes available. As stated in 4.1.6, this leads to a result which is identical with (1.18) except that a re-interpretation of matrices is necessary in view of the fact that $x_1 = \tilde{x}_1$ and $\mathscr{I}_0$ is replaced by $\mathscr{I}_1$. The result is the second-period decision of the maximizing strategy, $\tilde{x}_2$, together with the forecasts $\mathscr{E}(\tilde{x}_3|\mathscr{I}_1)$, $\mathscr{E}(\tilde{x}_4|\mathscr{I}_1), \ldots$, for short $\mathscr{E}_1\tilde{x}_3, \mathscr{E}_1\tilde{x}_4, \ldots$ These predictions are of course conditionally unbiased, given $\mathscr{I}_1$. Also, if $\mathscr{I}_1$ includes complete knowledge of s_1, we know $\tilde{y}_1$; and we can compute $\mathscr{E}_1\tilde{y}_2$, $\mathscr{E}_1\tilde{y}_3, \ldots$, which are unbiased predictions of noncontrolled values, given $\mathscr{I}_1$. In other words, the predictions $\mathscr{E}_0\tilde{x}_2, \mathscr{E}_0\tilde{x}_3, \ldots, \mathscr{E}_0\tilde{y}_1, \mathscr{E}_0\tilde{y}_2, \ldots$ are *revised* at the end of the first period to include that period's information. We have realizations for $\tilde{x}_2$ and $\tilde{y}_1$ and new forecasts for $\tilde{x}_3, \tilde{x}_4, \ldots$, $\tilde{y}_2, \tilde{y}_3, \ldots$ Insofar as the information $\mathscr{I}_1$ is "better" than $\mathscr{I}_0$ one should expect the new forecasts to be closer to the later realizations than

[1] According to this notation, the expectation operators of (1.18) should both be written as $\mathscr{E}_0$.

their predecessors. This is of course not the Law of the Medes and the Persians, but it would be surprising if it would not be true in most cases. We also note that it is not necessarily true that $\mathscr{I}_1$ includes complete knowledge of s_1. If this is untrue, then $\mathscr{E}_1 \tilde{y}_1 \neq \tilde{y}_1$, so that at the end of the first period we do not know the first-period noncontrolled vector $\tilde{y}_1$ although it has in fact been realized. The vector $\mathscr{E}_1 \tilde{y}_1 = R_{11}\tilde{x}_1 + \mathscr{E}_1 s_1$ is then a conditionally unbiased estimate based on the conditionally unbiased estimate of s_1 (the condition being again the information $\mathscr{I}_1$).

We can go on in this way for later periods. At the end of the tth period our information is $\mathscr{I}_t$, which includes $\tilde{x}_1, \ldots, \tilde{x}_t$ and $\mathscr{E}_t s_1, \ldots, \mathscr{E}_t s_t$. On the basis of $\mathscr{I}_t$ we can compute, using (1.18) in its appropriate interpretation, the decision $\tilde{x}_{t+1}$ together with the forecasts $\mathscr{E}_t \tilde{x}_{t+2}, \ldots,$ $\mathscr{E}_t \tilde{x}_T$, $\mathscr{E}_t \tilde{y}_{t+1}, \ldots, \mathscr{E}_t \tilde{y}_T$ and the estimates of past values: $\mathscr{E}_t \tilde{y}_1, \ldots,$ $\mathscr{E}_t \tilde{y}_t$. These forecasts and estimates are all conditionally unbiased, given $\mathscr{I}_t$, and they are all revisions of the previous forecasts $\mathscr{E}_{t-1} \tilde{x}_{t+2}, \ldots$ Moreover, if $\mathscr{I}_t$ includes complete knowledge of such previous vectors as $s_1, s_2, \ldots$, then the corresponding estimates $\mathscr{E}_t \tilde{y}_1, \mathscr{E}_t \tilde{y}_2, \ldots$ are identical with the vectors estimated. A more complete survey is presented in Table 4.1.

In concluding we wish to stress that for this type of analysis the distinction between forecasts of future events, such as $\mathscr{E}_0 \tilde{y}_1$, and estimates of past events, such as $\mathscr{E}_1 \tilde{y}_1$, tends to disappear. Of course, the fundamental difference remains that "bygones are bygones" while the future remains open and is subject to changes caused by the decision maker's actions. But this is not the main point. As long as a value taken by some variable belongs to the future, it has to be predicted; and as soon as it has become past, it has to be estimated. In both cases there is uncertainty as to the precise value. One should expect that the discrepancy tends to diminish in the course of time, the variance of the forecast error becoming smaller as the future becomes less distant and, similarly, the variance of the estimation error becoming smaller still when more and more information becomes available. But in many cases there is no a priori reason for believing that the transition from prediction to estimation is accompanied by an abrupt reduction of uncertainty.

4.1.8. Summary

(1) In the dynamic theory we introduce a horizon consisting of T consecutive periods, each of which is characterized by m instruments and n noncontrolled variables. This leads to $(m+n)T$ variables as a whole, all

TABLE 4.1

PREDICTIONS, ESTIMATES, AND REALIZATIONS OF THE MAXIMIZING STRATEGY

At the beginning of period	Available information	Decisions in periods 1, 2, . . ., T					Noncontrolled values in periods 1, 2, . . ., T				
1	$\mathscr{I}_0$	$\tilde{x}_1$	$\mathscr{E}_0\tilde{x}_2$	$\mathscr{E}_0\tilde{x}_3 \ldots$	$\mathscr{E}_0\tilde{x}_{T-1}$	$\mathscr{E}_0\tilde{x}_T$	$\mathscr{E}_0\tilde{y}_1$	$\mathscr{E}_0\tilde{y}_2$	$\mathscr{E}_0\tilde{y}_3 \ldots$	$\mathscr{E}_0\tilde{y}_{T-1}$	$\mathscr{E}_0\tilde{y}_T$
2	$\mathscr{I}_1$	$\tilde{x}_1$	$\tilde{x}_2$	$\mathscr{E}_1\tilde{x}_3 \ldots$	$\mathscr{E}_1\tilde{x}_{T-1}$	$\mathscr{E}_1\tilde{x}_T$	$\mathscr{E}_1\tilde{y}_1$	$\mathscr{E}_1\tilde{y}_2$	$\mathscr{E}_1\tilde{y}_3 \ldots$	$\mathscr{E}_1\tilde{y}_{T-1}$	$\mathscr{E}_1\tilde{y}_T$
3	$\mathscr{I}_2$	$\tilde{x}_1$	$\tilde{x}_2$	$\tilde{x}_3$	$\ldots \mathscr{E}_2\tilde{x}_{T-1}$	$\mathscr{E}_2\tilde{x}_T$	$\mathscr{E}_2\tilde{y}_1$	$\mathscr{E}_2\tilde{y}_2$	$\mathscr{E}_2\tilde{y}_3 \ldots$	$\mathscr{E}_2\tilde{y}_{T-1}$	$\mathscr{E}_2\tilde{y}_T$
$\vdots$	$\vdots$	$\vdots$	$\vdots$	$\vdots$	$\vdots$	$\vdots$	$\vdots$	$\vdots$	$\vdots$	$\vdots$	$\vdots$
$T-1$	$\mathscr{I}_{T-2}$	$\tilde{x}_1$	$\tilde{x}_2$	$\tilde{x}_3$	$\ldots \tilde{x}_{T-1}$	$\mathscr{E}_{T-2}\tilde{x}_T$	$\mathscr{E}_{T-2}\tilde{y}_1$	$\mathscr{E}_{T-2}\tilde{y}_2$	$\mathscr{E}_{T-2}\tilde{y}_3 \ldots$	$\mathscr{E}_{T-2}\tilde{y}_{T-1}$	$\mathscr{E}_{T-2}\tilde{y}_T$
T	$\mathscr{I}_{T-1}$	$\tilde{x}_1$	$\tilde{x}_2$	$\tilde{x}_3$	$\ldots \tilde{x}_{T-1}$	$\tilde{x}_T$	$\mathscr{E}_{T-1}\tilde{y}_1$	$\mathscr{E}_{T-1}\tilde{y}_2$	$\mathscr{E}_{T-1}\tilde{y}_3 \ldots$	$\mathscr{E}_{T-1}\tilde{y}_{T-1}$	$\mathscr{E}_{T-1}\tilde{y}_T$

Note: For $t < t'$, $\mathscr{E}_t\tilde{y}_{t'}$ is a prediction; for $t \geqq t'$ it is an estimate of a past realization.

of which are arguments of a quadratic preference function. The objective is to maximize this function subject to a set of linear constraints, each of which describes one of the nT noncontrolled variables in terms of the instruments. This generalization of the static theory is entirely straightforward except that the multiplicative structure of the constraints is supposed to be such that no noncontrolled variable depends on later instruments.

(2, 3) The assumptions are generalized to allow for the possibility that the additive structure of the constraints is random. Maximizing expected utility in the dynamic case requires the use of a strategy, i.e., a decision rule according to which later-period decisions are made dependent on the information that will have become available at the time when the decision has to be taken. A very simple example is used to show that the first-period decision of the strategy which maximizes expected utility (the maximizing strategy) may deviate from the first-period decision which is obtained when no account is taken of the possibility that later-period decisions are made dependent on relevant information.

(4, 5, 6) If the additive structure of the constraints is random but such that the decision maker is not in a position to affect its distribution, then there is a first-period certainty equivalence in the following sense: the first-period decision of the maximizing strategy is identical with the first-period decision which is obtained by maximizing the quadratic preference function subject to the linear constraints after their random additive structure is replaced by its expectation. This result can be generalized to include uncertainty at the level of the coefficients of the linear part of the preference function. The first-period certainty equivalence result can also be used for later-period decisions, viz., by reformulating the maximization problem in such a way that earlier decisions are taken as given, so that the decision to be derived becomes the first-period decision of a choice problem with a shorter horizon.

(7) The certainty equivalence procedure supplies not only the first-period decision of the maximizing strategy, but also unbiased forecasts of later-period decisions, where "unbiased" is to be interpreted conditionally, given the available information of the moment. It supplies also similar unbiased forecasts of future noncontrolled values. Furthermore, when the procedure is applied to the second-period decision on the basis of the information available at the end of the first period, one obtains revised forecasts as well as estimates of past realizations. These are conditionally unbiased too, the condition being the available information

at the end of the first period. This process of revision of forecasts and estimates continues period after period.

4.2. FURTHER DYNAMIC EXTENSIONS OF THE STATIC THEORY

4.2.1. Equilibrium Conditions, Substitution, and Related Issues in the T-Period Case

We now return to Assumptions 4.1 and 4.2, which have not been used until now, and we shall consider the conditions under which the quadratic preference function (1.3) has a maximum subject to the linear constraints (1.4), all uncertainty being disregarded. It will be clear that this must be a completely straightforward generalization of the static theory which was expounded in Section 2.1. For the optimal decision, which maximizes (1.3) subject to (1.4), is of course

$$\mathbf{x}^0 = -\mathbf{K}^{-1}\mathbf{k}, \tag{2.1}$$

where $\mathbf{K}$ and $\mathbf{k}$ are defined in (1.11); in fact, we already used this result in 4.1.5. The condition under which the vector (2.1) exists and is at the same time the unique optimal decision is that $\mathbf{K}$ be negative definite; and this condition has already been imposed in Theorem 4.1. It will be noted that $\mathbf{x}^0$ specifies all decisions in all T periods completely, contrary to (1.18) which specifies only the first-period decision of the maximizing strategy (plus expectations of later-period decisions). This difference is natural, however, for if there is no uncertainty as under Assumptions 4.1 and 4.2, the decision maker should be able to formulate his best line of action right at the beginning.

The comparative statics of Section 2.1 are indeed completely applicable to the dynamic case under the uncertainty-excluding Assumptions 4.1 and 4.2, apart from one (unimportant) exception. According to (1.5), the dynamic $\mathbf{R}$-matrix can be partitioned such that the elements Northeast of the diagonal blocks vanish, whereas a similar rule does not hold for the $\mathbf{R}$-matrix of the static theory. This means that if we consider changes in the multiplicative structure of the constraints as in Theorem 2.4, then, in the dynamic case, it does not make much sense to consider changes in such elements which have to be zero anyhow. But this implies only that $\mathbf{R}$-changes are restricted to the diagonal blocks and Southwest, which has no further implications.

It is of some use to introduce explicitly the dynamic extensions of the more important concepts of Section 2.1. By bordering the second-order derivatives of the preference function (1.3) by the multiplicative structure of the constraints (1.4), we obtain an $(m+2n)T \times (m+2n)T$ matrix which is the dynamic generalization of W defined in (2.1.17). If we invert this matrix, like in (2.1.28), we obtain another square matrix whose first mT rows can be written in the form:

$$[(\mathbf{xx}) \quad (\mathbf{xy}) \quad (\mathbf{x}\cdot)],$$

where $(\mathbf{xx})$ is the substitution matrix of the mT instruments, $(\mathbf{xy})$ the mixed substitution matrix of the mT instruments and the nT noncontrolled variables, and $(\mathbf{x}\cdot)$ minus the matrix of slopes of the Tinbergen surfaces of all mT instruments. These matrices can all be expressed in terms of $\mathbf{A}$, $\mathbf{B}$, $\mathbf{C}$ and $\mathbf{R}$:

$$(2.2) \qquad (\mathbf{xx}) = \mathbf{K}^{-1}, \quad (\mathbf{xy}) = \mathbf{K}^{-1}\mathbf{R}', \quad (\mathbf{x}\cdot) = \mathbf{K}^{-1}(\mathbf{C}+\mathbf{R}'\mathbf{B}),$$

where $\mathbf{K}$ is given in (1.11). This is completely analogous to (2.1.30). The dynamic extension implies that these matrices can be partitioned into T^2 submatrices according to pairs of periods, e.g.,

$$(2.3) \qquad (\mathbf{xx}) = \begin{bmatrix} (\mathsf{xx})_{11} & \cdots & (\mathsf{xx})_{1T} \\ \vdots & & \vdots \\ (\mathsf{xx})_{T1} & \cdots & (\mathsf{xx})_{TT} \end{bmatrix},$$

where $(\mathsf{xx})_{tt'}$ contains the substitution terms of $x_h(t)$ and $x_k(t')$ for $h, k = 1, \ldots, m$. It will be noted that it is conceivable that $x_1(1)$ and $x_2(1)$ are complementary, say, whereas $x_1(1)$ and $x_2(2)$ are substitutes. In fact, an example of this nature was already obtained in the production-employment analysis of Section 3.2, since the first-period production decision turned out to be complementary with the first-period work force decision but a substitute of the second-period work force decision (see Table 3.8).

The further results are straightforward and can be easily summarized in:

THEOREM 4.2. *Suppose that Assumptions* 4.1 *and* 4.2 *are satisfied. Then Theorems* 2.1 *through* 2.6 *are all applicable in dynamic form, the vectors and matrices in sanserif type* (a, b, A, . . .) *being replaced by corresponding symbols in bold-face roman type* ($\mathbf{a}$, $\mathbf{b}$, $\mathbf{A}$, . . .), *and m and n by mT and nT respectively.*

4.2.2. The First-Period Loss Due to a First-Period Decision Error; Optimal Decision Revisions

We proceed to consider losses due to suboptimal decisions. The highest attainable utility level is, of course, $w^0 = w(\mathbf{x}^0, \mathbf{R}\mathbf{x}^0+\mathbf{s})$, and the loss associated with any mT-element decision vector $\mathbf{x}$ is then

$$
\begin{aligned}
(2.4) \qquad w^0 - w_{\mathbf{x}} &= -\tfrac{1}{2}(\mathbf{x}-\mathbf{x}^0)'(\mathbf{xx})^{-1}(\mathbf{x}-\mathbf{x}^0) \\
&= -\tfrac{1}{2}\sum_t \sum_{t'} (x_t - x_t^0)'(xx)^{tt'}(x_{t'} - x_{t'}^0),
\end{aligned}
$$

where $(xx)^{tt'}$ is one of the T^2 submatrices of $(\mathbf{xx})^{-1}$ (all of them being of order $m \times m$), and x_t, x_t^0 the tth subvector of $\mathbf{x}$ and $\mathbf{x}^0$ respectively. The first line of (2.4) represents a straightforward extension of the static result (2.3.3) and states that, if we specify a complete mT-element decision error vector, the result is a loss which is a quadratic form in this vector whose matrix is $-\frac{1}{2}$ times the inverse of the complete $mT \times mT$ instrumental substitution matrix. In the second line this form is split up into T^2 quadratic and bilinear forms corresponding to separate periods and to pairs of periods respectively. If there is neither substitution nor complementarity among instruments of different periods, then $(xx)_{tt'} = \mathbf{0}$ whenever $t \neq t'$, so that

$$
(\mathbf{xx})^{-1} = \begin{bmatrix} (xx)_{11}^{-1} & \mathbf{0} & \dots & \mathbf{0} \\ \mathbf{0} & (xx)_{22}^{-1} & \dots & \mathbf{0} \\ \vdots & \vdots & & \vdots \\ \mathbf{0} & \mathbf{0} & \dots & (xx)_{TT}^{-1} \end{bmatrix},
$$

which implies that the loss associated with any vector $\mathbf{x}$ can be written as a single sum:

$$
w^0 - w_{\mathbf{x}} = -\tfrac{1}{2}\sum_t (x_t - x_t^0)'(xx)_{tt}^{-1}(x_t - x_t^0).
$$

In that case the extent to which an error $x_t - x_t^0$ affects the preference level attained is independent of the deviation $x_{t'} - x_{t'}^0$ of another period t'. In general, however, there will be at least some substitution or complementarity among instruments of different periods, in which case products of the type

$$
\{x_h(t) - x_h^0(t)\}\{x_k(t') - x_k^0(t')\} \qquad (t \neq t')
$$

will enter into (2.4) with nonzero coefficients. In fact, we found in Section 3.2 that substitution terms connecting different periods may be substantial, particularly when they refer to the same instrument [see, e.g., the lower right-hand block in (3.2.17) and in Table 3.8].

But there is a second approach to the loss analysis in the dynamic case which is even more interesting. The point is that the decision maker formulates his decisions period after period, not all at once as we assumed in the preceding paragraph (and also in Section 3.2!). Suppose then that he decides on x_1^*, say, in the first period; for example, we may have $x_1^* = \tilde{x}_1$ on the basis of the first-period certainty equivalence procedure. We may then ask what is the loss associated with x_1^*; more precisely, what is the reduction of the attainable preference level given that the decision maker has decided on x_1^* in the first period but is still free as to his later-period decisions. This reduction will be called the *first-period loss* associated with x_1^*. It will be noticed that this line of thought has a close resemblance to that of 4.1.6 where we considered the derivation of the second-period decision of the maximizing strategy; but it will prove more convenient to proceed in a mathematically different manner, viz., that of the Lagrangean technique.

The preference level which is still attainable, given $x_1 = x_1^*$, is a conditional maximum. Hence we introduce an m-element column vector $\boldsymbol{\mu}$ of Lagrangean multipliers and consider:

$$k_0 + \mathbf{k}'\mathbf{x} + \tfrac{1}{2}\mathbf{x}'\mathbf{K}\mathbf{x} - \boldsymbol{\mu}'(x_1 - x_1^*).$$

On differentiating and putting the result equal to zero we obtain

$$\mathbf{k} + \mathbf{K}\mathbf{x}^1 - \begin{bmatrix} \boldsymbol{\mu} \\ \mathbf{0} \end{bmatrix} = \mathbf{0}, \tag{2.5}$$

where $\mathbf{x}^1$ is the vector of the conditional maximum and the zeros are both column vectors, the first containing $m(T-1)$ and the second mT elements. On premultiplying (2.5) by $\mathbf{K}^{-1} = (\mathbf{xx})$ we obtain

$$\mathbf{x}^1 = -\mathbf{K}^{-1}\mathbf{k} + \mathbf{K}^{-1}\begin{bmatrix} \boldsymbol{\mu} \\ \mathbf{0} \end{bmatrix} = \mathbf{x}^0 + (\mathbf{xx})\begin{bmatrix} \boldsymbol{\mu} \\ \mathbf{0} \end{bmatrix} = \mathbf{x}^0 + \begin{bmatrix} (xx)_{11} \\ \vdots \\ (xx)_{T1} \end{bmatrix}\boldsymbol{\mu},$$

the first m components of which imply $x_1^1 = x_1^0 + (xx)_{11}\boldsymbol{\mu}$. But it is given that $x_1^1 = x_1^*$. Hence $\boldsymbol{\mu} = (xx)_{11}^{-1}(x_1^* - x_1^0)$, so that

$$\mathbf{x}^1 - \mathbf{x}^0 = \begin{bmatrix} (xx)_{11} \\ \vdots \\ (xx)_{T1} \end{bmatrix} (xx)_{11}^{-1}(x_1^* - x_1^0). \tag{2.6}$$

This specifies the best decision ($\mathbf{x}^1$) that can be made when it is given that the first-period decision is x_1^*. At the same time, (2.6) specifies a decision error ($\mathbf{x}^1 - \mathbf{x}^0$) for the whole period 1, 2, . . ., T when it is given that $x_1 = x_1^*$, so that we can use (2.4) to compute its loss. This loss is

$$(2.7)\quad -\tfrac{1}{2}(\mathbf{x}^1-\mathbf{x}^0)'(\mathbf{xx})^{-1}(\mathbf{x}^1-\mathbf{x}^0)$$

$$= -\tfrac{1}{2}(x_1^*-x_1^0)'(xx)_{11}^{-1}[(xx)_{11}\dots(xx)_{1T}](\mathbf{xx})^{-1}\begin{bmatrix}(xx)_{11}\\ \vdots\\ (xx)_{T1}\end{bmatrix}(xx)_{11}^{-1}(x_1^*-x_1^0)$$

$$= -\tfrac{1}{2}(x_1^*-x_1^0)'(xx)_{11}^{-1}(x_1^*-x_1^0),$$

where use has been made of the fact that the product matrix

$$[(xx)_{11}\dots(xx)_{1T}](\mathbf{xx})^{-1} = [(xx)_{11}\dots(xx)_{1T}]\begin{bmatrix}(xx)^{11} & \dots & (xx)^{1T}\\ \vdots & & \vdots\\ (xx)^{T1} & \dots & (xx)^{TT}\end{bmatrix}$$

is the submatrix of the $mT\times mT$ unit matrix consisting of the first m rows; i.e., it is of the form $[\mathbf{I}\ \mathbf{0}]$ where $\mathbf{I}$ is $m\times m$ and $\mathbf{0}$ is $m\times m(T-1)$.

The loss (2.7) is the minimum loss for the whole period, given that $x_1 = x_1^*$; in other words, it is the first-period loss associated with x_1^*. It is a positive definite form in the first-period decision error, its matrix being $-\tfrac{1}{2}$ times the inverse of the substitution matrix of the instruments of the first period.

The results (2.4) and (2.7) are summarized in the first two parts of

THEOREM 4.3. *Suppose that Assumptions* 4.1 *and* 4.2 *are satisfied; suppose also that the matrix* $\mathbf{K}$ *as specified in* (1.11) *is negative definite. Then the loss associated with any decision vector* $\mathbf{x}$ *which is specified for the whole period* 1, 2, . . ., T *is the positive definite quadratic form* (2.4) *in the decision error* $\mathbf{x}-\mathbf{x}^0$, *where* $\mathbf{x}^0$ *is the optimal decision as specified in* (2.1) *and* $(\mathbf{xx})$ *the substitution matrix of all mT instruments as specified in* (2.2), (1.11). *Furthermore, the first-period loss associated with any first-period decision* x_1 *is the positive definite quadratic form*

$$(2.8)\qquad -\tfrac{1}{2}(x_1-x_1^0)'(xx)_{11}^{-1}(x_1-x_1^0),$$

where x_1^0 *is the optimal first-period decision and* $(xx)_{11}$ *the substitution matrix of the first-period instruments as specified in* (2.3). *Finally, the optimal decision revisions from the second period onward, given any first-period decision* x_1, *are the following homogeneous linear combinations of the first-period decision error*:

$$(2.9)\qquad \begin{bmatrix}x_2^1-x_2^0\\ \vdots\\ x_T^1-x_T^0\end{bmatrix} = \begin{bmatrix}(xx)_{21}\\ \vdots\\ (xx)_{T1}\end{bmatrix}(xx)_{11}^{-1}(x_1-x_1^0),$$

where $(xx)_{21}, \ldots, (xx)_{T1}$ *are the submatrices of the substitution matrix connecting later-period instruments with first-period instruments.*

Regarding the last part of the theorem, which deals with optimal decision revisions, we note that (2.6) specifies the "new" optimal decision $\mathbf{x}^1$, given the first-period decision error. The difference between $\mathbf{x}^1$ and the original optimal decision $\mathbf{x}^0$ (before the error was made) is therefore termed the optimal decision revision. The first m components of $\mathbf{x}^1 - \mathbf{x}^0$ are of course identical with the first-period decision error, hence the last $m(T-1)$ components only are revisions in the real sense. It follows from (2.9) that any first-period decision error leads to nonzero optimal revisions in all later periods except when there is neither substitution nor complementarity between the first-period instruments and those of such a later period.

4.2.3. *The Maximizing Strategy in Explicit Form*

We shall now apply the same mathematical argument to derive a recursive formula from which the successive subvectors of the maximizing strategy can be derived. The approach is completely analogous to that of 4.1.6 except that a Lagrangean procedure will be used. Thus at the beginning of the second period we consider the Lagrangean expression

$$\mathscr{E}_1 k_0 + (\mathscr{E}_1 \mathbf{k})' \mathbf{x} + \tfrac{1}{2} \mathbf{x}' \mathbf{K} \mathbf{x} - \boldsymbol{\mu}_1' (x_1 - \tilde{x}_1),$$

since we wish to maximize the conditional expectation of utility, given the available information at the end of the first period and given that the first-period decision made is $\tilde{x}_1$. The result is

$$\text{(2.10)} \qquad \mathbf{x} = -\mathbf{K}^{-1} \mathscr{E}_1 \mathbf{k} + \begin{bmatrix} (xx)_{11} \\ (xx)_{21} \\ \vdots \\ (xx)_{T1} \end{bmatrix} \boldsymbol{\mu}_1 .$$

But $-\mathbf{K}^{-1} \mathscr{E}_1 \mathbf{k}$ is nothing else than $\mathscr{E}_1 \mathbf{x}^0$, which is the conditional expectation of the (truly) optimal decision, given the available information at the end of the first period. This is a special case of

$$\text{(2.11)} \quad \mathscr{E}_t \mathbf{x}^0 = -\mathbf{K}^{-1} \mathscr{E}_t \mathbf{k} = -\mathbf{K}^{-1} [\mathscr{E}_t \mathbf{a} + \mathbf{R}' \mathscr{E}_t \mathbf{b} + (\mathbf{C} + \mathbf{R}' \mathbf{B}) \mathscr{E}_t \mathbf{s}],$$

where the condition refers now to the information available at the end of the tth period. It will be clear that the vector $\mathscr{E}_t \mathbf{x}^0$ can be derived numerically at that moment; also, that the expressions $\mathscr{E}_t \mathbf{a}$ and $\mathscr{E}_t \mathbf{b}$

imply that we want to take account of the possibility that the coefficients of the linear part of the preference function are random.

We find $(xx)_{11}\mu_1 = \tilde{x}_1 - \mathscr{E}_1 x_1^0$ from (2.10) and from $x_1 = \tilde{x}_1$, so that the $\mathbf{x}$ of (2.10) — written as $\mathscr{E}_1\tilde{\mathbf{x}}$ — is obtained from:

$$\mathscr{E}_1\tilde{\mathbf{x}} - \mathscr{E}_1\mathbf{x}^0 = \begin{bmatrix}(xx)_{11}\\(xx)_{21}\\\vdots\\(xx)_{T1}\end{bmatrix}(xx)_{11}^{-1}(\tilde{x}_1 - \mathscr{E}_1 x_1^0). \tag{2.12}$$

The first-period subvector of $\mathscr{E}_1\tilde{\mathbf{x}}$ is $\tilde{x}_1$, which is as it should be; that of the second period is given by

$$\tilde{x}_2 - \mathscr{E}_1 x_2^0 = (xx)_{21}(xx)_{11}^{-1}(\tilde{x}_1 - \mathscr{E}_1 x_1^0). \tag{2.13}$$

The left-hand side is the second-period decision of the maximizing strategy measured as a deviation from the conditional expectation of the optimal second-period decision, the condition being the available information at the end of the first period. The right-hand side contains the analogous difference of first-period decisions; note that its expectation operator is $\mathscr{E}_1$, not the $\mathscr{E}_0$ which is used for the derivation of $\tilde{x}_1$! We have to premultiply the latter difference by $(xx)_{21}(xx)_{11}^{-1}$ to obtain the former.

The other equations of (2.12) take the form:

$$\begin{bmatrix}\mathscr{E}_1\tilde{x}_3 - \mathscr{E}_1 x_3^0\\\vdots\\\mathscr{E}_1\tilde{x}_T - \mathscr{E}_1 x_T^0\end{bmatrix} = \begin{bmatrix}(xx)_{31}\\\vdots\\(xx)_{T1}\end{bmatrix}(xx)_{11}^{-1}(\tilde{x}_1 - \mathscr{E}_1 x_1^0). \tag{2.14}$$

They are entirely comparable with (2.13) for the second period; but they do not specify the actual decisions $\tilde{x}_3, \ldots, \tilde{x}_T$ of the maximizing strategy but only $\mathscr{E}_1\tilde{x}_3, \ldots, \mathscr{E}_1\tilde{x}_T$, i.e., their conditional expectations given the information which is available at the end of the first period.

The procedure for $\tilde{x}_3$ is completely analogous. The Lagrangean expression is now:

$$\mathscr{E}_2 k_0 + (\mathscr{E}_2\mathbf{k})'\mathbf{x} + \tfrac{1}{2}\mathbf{x}'\mathbf{K}\mathbf{x} - \mu_2'(x_1 - \tilde{x}_1) - \mu_3'(x_2 - \tilde{x}_2).$$

By differentiating and putting the result equal to zero we obtain:

$$\mathbf{x} = -\mathbf{K}^{-1}\mathscr{E}_2\mathbf{k} + \begin{bmatrix}(xx)_{11} & (xx)_{12}\\(xx)_{21} & (xx)_{22}\\\vdots & \vdots\\(xx)_{T1} & (xx)_{T2}\end{bmatrix}\begin{bmatrix}\mu_2\\\mu_3\end{bmatrix},$$

from which we derive:

$$\mathscr{E}_2\tilde{\mathbf{x}} - \mathscr{E}_2\mathbf{x}^0 = \begin{bmatrix} (xx)_{11} & (xx)_{12} \\ (xx)_{21} & (xx)_{22} \\ \vdots & \vdots \\ (xx)_{T1} & (xx)_{T2} \end{bmatrix} \begin{bmatrix} (xx)_{11} & (xx)_{12} \\ (xx)_{21} & (xx)_{22} \end{bmatrix}^{-1} \begin{bmatrix} \tilde{x}_1 - \mathscr{E}_2 x_1^0 \\ \tilde{x}_2 - \mathscr{E}_2 x_2^0 \end{bmatrix}.$$

The first two subvectors give

$$\mathscr{E}_2\tilde{x}_1 - \mathscr{E}_2 x_1^0 = \tilde{x}_1 - \mathscr{E}_2 x_1^0, \quad \mathscr{E}_2\tilde{x}_2 - \mathscr{E}_2 x_2^0 = \tilde{x}_2 - \mathscr{E}_2 x_2^0$$

and hence $\mathscr{E}_2\tilde{x}_1 = \tilde{x}_1$, $\mathscr{E}_2\tilde{x}_2 = \tilde{x}_2$, which is as it should be. The third subvector gives:

$$\tilde{x}_3 - \mathscr{E}_2 x_3^0 = [(xx)_{31} \quad (xx)_{32}] \begin{bmatrix} (xx)_{11} & (xx)_{12} \\ (xx)_{21} & (xx)_{22} \end{bmatrix}^{-1} \begin{bmatrix} \tilde{x}_1 - \mathscr{E}_2 x_1^0 \\ \tilde{x}_2 - \mathscr{E}_2 x_2^0 \end{bmatrix},$$

which is the straightforward extension of (2.13). The fourth, fifth, ... subvectors take the form:

$$\begin{bmatrix} \mathscr{E}_2\tilde{x}_4 - \mathscr{E}_2 x_4^0 \\ \vdots \\ \mathscr{E}_2\tilde{x}_T - \mathscr{E}_2 x_T^0 \end{bmatrix} = \begin{bmatrix} (xx)_{41} & (xx)_{42} \\ \vdots & \vdots \\ (xx)_{T1} & (xx)_{T2} \end{bmatrix} \begin{bmatrix} (xx)_{11} & (xx)_{12} \\ (xx)_{21} & (xx)_{22} \end{bmatrix}^{-1} \begin{bmatrix} \tilde{x}_1 - \mathscr{E}_2 x_1^0 \\ x_2 - \mathscr{E}_2 x_2^0 \end{bmatrix}$$

and these give conditional expectations of future decisions of the maximizing strategy, given the information available at the end of the second period.

The derivations for the general case are now straightforward. At the end of the tth period the relevant conditional expectation is $\mathscr{E}_t$ and the decision of the maximizing strategy for the next period is obtained from

$$(2.15) \quad \tilde{x}_{t+1} - \mathscr{E}_t x_{t+1}^0$$
$$= [(xx)_{t+1,1} \quad \dots \quad (xx)_{t+1,t}] \begin{bmatrix} (xx)_{11} & \dots & (xx)_{1t} \\ \vdots & & \vdots \\ (xx)_{t1} & \dots & (xx)_{tt} \end{bmatrix}^{-1} \begin{bmatrix} \tilde{x}_1 - \mathscr{E}_t x_1^0 \\ \vdots \\ \tilde{x}_t - \mathscr{E}_t x_t^0 \end{bmatrix};$$

and the conditional expectation of the future decisions (for periods $t+2$, $t+3$, ...) is obtained from:

$$(2.16) \quad \begin{bmatrix} \mathscr{E}_t\tilde{x}_{t+2} - \mathscr{E}_t x_{t+2}^0 \\ \vdots \\ \mathscr{E}_t\tilde{x}_T - \mathscr{E}_t x_T^0 \end{bmatrix}$$
$$= \begin{bmatrix} (xx)_{t+2,1} & \dots & (xx)_{t+2,t} \\ \vdots & & \vdots \\ (xx)_{T1} & \dots & (xx)_{Tt} \end{bmatrix} \begin{bmatrix} (xx)_{11} & \dots & (xx)_{1t} \\ \vdots & & \vdots \\ (xx)_{t1} & \dots & (xx)_{tt} \end{bmatrix}^{-1} \begin{bmatrix} \tilde{x}_1 - \mathscr{E}_t x_1^0 \\ \vdots \\ \tilde{x}_t - \mathscr{E}_t x_t^0 \end{bmatrix}.$$

Summarizing our results:

THEOREM 4.4. *Suppose that Assumptions* 4.3 *and* 4.4 *are satisfied; suppose also that the matrix* **K** *defined in* (1.11) *is negative definite. Then for each* $t = 0, 1, \ldots, T-1$, *given the decisions* $\tilde{x}_1, \ldots, \tilde{x}_t$ *of the maximizing strategy, the decision* $\tilde{x}_{t+1}$ *is obtained from* (2.15), *where* $(xx)_{tt'}$ *is a submatrix of the instrumental substitution matrix defined in* (2.3) *and* $\mathscr{E}_t x^0_{t'}$ *is the conditional expectation, given the information available at the end of the* t^{th} *period, of the optimal decision in period* t' *as defined in* (2.11). *This result includes the first-period certainty equivalence theorem as a special case when the right-hand side of* (2.15) *is interpreted as zero for* $t = 0$. *Furthermore, the conditional expectation of the decisions for periods* $t+2, \ldots, T$ *of the maximizing strategy, given the information available at the end of the* t^{th}, *is given by* (2.16). *Finally, the conditional expectations of the values taken by the noncontrolled variables under the same condition follow from*

$$\mathscr{E}_t\tilde{\mathbf{y}} = \mathbf{R}\mathscr{E}_t\tilde{\mathbf{x}} + \mathscr{E}_t\mathbf{s}. \tag{2.17}$$

The last part of the theorem, dealing with forecasts and estimates of noncontrolled values, is straightforward and needs no further comments. It is more useful to comment on (2.15) and (2.16) by means of a least-squares interpretation. For this purpose we note that under our assumptions $-(\mathbf{xx})$ is a positive definite matrix, so that it can be written as $\mathbf{P'P}$ for some matrix $\mathbf{P}$ whose columns are linearly independent. In partitioned form:

$$-(\mathbf{xx}) = \mathbf{P'P} = \begin{bmatrix} P_1'P_1 & P_1'P_2 & \ldots & P_1'P_T \\ P_2'P_1 & P_2'P_2 & \ldots & P_2'P_T \\ \vdots & \vdots & & \vdots \\ P_T'P_1 & P_T'P_2 & \ldots & P_T'P_T \end{bmatrix},$$

where

$$\mathbf{P} = [P_1 \quad P_2 \quad \ldots \quad P_T]$$

such that $P_1'P_1 = -(xx)_{11}$, $P_1'P_2 = -(xx)_{12}$, and so on. Consider then the matrix

$$[(xx)_{t+\tau,1} \quad \ldots \quad (xx)_{t+\tau,t}] \begin{bmatrix} (xx)_{11} & \ldots & (xx)_{1t} \\ \vdots & & \vdots \\ (xx)_{t1} & \ldots & (xx)_{tt} \end{bmatrix}^{-1}$$

$$= [P_{t+\tau}'P_1 \quad \ldots \quad P_{t+\tau}'P_t] \begin{bmatrix} P_1'P_1 & \ldots & P_1'P_t \\ \vdots & & \vdots \\ P_t'P_1 & \ldots & P_t'P_t \end{bmatrix}^{-1},$$

which can be interpreted as the coefficient matrix of a set of least-squares regressions in which the columns of $P_{t+\tau}$ contain the values taken by the dependent variables and those of $[P_1 \ldots P_t]$ the values taken by the independent variables. Now (2.16) specifies that if we postmultiply this coefficient matrix by

$$\begin{bmatrix} \tilde{x}_1 - \mathscr{E}_t x_1^0 \\ \vdots \\ \tilde{x}_t - \mathscr{E}_t x_t^0 \end{bmatrix},$$

we obtain $\mathscr{E}_t \tilde{x}_{t+\tau} - \mathscr{E}_t x_{t+\tau}^0$. Next, we consider what happens when we are one period later, so that we compute the $\mathscr{E}_{t+1}$ of $\tilde{x}_{t+\tau}$. Actually, two things happen. One is that the set of independent variables of our auxiliary regressions is enlarged, because $[P_1 \ldots P_t]$ is replaced by $[P_1 \ldots P_{t+1}]$. This implies that in general the way in which $\mathscr{E}_{t+1}\tilde{x}_{t+\tau} - \mathscr{E}_{t+1} x_{t+\tau}^0$ depends on $\tilde{x}_1 - \mathscr{E}_{t+1} x_1^0$, $\tilde{x}_2 - \mathscr{E}_{t+1} x_2^0, \ldots$ is different from the way in which $\mathscr{E}_t \tilde{x}_{t+\tau} - \mathscr{E}_t x_{t+\tau}^0$ depends on $\tilde{x}_1 - \mathscr{E}_t x_1^0, \ldots$; in other words, the reaction to discrepancies between past decisions of the maximizing strategy and the corresponding estimated optimal decisions has changed. But these estimates have changed too, since $\tilde{x}_1 - \mathscr{E}_{t+1} x_1^0$ is in general different from $\tilde{x}_1 - \mathscr{E}_t x_1^0$. (In addition to this there is now also the "new" vector $\tilde{x}_{t+1} - \mathscr{E}_{t+1} x_{t+1}^0$.) It follows that the formulas (2.15) and (2.16), which enable us to compute the relevant decision of the maximizing strategy as well as revised forecasts of later decisions, are such that they imply a linear feedback with respect to estimated decision errors in the past; and the coefficient matrix of this feedback as well as the estimates of the decision errors change in principle from period to period. It will be noted that if the least-squares coefficient matrix introduced above is zero, there is no reaction to past errors; this case corresponds to absence of substitution and complementarity between the instruments in period $t+\tau$ and those in periods $1, 2, \ldots, t$.

4.2.4. The First-Period Loss Due to Specification Errors in Constraints and Preference Function

The extension of the loss concept to the causes of the suboptimal decisions, viz., erroneous specifications of the determining vectors and matrices **a**, **b**, **A**, **B**, **C**, **R**, **s**, is straightforward. We recall that according to Theorem 4.2, Theorem 2.6 is applicable to the T-period case, which means that the decision error $\mathbf{x} - \mathbf{x}^0$ can be approximated by a homogeneous linear combination of the specification errors in these determining matrices, see (2.1.43). On applying (2.4), we find that the latter errors lead to a loss that can be written in quadratic form, or, as in Theorem 2.11, as the sum of a substitution component, a constant-term component, and a mixed component. This is indeed perfectly straightforward, the only alterations being that the order of certain matrices is enlarged from m to mT or from n to nT.

The generalization to the first-period loss associated with specification errors in $\mathbf{a}$, $\mathbf{b}$, $\mathbf{A}, \ldots, \mathbf{s}$ is almost equally simple. The quadratic form in the decision error is now (2.8), which shows that we need only $x_1 - x_1^0$ rather than the complete mT-element vector $\mathbf{x}-\mathbf{x}^0$. The way in which the latter vector is derived from the specification errors in $\mathbf{a}$, $\mathbf{b}, \ldots, \mathbf{s}$ has been described in the preceding paragraph, and to obtain $x_1 - x_1^0$ we should consider only the first m elements and disregard the $m(T-1)$ other elements. In other words, if we interpret (2.1.43) in the T-period manner, so that there are mT-element vectors on the left and on the right of its equation sign, we should take the first m elements which express $x_1 - x_1^0$ in terms of the determining specification errors:

$$
\begin{aligned}
(2.18) \qquad x_1 - x_1^0 \approx & -[(x\cdot)_{11} \ldots (x\cdot)_{1T}][(\mathbf{dR})\mathbf{x}^0 + \mathbf{ds}] \\
& -[(xx)_{11} \ldots (xx)_{1T}](\mathbf{dR})'\boldsymbol{\lambda}^0 \\
& -[(xx)_{11} \ldots (xx)_{1T}][\mathbf{da} + (\mathbf{dA})\mathbf{x}^0 + (\mathbf{dC})\mathbf{y}^0] \\
& -[(xy)_{11} \ldots (xy)_{1T}][\mathbf{db} + (\mathbf{dC})'\mathbf{x}^0 + (\mathbf{dB})\mathbf{y}^0],
\end{aligned}
$$

where $(x\cdot)_{1t}$, $(xx)_{1t}$, $(xy)_{1t}$ are matrices whose interpretation should be self-evident. On combining (2.18) with (2.8) we obtain the first-period loss associated with these specification errors. This is again a quadratic form which can be written as the sum of a substitution component, a constant-term component, and a mixed component. It will be noted that there is in general a first-period decision error (and hence also a first-period loss) even if the specification errors refer to periods after the first. This follows immediately from (2.18), which shows that an error like $\mathbf{ds}$ affects the first-period decision even if its first n components are all zero.

In concluding, we shall consider the *first-period failure* and *success* concepts, which are similar extensions of the static theory. Suppose that the decision maker uses $\mathbf{s}_e$ as a forecast of $\mathbf{s}$, all other determining vectors and matrices being specified without error. The resulting first-period decision error is then

$$
(2.19) \qquad x_1 - x_1^0 = -[(x\cdot)_{11} \ldots (x\cdot)_{1T}](\mathbf{s}_e - \mathbf{s}),
$$

where the equation holds exactly because the optimal reaction functions are linear in **s** as in the static case. On substituting (2.19) into (2.8) we obtain the first-period loss associated with the forecast $\mathbf{s}_e$:

$$-\tfrac{1}{2}(\mathbf{s}_e-\mathbf{s})'\mathbf{F}_1(\mathbf{s}_e-\mathbf{s}), \tag{2.20}$$

where $\mathbf{F}_1$ takes the form

$$\mathbf{F}_1 = \begin{bmatrix} (\cdot x)_{11} \\ \vdots \\ (\cdot x)_{1T} \end{bmatrix} (xx)_{11}^{-1}[(x\cdot)_{11} \dots (x\cdot)_{1T}], \tag{2.21}$$

which is a negative definite or negative semi-definite matrix. Its order is $nT \times nT$, its rank is at most m.

Let us go back to 2.3.3, where the static failure concept was introduced. In the T-period case the additive structure of the constraints depends on events that took place in the past as well as on events that will take place in the future, up till the Tth period. We shall therefore generalize (2.3.9) as follows:

$$\begin{aligned} \mathbf{s} &= \mathbf{f}(q_T, q_{T-1}, \dots, q_1, q_0, q_{-1}, \dots) \\ \mathbf{s}_0 &= \mathbf{f}(q_0, q_0, \quad \dots, q_0, q_0, q_{-1}, \dots), \end{aligned} \tag{2.22}$$

i.e., we define an extrapolated additive structure which is identical with the "true" additive structure except that the future determining factors $(q_1, \dots, q_T)$ are all replaced by the most recent observed values (q_0). For example, in the production-work force example of Section 3.2 we replace all shipments of the additive structure in (3.2.12) by the shipments of last month. The first-period failure of the forecast $\mathbf{s}_e$ is then defined as

$$\text{fail}_1\ \mathbf{s}_e = \frac{(\mathbf{s}_e-\mathbf{s})'\mathbf{F}_1(\mathbf{s}_e-\mathbf{s})}{(\mathbf{s}_0-\mathbf{s})'\mathbf{F}_1(\mathbf{s}_0-\mathbf{s})}, \tag{2.23}$$

i.e., as the ratio of the first-period loss of $\mathbf{s}_e$ to that of the no-change extrapolation. The first-period success of $\mathbf{s}_e$ ($\text{suc}_1\,\mathbf{s}_e$) can then be defined as one minus the first-period failure.

4.2.5. On Infinite and Moving Horizons

The choice of T, the length of the horizon, is in many cases somewhat arbitrary. One might say that the four-year horizon which was introduced in Section 3.1 is a natural choice, since it corresponds to the American Presidential administration period; but one will have to admit that, in the example of Section 3.2, there is no special reason why a six-month horizon is to be preferred to a twelve-month horizon, say. Also, one should take account of the fact that the diminishing horizon has sometimes unrealistic features. For a six-month horizon implies a five-month horizon in the second month, and a four-month horizon in the third, and so on; clearly, such a procedure is justifiable only when the decision maker's interest is completely confined to the six-month period. In fact, however, a factory manager will usually be interested in continuing the operations of his factory during a period of indefinite length.

The objection just raised applies to any finite horizon. Accordingly, it is worthwhile to investigate under what circumstances we can derive a well-defined first-period decision of a maximizing strategy which corresponds with an infinite horizon. This requires that we carry out a limiting process, and the existence of the limit is something that will have to be proved in every particular case. We shall do so here for the factory manager example of Section 2.1, for which the limit can be derived fairly easily. At the same time, the example is convenient for the illustration of the concept of a *moving horizon*. In the infinite-horizon case, all successive decisions are first-period decisions corresponding with an infinite horizon. This requires forecasts for an indefinite future, and it is therefore frequently convenient to "truncate" this horizon to one of finite length, say 12 months. Every decision made is then a first-period decision corresponding with a twelve-month horizon. This is to be interpreted as an approximation to the infinite-horizon case; not as a twelve-month horizon application of the analysis of the preceding pages, since this would imply an eleven-month horizon in the second month, a ten-month horizon in the third, and so on.

We shall apply the infinite-horizon idea to the factory manager example of 2.1.1. For every finite horizon T, the instrument vector $\mathbf{x}$ and the vector of noncontrolled variables $\mathbf{y}$ are then

$$\mathbf{x} = \begin{bmatrix} P_1 \\ \vdots \\ P_T \end{bmatrix}, \qquad \mathbf{y} = \begin{bmatrix} I_1 \\ \vdots \\ I_T \end{bmatrix}, \tag{2.24}$$

respectively, where P_t is production in month t and I_t is the inventory level at the end of that month. The cost function (2.1.3) implies the following coefficient matrices of the dynamic preference function:

$$\mathbf{a} = -\begin{bmatrix} b \\ \vdots \\ b \end{bmatrix}, \quad \mathbf{b} = -\begin{bmatrix} b' \\ \vdots \\ b' \end{bmatrix}, \quad \mathbf{A} = -2c\mathbf{I}, \ \mathbf{B} = -2c'\mathbf{I}, \ \mathbf{C} = \mathbf{0}, \tag{2.25}$$

the first two being $T \times 1$ and the last three $T \times T$. The constraints (2.1.4) are written as

$$\begin{aligned} I_1 &= P_1+(I_0-S_1) \\ I_2 &= P_1+P_2+(I_0-S_1-S_2) \\ &\vdots \end{aligned}$$

so that we have $\mathbf{y} = \mathbf{R}\mathbf{x}+\mathbf{s}$ with

$$\mathbf{R} = \begin{bmatrix} 1 & 0 & \dots & 0 \\ 1 & 1 & \dots & 0 \\ \vdots & \vdots & & \vdots \\ 1 & 1 & \dots & 1 \end{bmatrix} \tag{2.26}$$

and

$$\mathbf{s} = \begin{bmatrix} I_0-S_1 \\ I_0-S_1-S_2 \\ \vdots \\ I_0-\sum_1^T S_t \end{bmatrix} = -\mathbf{R}\begin{bmatrix} S_1-I_0 \\ S_2 \\ \vdots \\ S_T \end{bmatrix}, \tag{2.27}$$

the vectors and matrices of (2.26) and (2.27) being all $T\times 1$ and $T\times T$, respectively.

The optimal decision is $\mathbf{x}^0 = -\mathbf{K}^{-1}\mathbf{k}$, so we need the inverse of

$$\mathbf{K} = \mathbf{A}+\mathbf{R}'\mathbf{B}\mathbf{R} = -2(c\mathbf{I}+c'\mathbf{R}'\mathbf{R}), \tag{2.28}$$

the **C**-matrix being zero. Now $\mathbf{R}^{-1}$ and $\mathbf{R}'^{-1}\mathbf{R}^{-1}$ take particularly simple forms:

$$\mathbf{R}^{-1} = \begin{bmatrix} 1 & 0 & 0 & \dots & 0 & 0 \\ -1 & 1 & 0 & \dots & 0 & 0 \\ 0 & -1 & 1 & \dots & 0 & 0 \\ \vdots & \vdots & \vdots & & \vdots & \vdots \\ 0 & 0 & 0 & \dots & 1 & 0 \\ 0 & 0 & 0 & \dots & -1 & 1 \end{bmatrix},$$

(2.29)

$$\mathbf{R}'^{-1}\mathbf{R}^{-1} = \begin{bmatrix} 2 & -1 & 0 & \dots & 0 & 0 \\ -1 & 2 & -1 & \dots & 0 & 0 \\ 0 & -1 & 2 & \dots & 0 & 0 \\ \vdots & \vdots & \vdots & & \vdots & \vdots \\ 0 & 0 & 0 & \dots & 2 & -1 \\ 0 & 0 & 0 & \dots & -1 & 1 \end{bmatrix},$$

and the computation of $\mathbf{K}^{-1}$ is therefore simplified if we write **K** in the form

$$\mathbf{K} = -2c\mathbf{R}'\left(\mathbf{R}'^{-1}\mathbf{R}^{-1}+\frac{c'}{c}\mathbf{I}\right)\mathbf{R},$$

so that

$$\mathbf{K}^{-1} = \frac{-1}{2c}\mathbf{R}^{-1}\left(\mathbf{R}'^{-1}\mathbf{R}^{-1}+\frac{c'}{c}\mathbf{I}\right)^{-1}\mathbf{R}'^{-1}. \tag{2.30}$$

The first and the last inverse on the right follow immediately from (2.29), and the matrix in the middle is the inverse of

$$\begin{bmatrix} 2+\frac{c'}{c} & -1 & 0 & \cdots & 0 & 0 \\ -1 & 2+\frac{c'}{c} & -1 & \cdots & 0 & 0 \\ 0 & -1 & 2+\frac{c'}{c} & \cdots & 0 & 0 \\ \vdots & \vdots & \vdots & & \vdots & \vdots \\ 0 & 0 & 0 & \cdots & 2+\frac{c'}{c} & -1 \\ 0 & 0 & 0 & \cdots & -1 & 1+\frac{c'}{c} \end{bmatrix}, \tag{2.31}$$

i.e., it is the inverse of a matrix whose diagonal elements are all $2+c'/c$ and whose elements immediately above and below the diagonal are all -1, all other elements being zero. There is a terminal effect implying that the last diagonal element is $1+c'/c$ rather than $2+c'/c$, but this is immaterial when we take the limit for $T \to \infty$. Now we need only the first row of $\mathbf{K}^{-1}$ and hence the first row of $\mathbf{R}^{-1}$ [see (2.30)] for the first-period decision; and since the first row of $\mathbf{R}^{-1}$ is of the form $[1\ 0 \ldots 0]$ we need only the first row of the inverse of (2.31). On taking the limit for $T \to \infty$ we find for this row:

$$\mathbf{g}_1 = [\gamma\ \gamma^2\ \gamma^3\ \ldots], \tag{2.32}$$

where

$$\gamma = 1 - \frac{1}{2c}\{-c'+\sqrt{4cc'+c'^2}\}, \tag{2.33}$$

which satisfies

$$0 < \gamma < 1 \text{ if } c,\ c' > 0. \tag{2.34}$$

That $\mathbf{g}_1$ is indeed the first row of

$$\left(\mathbf{R}'^{-1}\mathbf{R}^{-1}+\frac{c'}{c}\mathbf{I}\right)^{-1} \quad \text{and} \quad \mathbf{R}^{-1}\left(\mathbf{R}'^{-1}\mathbf{R}^{-1}+\frac{c'}{c}\mathbf{I}\right)^{-1}$$

is easily verified by computing

$$[\gamma \quad \gamma^2 \quad \gamma^3 \quad \ldots]\left(\mathbf{R}'^{-1}\mathbf{R}^{-1}+\frac{c'}{c}\mathbf{I}\right),$$

γ being specified as in (2.33). The result is [1 0 0 . . .], which is as it should be. Further, by postmultiplying $\mathbf{g}_1$ by $-(1/2c)\mathbf{R}'^{-1}$ we obtain

$$\text{(2.35)} \qquad \mathbf{g}_2 = \frac{-1}{2c}[\gamma \quad -\gamma(1-\gamma) \quad -\gamma^2(1-\gamma) \quad -\gamma^3(1-\gamma) \quad \ldots],$$

which is the first row of $\mathbf{K}^{-1}$ in the infinite-horizon case.

To find the optimal first-period decision we should postmultiply $\mathbf{g}_2$ by

$$\text{(2.36)} \quad \mathbf{k} = \mathbf{a}+\mathbf{R}'\mathbf{b}+\mathbf{R}'\mathbf{B}\mathbf{s} = -\begin{bmatrix} b \\ b \\ \vdots \end{bmatrix} - \mathbf{R}'\begin{bmatrix} b' \\ b' \\ \vdots \end{bmatrix} + 2c'\mathbf{R}'\mathbf{R}\begin{bmatrix} S_1 - I_0 \\ S_2 \\ \vdots \end{bmatrix},$$

which shows that $\mathbf{g}_2$ is to be postmultiplied by a column of identical elements, by $\mathbf{R}'$, and by $\mathbf{R}'\mathbf{R}$, all of which contain an infinite number of elements. Now we have

$$\mathbf{g}_2\begin{bmatrix} b \\ b \\ \vdots \end{bmatrix} = \frac{-b}{2c}\{\gamma-\gamma(1-\gamma)-\gamma^2(1-\gamma)- \ldots\} = 0;$$

$$\mathbf{g}_2\mathbf{R}' = \frac{-1}{2c}[\gamma \quad \gamma^2 \quad \gamma^3 \quad \ldots];$$

$$\mathbf{g}_2\mathbf{R}'\mathbf{R} = \frac{-1}{2c(1-\gamma)}[\gamma \quad \gamma^2 \quad \gamma^3 \quad \ldots].$$

Then, by using the relation $\gamma c'/c = (1-\gamma)^2$, we obtain the optimal first-period production decision:

$$\text{(2.37)} \qquad P_1^0 = -\mathbf{g}_2\mathbf{k} = (1-\gamma)\sum_{t=1}^{\infty}\gamma^{t-1}S_t+(1-\gamma)(I^*-I_0),$$

where

$$\text{(2.38)} \qquad I^* = -\frac{b'}{2c'}.$$

The first-period decision of the maximizing strategy is identical with (2.37) except that future sales are replaced by their conditional expectations, given the available information.

The result (2.37) shows clearly that there is production for sales and production for stocks. Regarding the latter part, we recall that the inventory cost function for each month is of the type $a'+b'I_t+c'I_t^2$, so that the minimum-cost inventory level is $I^* = -b'/2c'$ (assuming $b' \leqq 0$, $c' > 0$). Then (2.37) specifies that in each month there should be a certain volume of production for stocks, and that this volume should be a constant fraction $(1-\gamma)$ of the excess of the minimum-cost inventory level over the actual initial inventory level. [Note that this excess may be negative, so that the corresponding production volume should then be subtracted from production for sales.] To obtain the optimal end-of-period inventory level, I_1^0, we apply

$$I_1^0 - I_0 = P_1^0 - S_1,$$

which gives:

$$I_1^0 = (1-\gamma)\sum_{t=2}^{\infty}\gamma^{t-1}S_t + \{\gamma(I_0-S_1)+(1-\gamma)I^*\}. \tag{2.39}$$

This shows that I_1^0 consists of two components, just like P_1^0. One is that part of the optimal production decision that refers to sales in periods later than the first; the other is a weighted average of the minimum-cost inventory level (I^*) and the excess of the initial stocks over the first period's sales (I_0-S_1).

Regarding production for sales, we see from (2.37) that the effect of the successive S's on P_1^0 is of the decreasing exponential type and such that the weights add up to 1:

$$(1-\gamma)(1+\gamma+\gamma^2+\ldots) = 1.$$

This reflects the fact that an additional unit sold at some point of time must be produced at some moment. Further, if sales increase exponentially, i.e., if $S_t = S_0(1+r)^t$ with $r > 0$, then the sales term of (2.37) is simplified to

$$\frac{(1-\gamma)(1+r)S_0}{1-\gamma(1+r)},$$

provided that $\gamma(1+r) < 1$. If sales increase so fast that $\gamma(1+r) \geqq 1$, we are faced with the problem of divergence so that there is then no maximizing strategy with a unique first-period decision in the infinite-horizon case.

The dependence of the optimal first-period decision on future sales is completely determined by γ; and γ, in turn, is completely determined by the ratio of c' to c, see (2.33). Consider then $c'/(c+c')$, which can be regarded as the share of inventory costs in the "total curvilinearity" of the cost function. This ratio is also the coefficient of S_1 in the optimal production decision in the case of a one-period horizon, see (2.1.20). It is evidently interesting to compare this coefficient with $1-\gamma$, which is the S_1-coefficient in the infinite-horizon case. This comparison is made in Table 4.2, which shows that the first-period sales have a larger influence on the first-period production decision in the case of an infinite horizon, for whatever (positive) values of c and c'.

TABLE 4.2

COEFFICIENTS OF THE FIRST-PERIOD SALES IN THE OPTIMAL PRODUCTION DECISION: THE ONE-PERIOD HORIZON VERSUS THE INFINITE HORIZON

$\frac{c'}{c+c'}$ (for $T=1$)	$1-\gamma$ (for $T=\infty$)
0.01	0.096
0.05	0.205
0.1	0.282
0.2	0.390
0.3	0.475
0.4	0.549
0.5	0.618
0.6	0.686
0.7	0.755
0.8	0.828
0.9	0.908
0.95	0.952
0.99	0.990

The leading element of $(\mathbf{xx}) = \mathbf{K}^{-1}$ is the first element of $\mathbf{g}_2$ and therefore equal to $-\gamma/2c$, see (2.35). Hence the first-period loss associated with a first-period decision error $P_1-P_1^0$ is $(c/\gamma)(P_1-P_1^0)^2$. The other elements of $\mathbf{g}_2$ are the substitution terms connecting first-period and later-period decisions. They are of the form $\gamma^{t-1}(1-\gamma)/2c$, so that the matrix product $(xx)_{t1}(xx)_{11}^{-1}$ is a scalar and equal to $-\gamma^{t-2}(1-\gamma)$. On comparing this with (2.9) we conclude that a unit first-period decision error implies an optimal decision revision in the tth period of opposite sign, completely determined by γ, and decreasing geometrically: $-(1-\gamma)$ in the next period, $-\gamma(1-\gamma)$ in the third, and so on. It follows from Table 4.2 that if the inventory share in the total curvilinearity of the cost function is small (large), the optimal revision in the second period is also small (large) and that the successive reductions of these revisions are small (large) too. The sum of all these revisions is -1, which means that the initial decision error is compensated exactly in the course of time.

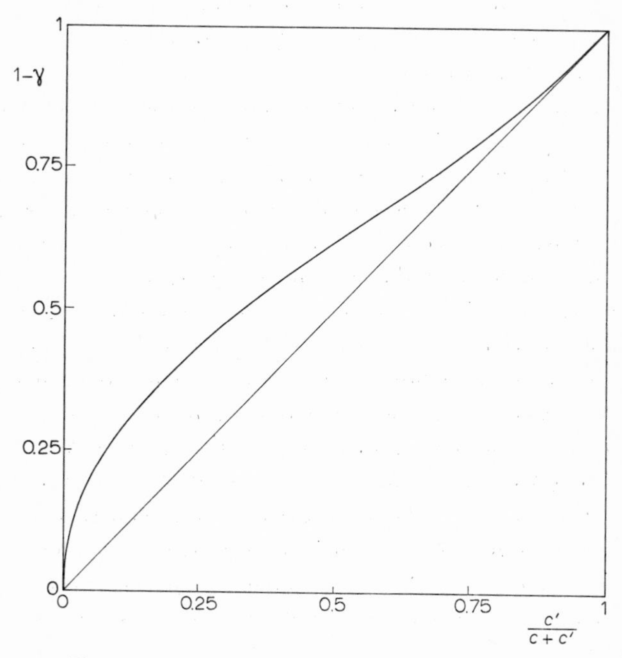

Figure 4.3. The relation between $1-\gamma$ and $c'/(c+c')$

4.2.6. *Summary*

(1) When there is no uncertainty, the equilibrium conditions and the comparative statics of the one-period theory can be carried over completely to the T-period case. This applies to the optimal reaction functions, to substitution and complementarity relationships, and to the Tinbergen surfaces.

(2) A similar straightforward extension can be made for the loss associated with a decision which is specified for all T periods. A new extension is the first-period loss associated with any given first-period decision, which is defined as the reduction in the attainable preference level due to the first-period error. This is a positive definite quadratic form in this error, the matrix being $-\frac{1}{2}$ times the inverse of the substitution matrix of the first-period instruments. Another extension is that of the optimal

decision revisions for later periods, given a first-period decision error made, and these appear to be equal to a homogeneous linear combination of the first-period decision error components. The matrix of this combination is determined by substitution terms of the instruments of the various periods, and the optimal revision for any period t is zero only if the instruments of that period are neither substitutes of nor complementary with the first-period instruments.

(3) The successive decisions of the maximizing strategy can be expressed in terms of the discrepancies between the previous decisions of that strategy and the conditional expectations of the corresponding optimal decisions, given the information available at the moment when the decision has to be made. The same applies to the successive forecast revisions of the future decisions of the maximizing strategy.

(4) The extension of the loss and the first-period loss associated with specification errors in the coefficient matrices of constraints and preference function is also straightforward. The same applies to the first-period failure, which measures the first-period loss due to an error in the additive structure of the constraints relative to that of no-change extrapolation.

(5) The analysis can be extended to include the case of an infinite horizon. The first-period decision of the maximizing strategy is then found by applying a limiting process, which is illustrated for a simple case of production programming. We speak about moving horizons when the infinite horizon is "truncated" to one of finite but constant length in all successive periods.

CHAPTER 5

Dynamics of Production and Employment Scheduling [1]

5.1. DECISION RULES AND LOSSES FOR A GIVEN COST FUNCTION

5.1.1. Statement of the Dynamic Problem; The First-Period Decision of the Maximizing Strategy

We return to the paint factory of Section 3.2, particularly to 3.2.2 where the problem in static form was formulated algebraically. It will be clear that little has to be changed to put the problem in dynamic form. If we assume that there is no uncertainty, the analysis of 3.3.2 is completely applicable and Table 3.7 specifies the optimal decisions in terms of the shipments of the various months, given (i) the cost function to be minimized, (ii) the (very simple) multiplicative structure of the constraints, and (iii) the choice of a six-month horizon. But if we make the realistic assumption that future shipments are not known with certainty, then, given the dynamic character of the problem, a maximizing strategy is needed. The analysis of this strategy, in particular its first-period decision, is the objective of the present discussion.

The vectors of instruments and noncontrolled variables are given in (3.2.8). In the present dynamic context we should write them in bold-face roman type rather than the sanserif type; but in addition to this, there is the problem that the instruments are not partitioned by periods (which is the procedure of Chapter 4) but by variables. We could of course partition by periods, which implies that the complete T-period instrument vector (dealing with production, p, and work force, q) is written

$$\mathbf{x} = \{p_1 \quad q_1 \quad p_2 \quad q_2 \quad \dots \quad p_T \quad q_T\} \tag{1.1}$$

---

[1] It is advised to re-read Section 3.2 before reading this chapter. See also the references quoted at the beginning of that section, particularly the articles by C. VAN DE PANNE.

instead of

$$\mathbf{x}^* = \{p_1 \quad p_2 \quad \ldots \quad p_T \quad q_1 \quad q_2 \quad \ldots \quad q_T\}. \tag{1.2}$$

However, this has the disadvantage that the matrix of the quadratic part of the cost function becomes rather complicated notationally. We shall therefore continue to use (1.2); and to distinguish it from the decision vector of Chapter 4 we shall write it as $\mathbf{x}^*$, and reserve $\mathbf{x}$ for (1.1). It is easily seen that $\mathbf{x}$ and $\mathbf{x}^*$ are connected by

$$\mathbf{x}^* = \mathbf{\Pi x}, \quad \mathbf{x} = \mathbf{\Pi}'\mathbf{x}^*, \tag{1.3}$$

where the orthogonal matrix $\mathbf{\Pi}$ is a $2T \times 2T$ permutation matrix of the form:[1]

$$\mathbf{\Pi} = \begin{bmatrix} 1 & 0 & 0 & 0 & 0 & 0 & \ldots & 0 & 0 \\ 0 & 0 & 1 & 0 & 0 & 0 & \ldots & 0 & 0 \\ 0 & 0 & 0 & 0 & 1 & 0 & \ldots & 0 & 0 \\ 0 & 0 & 0 & 0 & 0 & 0 & \ldots & 0 & 0 \\ \vdots & \vdots & \vdots & \vdots & \vdots & \vdots & & \vdots & \vdots \\ 0 & 0 & 0 & 0 & 0 & 0 & \ldots & 1 & 0 \\ \hdashline 0 & 1 & 0 & 0 & 0 & 0 & \ldots & 0 & 0 \\ 0 & 0 & 0 & 1 & 0 & 0 & \ldots & 0 & 0 \\ 0 & 0 & 0 & 0 & 0 & 1 & \ldots & 0 & 0 \\ 0 & 0 & 0 & 0 & 0 & 0 & \ldots & 0 & 0 \\ \vdots & \vdots & \vdots & \vdots & \vdots & \vdots & & \vdots & \vdots \\ 0 & 0 & 0 & 0 & 0 & 0 & \ldots & 0 & 1 \end{bmatrix}, \tag{1.4}$$

that is, there is a unit element on the $(2t-1)^{st}$ place of the tth row of $\mathbf{\Pi}$ if $t \leqq T$, and in the last T rows there is a unit element on the $2t'^{\text{th}}$ place, the latter rows being numbered $T+t'$ where $t' = 1, \ldots, T$. There is no similar partitioning problem with respect to noncontrolled variables (inventories) because there is only one such variable in every period. Hence the preference function to be maximized (i.e., minus the cost function to be minimized) takes now the form:

$$w(\mathbf{x}^*, \mathbf{y}) = \mathbf{a}^{*\prime}\mathbf{x}^* + \mathbf{b}'\mathbf{y} + \tfrac{1}{2}(\mathbf{x}^{*\prime}\mathbf{A}^*\mathbf{x}^* + \mathbf{y}'\mathbf{B}\mathbf{y}), \tag{1.5}$$

[1] A square matrix $\mathbf{A}$ is said to be orthogonal if $\mathbf{A}'\mathbf{A} = \mathbf{A}\mathbf{A}' = \mathbf{I}$, i.e., if it is nonsingular and if the inverse is equal to the transpose. A permutation matrix is square and contains exactly one unit element in each row and each column, all other elements being zero; it is always orthogonal.

where use is made of the fact that there are no bilinear terms in instruments and noncontrolled variables so that $\mathbf{C} = \mathbf{0}$. The starred coefficient matrices of (1.5) are

$$\text{(1.6)} \qquad \mathbf{a}^* = \mathbf{\Pi a} = \begin{bmatrix} \mathbf{a}_p \\ \mathbf{a}_q \end{bmatrix}, \qquad \mathbf{A}^* = \mathbf{\Pi A \Pi}' = \begin{bmatrix} \mathbf{A}_{pp} & \mathbf{A}_{pq} \\ \mathbf{A}_{qp} & \mathbf{A}_{qq} \end{bmatrix},$$

where $\mathbf{a}_p$, $\mathbf{a}_q$, $\mathbf{A}_{pp}$, $\mathbf{A}_{pq}$, $\mathbf{A}_{qq}$ as well as the other coefficient matrices occurring in (1.5), $\mathbf{b}$ and $\mathbf{B}$, are given in (3.2.9)-(3.2.11) and expressed there in terms of the cost function coefficients, the c's. In this section we will specify the c's according to (3.2.6) insofar as we shall proceed numerically rather than algebraically; an analysis of the consequences of erroneous specifications of the c's will be carried out in Section 5.2. No stars have been added to the submatrices of (1.6), because it is sufficiently clear that they are obtained by partitioning by variables.

Essentially, the development of the preceding paragraph amounts to typographical changes compared with Section 3.2, implying the use of the bold-face type and the addition of stars as superscripts so as to bring the notation in line with that of Chapter 4. The same procedure applied to the constraints (according to which the change in inventories is equal to the excess of production over shipments) leads to

$$\text{(1.7)} \qquad \mathbf{y} = \mathbf{R}^*\mathbf{x}^* + \mathbf{s},$$

where

$$\text{(1.8)} \qquad \mathbf{R}^* = \mathbf{R\Pi}' = [\mathbf{R}_p \quad \mathbf{0}],$$

the zero submatrix being of order $T \times T$. The triangular matrix $\mathbf{R}_p$ and the cumulated-sales vector $\mathbf{s}$ have been specified in (3.2.12); they are similar in structure to the corresponding coefficient matrices (4.2.26)-(4.2.27) of 4.2.5.

The expectation of the maximizing strategy can then either be written in the form $\mathscr{E}\tilde{\mathbf{x}} = -\mathbf{K}^{-1}\mathscr{E}\mathbf{k}$ [see (4.1.18)] or in the form $\mathscr{E}\tilde{\mathbf{x}}^* = -\mathbf{K}^{*-1}\mathscr{E}\mathbf{k}^*$, depending on the type of partitioning. Given that the first-period decision of this strategy is nonstochastic, it is obtained from $\mathscr{E}\tilde{\mathbf{x}}$ or $\mathscr{E}\tilde{\mathbf{x}}^*$ as follows:

$$\text{(1.9)} \qquad \begin{bmatrix} \tilde{p}_1 \\ \tilde{q}_1 \end{bmatrix} = [\mathbf{I} \quad \mathbf{0}]\mathscr{E}\tilde{\mathbf{x}} = \begin{bmatrix} \mathbf{e}_1' & \mathbf{0} \\ \mathbf{0} & \mathbf{e}_1' \end{bmatrix} \mathscr{E}\tilde{\mathbf{x}}^*,$$

where $\mathbf{I}$ and $\mathbf{0}$ in $[\mathbf{I}\ \mathbf{0}]$ are the 2×2 unit matrix and the $2 \times (2T-2)$ zero matrix, respectively; $\mathbf{e}_1$ is the first column of the $T \times T$ unit matrix (hence $\mathbf{e}_1'$ its first row) and the zeros behind the last equation sign are rows of T zero elements. Obviously, $\tilde{p}_1$ and $\tilde{q}_1$ are precisely the same first-period decisions as those of the optimal vector $\mathbf{x}^0$ except that future shipments are to be replaced by their expectations. But the latter vector has already been given in Table 3.7 for a six-month horizon and for the numerical cost coefficient specification (3.2.6). Hence the first-period decision of the maximizing strategy in that case is

$$\begin{aligned} \tilde{p}_1 &= 152.8+0.902q_0+0.460(\mathscr{E}v_1-y_0)+0.231\mathscr{E}v_2 \\ &\quad + 0.106\mathscr{E}v_3+0.040\mathscr{E}v_4+0.008\mathscr{E}v_5-0.004\mathscr{E}v_6; \\ \tilde{q}_1 &= 1.18+0.760q_0+0.0106(\mathscr{E}v_1-y_0)+0.0094\mathscr{E}v_2 \\ &\quad + 0.0080\mathscr{E}v_3+0.0065\mathscr{E}v_4+0.0049\mathscr{E}v_5+0.0030\mathscr{E}v_6, \end{aligned} \tag{1.10}$$

compare (3.2.22).

In concluding we note that the assumptions underlying this result imply that in each future period t, the distribution of the shipments v_t cannot be affected by production and work force decisions for that period and earlier, and that the variances of the v's are finite. It is not necessary to assume that these variances are constant over time. Clearly, these assumptions are not very restrictive.

5.1.2. Alternative Horizons and Their Implications for the First-Period Decision

It was observed in 4.2.5 that the choice of a six-month horizon is somewhat arbitrary. We shall consider this here in more detail by analyzing the impact of alternative horizons on the first-period decision of the maximizing strategy corresponding with any given horizon. Whenever such a horizon consists of a finite number of months, the computations are straightforward. For example, the coefficient vector and matrix of the noncontrolled variables (inventories) in the case $T = 2$ take the form

$$\mathbf{b} = 2c_7c_8\begin{bmatrix}1\\1\end{bmatrix}, \qquad \mathbf{B} = -2c_7\begin{bmatrix}1 & 0\\0 & 1\end{bmatrix}, \tag{1.11}$$

as is easily verified from (3.2.9), whilce $\mathbf{C}$ is now the 4×2 zero matrix. Similarly, we then have

$$\mathbf{a}^* = -\begin{bmatrix} c_5 \\ c_5 \\ c_1-c_6-2c_2q_0 \\ c_1-c_6 \end{bmatrix} \begin{matrix} (p_1) \\ (p_2) \\ (q_1) \\ (q_2) \end{matrix} \tag{1.12}$$

for the coefficient vector of the instruments in the linear part of the preference function. And for the matrix of the quadratic part:

$$\text{(1.13)}\quad \mathbf{A}^* = -2\begin{bmatrix} c_3 & 0 & -c_3c_4 & 0 \\ 0 & c_3 & 0 & -c_3c_4 \\ -c_3c_4 & 0 & 2c_2+c_3c_4^2 & -c_2 \\ 0 & -c_3c_4 & -c_2 & c_2+c_3c_4^2 \end{bmatrix} \begin{matrix} (p_1) \\ (p_2) \\ (q_1) \\ (q_2) \end{matrix}$$

(columns: (p_1), (p_2), (q_1), (q_2))

In precisely the same way, the coefficient matrices of the constraints are now

$$\text{(1.14)}\qquad \mathbf{R}^* = \begin{bmatrix} 1 & 0 & 0 & 0 \\ 1 & 1 & 0 & 0 \end{bmatrix}, \qquad \mathbf{s} = -\begin{bmatrix} v_1 - y_0 \\ v_1 + v_2 - y_0 \end{bmatrix}.$$

Evidently, the shipments of the next two months only enter into the picture, which means that the first-period decision of the maximizing strategy, given the horizon $T = 2$, will depend only on $\mathscr{E}v_1$ and $\mathscr{E}v_2$. Also, there is a difference in the way in which the various cost components are weighted. The latter feature will be illustrated below.

Table 5.1 contains a survey of first-period decisions of the maximizing strategies for alternative horizons. The following have been chosen (all in months):

$$T = 1,\ 2,\ 3,\ 4,\ 6,\ 8,\ 10,\ 12,\ \infty,$$

where the case $T = 1$ corresponds, of course, to the static approach. It turns out that the first-period decisions converge rather rapidly, which suggests that in this case at least the use of a six-month horizon is an adequate approximation to that of an infinite horizon. (The mathematical derivations for $T = \infty$ will be considered below in 5.1.3.) If the horizon is very short, say 1 or 2 months, the differences are of course more substantial. The "weight" of the initial employment level (the coefficient of q_0 in the first-period decision) is then larger than in the case of a longer horizon, whereas the converse is true for the weight of future sales. This implies a tendency to keep employment and the production rate more stable, which is intuitively understandable. The analytic approach is as follows. For the two-month horizon we have, from (1.11)–(1.14),

$$\text{(1.15)}\quad \mathbf{K}^* = -2\begin{bmatrix} c_3+2c_7 & c_7 & -c_3c_4 & 0 \\ c_7 & c_3+c_7 & 0 & -c_3c_4 \\ -c_3c_4 & 0 & 2c_2+c_3c_4^2 & -c_2 \\ 0 & -c_3c_4 & -c_2 & c_2+c_3c_4^2 \end{bmatrix};$$

TABLE 5.1

FIRST-PERIOD PRODUCTION AND WORK FORCE DECISIONS OF THE MAXIMIZING STRATEGY UNDER ALTERNATIVE CHOICES OF THE HORIZON

	Horizon								
	1 month	2 months	3 months	4 months	6 months	8 months	10 months	12 months	∞
					Production $(\tilde{p}_1)$				
Constant term	1.2	80.2	118.8	137.8	152.8	155.9	155.5	154.7	153.1
q_0	3.900	2.180	1.274	0.946	0.902	0.966	0.995	1.003	1.007
$\mathscr{E}v_1 - y_0$	0.312	0.433	0.459	0.460	0.460	0.462	0.463	0.464	0.464
$\mathscr{E}v_2$		0.183	0.226	0.231	0.231	0.233	0.235	0.235	0.236
$\mathscr{E}v_3$			0.091	0.105	0.106	0.109	0.111	0.112	0.112
$\mathscr{E}v_4$				0.037	0.040	0.043	0.046	0.047	0.047
$\mathscr{E}v_5$					0.008	0.009	0.012	0.014	0.014
$\mathscr{E}v_6$					−0.004	−0.006	−0.003	−0.002	−0.001
$\mathscr{E}v_7$						−0.011	−0.010	−0.008	−0.007
$\mathscr{E}v_8$						−0.010	−0.012	−0.010	−0.008
$\mathscr{E}v_9$							−0.011	−0.010	−0.008
$\mathscr{E}v_{10}$							−0.007	−0.009	−0.007
$\mathscr{E}v_{11}$								−0.007	−0.005
$\mathscr{E}v_{12}$								−0.004	−0.004
					Work force $(\tilde{q}_1)$				
Constant term	−0.40	0.14	0.57	0.81	1.18	1.51	1.74	1.87	2.00
q_0	0.972	0.911	0.850	0.805	0.760	0.747	0.743	0.742	0.742
$\mathscr{E}v_1 - y_0$	0.0050	0.0093	0.0110	0.0113	0.0106	0.0102	0.0100	0.0100	0.0100
$\mathscr{E}v_2$		0.0065	0.0094	0.0100	0.0094	0.0089	0.0087	0.0087	0.0087
$\mathscr{E}v_3$			0.0061	0.0081	0.0080	0.0074	0.0071	0.0070	0.0070
$\mathscr{E}v_4$				0.0051	0.0065	0.0059	0.0056	0.0055	0.0054
$\mathscr{E}v_5$					0.0049	0.0046	0.0043	0.0041	0.0041
$\mathscr{E}v_6$					0.0030	0.0036	0.0032	0.0031	0.0030
$\mathscr{E}v_7$						0.0026	0.0024	0.0023	0.0022
$\mathscr{E}v_8$						0.0016	0.0018	0.0017	0.0016
$\mathscr{E}v_9$							0.0013	0.0012	0.0011
$\mathscr{E}v_{10}$							0.0008	0.0009	0.0008

$$\mathbf{k}^* = \begin{bmatrix} -c_5+4c_7c_8 \\ -c_5+2c_7c_8 \\ -c_1+c_6+2c_2q_0 \\ -c_1+c_6 \end{bmatrix} + 2c_7 \begin{bmatrix} 2v_1+v_2-2y_0 \\ v_1+v_2-y_0 \\ 0 \\ 0 \end{bmatrix}. \tag{1.16}$$

Since the optimal decision is $-\mathbf{K}^{*-1}\mathbf{k}^*$, we can conclude that the coefficient which measures the influence of q_0 on the first-period production

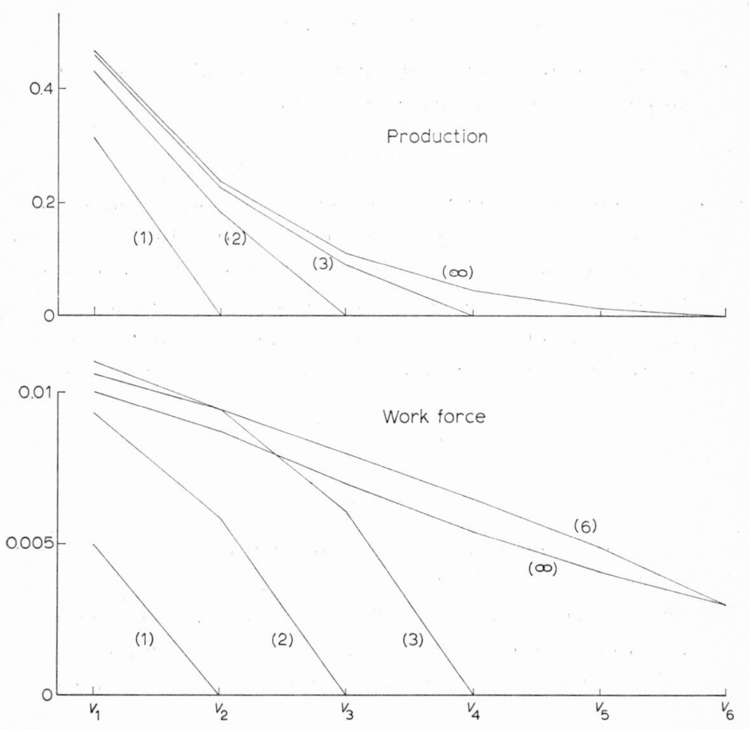

Figure 5.1. The coefficients describing the influence of the expectations of successive sales ($v_1, v_2, \ldots$) on the first-period decision of the maximizing strategy for alternative horizons. The length of the horizon (in months) is indicated in parentheses.

decision is $2c_2$ times the $(1, 3)^{\text{rd}}$ element of $\mathbf{K}^{*-1}$, and that the coefficient measuring the influence of q_0 on the first-period work force decision is $2c_2$ times the $(3, 3)^{\text{rd}}$ element of $\mathbf{K}^{*-1}$. For a one-month horizon we have

$$\begin{aligned} K^* &= -2\begin{bmatrix} c_3+c_7 & -c_3c_4 \\ -c_3c_4 & c_2+c_3c_4^2 \end{bmatrix}, \\ k^* &= \begin{bmatrix} -c_5+2c_7c_8 \\ -c_1+c_6+2c_2q_0 \end{bmatrix} + 2c_7\begin{bmatrix} v_1-y_0 \\ 0 \end{bmatrix}, \end{aligned} \tag{1.17}$$

in which case the influence of q_0 is (apart from the factor $2c_2$) the $(1, 2)^{\text{nd}}$ and the $(2, 2)^{\text{nd}}$ element of K^{*-1} for production and work force respectively. Consider production first, in particular the ratio of its q_0-coefficient in the two-month horizon case to that in the one-month horizon case. After some algebraic rearrangements it is found that this ratio is

$$\frac{D_1(D_1 - c_2 c_7)}{D_1^2 + c_2 c_3 c_7 (c_2 + 4c_3 c_4^2 + c_4^2 c_7)}, \tag{1.18}$$

where D_1 is the determinant of K^* in the case of a one-month horizon (disregarding the multiplicative factor -2):

$$D_1 = c_2 c_3 + c_2 c_7 + c_3 c_4^2 c_7. \tag{1.19}$$

Now all c's entering into (1.18)–(1.19) are positive according to (3.2.6), hence $0 < D_1 - c_2 c_7 < D_1$. The ratio (1.18) is therefore positive, and it is smaller than 1 since the numerator is smaller than the denominator. Therefore, the q_0-coefficient for first-period production is smaller in the case of a two-month horizon than in that of a one-month horizon. As to the first-period work force decision, the ratio corresponding to (1.18) is

$$\frac{D_1\left(D_1 + \dfrac{c_2 c_3 c_7}{c_3 + c_7}\right)}{D_1^2 + c_2 c_3 c_7 (c_2 + 4c_3 c_4^2 + c_4^2 c_7)}. \tag{1.20}$$

Its denominator is identical with that of (1.18), but its numerator is now larger than D_1^2. This means that (1.20) exceeds (1.18), which implies in turn that the relative difference of the q_0-coefficients for work force is not so large as that of the q_0-coefficients for production. But the numerator of (1.20) is still smaller than its denominator; this follows from

$$\frac{D_1}{c_3 + c_7} < c_2 + 4c_3 c_4^2 + c_4^2 c_7$$

as is easily verified.

The analysis of the v_1-coefficients is entirely similar. For example, the coefficient which measures the effect of the first-month shipments on the optimal first-month production in the two-month horizon case is $4c_7$ times the $(1, 1)^{\text{st}}$ element of $\mathbf{K}^{*-1}$ plus $2c_7$ times the $(1, 2)^{\text{nd}}$ element of $\mathbf{K}^{*-1}$, where $\mathbf{K}^*$ is as specified in (1.15). After applying some elementary algebra one finds that the v_1-coefficients of the two-month horizon are not larger than the corresponding one-month coefficients for all positive values of the c's, but this holds if and only if $c_2 > c_4^2 c_7$. This inequality is amply satisfied by the numerical specification (3.2.6), the left-hand side being more than 20 times larger than the right-hand side. Given c_4 (which measures the maximum output of one man), the inequality is violated only if the curvilinearity of the hiring and layoff cost function (measured by c_2) is insufficient compared with the curvilinearity of the inventory cost function (which is measured by c_7).

5.1.3. *Derivations for the Infinite-Horizon Case*

To handle the case of $T \to \infty$ we shall start by considering $\mathbf{W}^*$, which is the matrix of second-order derivatives of the preference function bordered by the multiplicative structure of the constraints. The asterisk indicates that partitioning is by variables, and accordingly $\mathbf{W}^*$ takes the following form:

$$\mathbf{W}^* = \begin{bmatrix} \mathbf{A}_{pp} & \mathbf{A}_{pq} & \mathbf{0} & \mathbf{R}_p' \\ \mathbf{A}_{qp} & \mathbf{A}_{qq} & \mathbf{0} & \mathbf{0} \\ \mathbf{0} & \mathbf{0} & \mathbf{B} & -\mathbf{I} \\ \mathbf{R}_p & \mathbf{0} & -\mathbf{I} & \mathbf{0} \end{bmatrix}, \tag{1.21}$$

where all submatrices are of order $T \times T$. These submatrices have been specified above; see, e.g., (1.11)–(1.14) for $T = 2$. The inverse can be written in the form

$$\mathbf{W}^{*-1} = \begin{bmatrix} (\mathbf{xx})_{pp} & (\mathbf{xx})_{pq} & (\mathbf{xy})_p & (\mathbf{x}\cdot)_p \\ (\mathbf{xx})_{qp} & (\mathbf{xx})_{qq} & (\mathbf{xy})_q & (\mathbf{x}\cdot)_q \\ (\mathbf{yx})_p & (\mathbf{yx})_q & (\mathbf{yy}) & (\mathbf{y}\cdot) \\ (\cdot\mathbf{x})_p & (\cdot\mathbf{x})_q & (\cdot\mathbf{y}) & (\cdot\,\cdot) \end{bmatrix}, \tag{1.22}$$

where $(\mathbf{xx})_{pp}$ is the substitution matrix dealing with production decisions only, $(\mathbf{xy})_q$ the mixed substitution matrix involving work force decisions on the one hand and inventory levels on the other hand, and so on.

We shall be concerned in particular with the first two rows of submatrices of $\mathbf{W}^{*-1}$ (or, what amounts to the same thing, the first two columns), which contain all relevant information on the instrument variables. Let us then postmultiply the second set of rows of $\mathbf{W}^{*-1}$ by the successive columns of $\mathbf{W}^*$:

$$(\mathbf{xx})_{qp}\mathbf{A}_{pp} + (\mathbf{xx})_{qq}\mathbf{A}_{qp} + (\mathbf{x}\cdot)_q\mathbf{R}_p = \mathbf{0} \tag{1.23}$$

$$(\mathbf{xx})_{qp}\mathbf{A}_{pq} + (\mathbf{xx})_{qq}\mathbf{A}_{qq} = \mathbf{I} \tag{1.24}$$

$$(\mathbf{xy})_q\mathbf{B} - (\mathbf{x}\cdot)_q = \mathbf{0} \tag{1.25}$$

$$(\mathbf{xx})_{qp}\mathbf{R}_p' - (\mathbf{xy})_q = \mathbf{0}. \tag{1.26}$$

From (1.25) and (1.26) we have

$$(1.27) \qquad (\mathbf{xy})_q = (\mathbf{xx})_{qp}\mathbf{R}'_p, \qquad (\mathbf{x}\cdot)_q = (\mathbf{xx})_{qp}\mathbf{R}'_p\mathbf{B},$$

which, when combined with (1.23), gives

$$(1.28) \qquad (\mathbf{xx})_{qq} = -(\mathbf{xx})_{qp}(\mathbf{A}_{pp}+\mathbf{R}'_p\mathbf{BR}_p)\mathbf{A}_{qp}^{-1}.$$

On combining this result with (1.24) we obtain

$$\begin{aligned}(1.29) \quad (\mathbf{xx})_{qp} &= [\mathbf{A}_{pq}-(\mathbf{A}_{pp}+\mathbf{R}'_p\mathbf{BR}_p)\mathbf{A}_{qp}^{-1}\mathbf{A}_{qq}]^{-1} \\ &= [\mathbf{R}'_p\mathbf{BR}_p\{\mathbf{R}_p^{-1}\mathbf{B}^{-1}\mathbf{R}_p'^{-1}(\mathbf{A}_{pq}-\mathbf{A}_{pp}\mathbf{A}_{qp}^{-1}\mathbf{A}_{qq})-\mathbf{A}_{qp}^{-1}\mathbf{A}_{qq}\}]^{-1} \\ &= \mathbf{Q}^{-1}\mathbf{R}_p^{-1}\mathbf{B}^{-1}\mathbf{R}_p'^{-1},\end{aligned}$$

where

$$(1.30) \qquad \mathbf{Q} = \mathbf{R}_p^{-1}\mathbf{B}^{-1}\mathbf{R}_p'^{-1}(\mathbf{A}_{pq}-\mathbf{A}_{pp}\mathbf{A}_{qp}^{-1}\mathbf{A}_{qq})-\mathbf{A}_{qp}^{-1}\mathbf{A}_{qq}.$$

Similar expressions for $(\mathbf{xy})_q$ and $(\mathbf{x}\cdot)_q$ are then obtained by applying (1.27):

$$(1.31) \qquad (\mathbf{xy})_q = \mathbf{Q}^{-1}\mathbf{R}_p^{-1}\mathbf{B}^{-1}; \qquad (\mathbf{x}\cdot)_q = \mathbf{Q}^{-1}\mathbf{R}_p^{-1},$$

while (1.28) gives for $(\mathbf{xx})_{qq}$:

$$(1.32) \qquad (\mathbf{xx})_{qq} = -\mathbf{Q}^{-1}(\mathbf{I}+\mathbf{R}_p^{-1}\mathbf{B}^{-1}\mathbf{R}_p'^{-1}\mathbf{A}_{pp})\mathbf{A}_{qp}^{-1}.$$

Regarding the submatrices of $\mathbf{W}^{*-1}$ involving production decisions [the first set of rows in (1.22)], we note that $(\mathbf{xx})_{pq}$ is the transpose of $(\mathbf{xx})_{qp}$ and can therefore be read directly from (1.29). Furthermore, we have $(\mathbf{xx})_{pp}\mathbf{A}_{pq}+(\mathbf{xx})_{pq}\mathbf{A}_{qq} = \mathbf{0}$ by postmultiplying the first set of rows of $\mathbf{W}^{*-1}$ by the second set of columns of $\mathbf{W}^*$. Hence:

$$\begin{aligned}(1.33) \qquad (\mathbf{xx})_{pp} &= -\mathbf{R}_p^{-1}\mathbf{B}^{-1}\mathbf{R}_p'^{-1}\mathbf{Q}'^{-1}\mathbf{A}_{qq}\mathbf{A}_{pq}^{-1} \\ &= -\mathbf{A}_{qp}^{-1}\mathbf{A}_{qq}\mathbf{Q}^{-1}\mathbf{R}_p^{-1}\mathbf{B}^{-1}\mathbf{R}_p'^{-1},\end{aligned}$$

where use is made of the symmetry of $(\mathbf{xx})_{pp}$. We have $(\cdot\mathbf{x})_p\mathbf{A}_{pq}+(\cdot\mathbf{x})_q\mathbf{A}_{qq} = \mathbf{0}$ by postmultiplying the last set of rows of $\mathbf{W}^{*-1}$ by the second set of columns of $\mathbf{W}^*$; hence, on applying (1.31):

$$(1.34) \qquad (\mathbf{x}\cdot)_p = -\mathbf{A}_{qp}^{-1}\mathbf{A}_{qq}\mathbf{Q}^{-1}\mathbf{R}_p^{-1}.$$

Finally we have $(\mathbf{xy})_p\mathbf{B}-(\mathbf{x}\cdot)_p = \mathbf{0}$ by postmultiplying the first set of rows of $\mathbf{W}^{*-1}$ by the third set of columns of $\mathbf{W}^*$. Hence:

$$(1.35) \qquad (\mathbf{xy})_p = -\mathbf{A}_{qp}^{-1}\mathbf{A}_{qq}\mathbf{Q}^{-1}\mathbf{R}_p^{-1}\mathbf{B}^{-1}.$$

We have thus succeeded in expressing the relevant submatrices of

$\mathbf{W}^{*-1}$ in $\mathbf{Q}^{-1}$, premultiplied and postmultiplied by various matrices. Now the latter matrices are all such that their behaviour for $T \to \infty$ does not lead to any difficulties. For example, in the case of $(\mathbf{x}\cdot)_q$ and $(\mathbf{x}\cdot)_p$ [see (1.31) and (1.34)] we have to postmultiply by $\mathbf{R}_p^{-1}$, which for $T \to \infty$ takes the form:

$$\mathbf{R}_p^{-1} = \begin{bmatrix} 1 & 0 & 0 & 0 & \dots \\ -1 & 1 & 0 & 0 & \dots \\ 0 & -1 & 1 & 0 & \dots \\ 0 & 0 & -1 & 1 & \dots \\ \vdots & \vdots & \vdots & \vdots & \end{bmatrix}. \tag{1.36}$$

Similarly, for $(\mathbf{xy})_q$ and $(\mathbf{xy})_p$ we have to postmultiply by $\mathbf{R}_p^{-1}\mathbf{B}^{-1}$, which is identical with the matrix (1.36) except that the elements which are ± 1 are replaced by $\mp 1/2c_7$. Further, in (1.29) we have to postmultiply by $\mathbf{R}_p^{-1}\mathbf{B}^{-1}\mathbf{R}_p'^{-1}$, which for $T \to \infty$ is

$$\mathbf{R}_p^{-1}\mathbf{B}^{-1}\mathbf{R}_p'^{-1} = \frac{-1}{2c_7}\begin{bmatrix} 1 & -1 & 0 & 0 & \dots \\ -1 & 2 & -1 & 0 & \dots \\ 0 & -1 & 2 & -1 & \dots \\ 0 & 0 & -1 & 2 & \dots \\ \vdots & \vdots & \vdots & \vdots & \end{bmatrix}; \tag{1.37}$$

and so on.

The problem is therefore to find the inverse of $\mathbf{Q}$ for $T \to \infty$. Now we have, from (1.30) and (1.37) and the specifications for $\mathbf{A}_{pp}$, $\mathbf{A}_{qp}$ and $\mathbf{A}_{qq}$:

$$\mathbf{Q} = -\frac{c_3 c_4}{c_7}\begin{bmatrix} 1 & -1 & 0 & 0 & \dots \\ -1 & 2 & -1 & 0 & \dots \\ 0 & -1 & 2 & -1 & \dots \\ 0 & 0 & -1 & 2 & \dots \\ \vdots & \vdots & \vdots & \vdots & \end{bmatrix}$$

$$+ \frac{1}{c_4 c_7}\begin{bmatrix} 1 & -1 & 0 & 0 & \dots \\ -1 & 2 & -1 & 0 & \dots \\ 0 & -1 & 2 & -1 & \dots \\ 0 & 0 & -1 & 2 & \dots \\ \vdots & \vdots & \vdots & \vdots & \end{bmatrix}\begin{bmatrix} 2c_2+c_3c_4^2 & -c_2 & 0 & \dots \\ -c_2 & 2c_2+c_3c_4^2 & -c_2 & \dots \\ 0 & -c_2 & 2c_2+c_3c_4^2 & \dots \\ \vdots & \vdots & \vdots & \end{bmatrix}$$

$$+ \frac{1}{c_3 c_4}\begin{bmatrix} 2c_2+c_3c_4^2 & -c_2 & 0 & \dots \\ -c_2 & 2c_2+c_3c_4^2 & -c_2 & \dots \\ 0 & -c_2 & 2c_2+c_3c_4^2 & \dots \\ \vdots & \vdots & \vdots & \end{bmatrix}.$$

After working this out, we find that **Q** is an infinite band matrix of the following form:

$$\mathbf{Q} = \begin{bmatrix} a' & b' & c & 0 & 0 & \cdots \\ b & a & b & c & 0 & \cdots \\ c & b & a & b & c & \cdots \\ 0 & c & b & a & b & \cdots \\ 0 & 0 & c & b & a & \cdots \\ \vdots & \vdots & \vdots & \vdots & \vdots & \end{bmatrix}, \tag{1.38}$$

where

$$a = \frac{6c_2c_3 + 2c_2c_7 + c_3c_4^2c_7}{c_3c_4c_7} = 943.8$$

$$a' = \frac{3c_2c_3 + 2c_2c_7 + c_3c_4^2c_7}{c_3c_4c_7} = 531.5$$

$$b = -\frac{4c_2c_3 + c_2c_7}{c_3c_4c_7} = -606.5$$

$$b' = -\frac{3c_2c_3 + c_2c_7}{c_3c_4c_7} = -469.1$$

$$c = \frac{c_2}{c_4c_7} = 137.5,$$

the numerical values being derived from the specification (3.2.6).

The inversion of the band matrix (1.38) is considered in more detail in the Appendix of this chapter (Section 5.A). The only elements of $\mathbf{Q}^{-1}$ which we need are those of the first two rows (to be denoted by q^{1t}, q^{2t}) and of the first two columns (q^{t1}, q^{t2}). The result is

$$\begin{aligned} q^{1t} &= 0.0776 \times 0.6638^t - 0.0677 \times 0.6143^t \\ q^{2t} &= 0.1896 \times 0.6638^t - 0.1841 \times 0.6143^t \\ q^{t1} &= 0.2013 \times 0.6638^t - 0.2013 \times 0.6143^t \\ q^{t2} &= 0.2656 \times 0.6638^t - 0.2728 \times 0.6143^t, \end{aligned} \tag{1.39}$$

from which it is evident that the elements of these rows and columns converge to zero when t increases beyond limits. On the basis of (1.39) it is now easy to derive the elements of the matrices $(\mathbf{xx})_{pp}$, $(\mathbf{xx})_{pq}$, ... which deal with first-period instruments. For example, if we use (1.31) for $(\mathbf{x}\cdot)_q$ and confine ourselves to the first-period work force decision, i.e., to the first row of that matrix, we obtain

$$[q^{11}\ q^{12}\ q^{13}\ \ldots]\begin{bmatrix} 1 & 0\,0 \ldots \\ -1 & 1\,0 \ldots \\ 0 & -1\,1 \ldots \\ \vdots & \vdots\ \vdots \end{bmatrix} = [q^{11}-q^{12}\ \ q^{12}-q^{13}\ \ q^{13}-q^{14}\ \ldots]$$

so that the $(1, t)^{\text{th}}$ element of $(\mathbf{x}\cdot)_q$ turns out to be:

$$\begin{aligned} q^{1t}-q^{1,t+1} &= 0.0776(1-0.6638)(0.6638)^t-0.0677(1-0.6143)(0.6143)^t \\ &= 0.0261\times 0.6638^t-0.0261\times 0.6143^t. \end{aligned}$$

Hence the slopes of the Tinbergen surface for first-period work force corresponding to the successive components of the additive structure of the constraints converge to zero. A slightly more complicated example is that of $(\mathbf{xx})_{pp}$, for which (1.33) specifies that $\mathbf{Q}'^{-1}$ is to be premultiplied by $-\mathbf{R}_p^{-1}\mathbf{B}^{-1}\mathbf{R}_p'^{-1}$ and to be postmultiplied by $\mathbf{A}_{qq}\mathbf{A}_{pq}^{-1}$. The first row of $-\mathbf{R}_p^{-1}\mathbf{B}^{-1}\mathbf{R}_p'^{-1}\mathbf{Q}'^{-1}$ is

$$\frac{1}{2c_7}[q^{11}-q^{12}\quad q^{21}-q^{22}\quad q^{31}-q^{32}\quad \ldots]$$

and this is to be postmultiplied by

$$\mathbf{A}_{qq}\mathbf{A}_{pq}^{-1} = \frac{-1}{c_3c_4}\begin{bmatrix} 2c_2+c_3c_4^2 & -c_2 & 0 & \ldots \\ -c_2 & 2c_2+c_3c_4^2 & -c_2 & \ldots \\ 0 & -c_2 & 2c_2+c_3c_4^2 & \ldots \\ \vdots & \vdots & \vdots & \end{bmatrix}.$$

Hence the leading element of $(\mathbf{xx})_{pp}$ is

$$\frac{-1}{2c_3c_4c_7}[(2c_2+c_3c_4^2)(q^{11}-q^{12})-c_2(q^{21}-q^{22})] = -1.384,$$

whereas the other elements of the first row [the $(1, t)^{\text{th}}$ element of $(\mathbf{xx})_{pp}$ for $t>1$] are

$$\begin{aligned} &\frac{-1}{2c_3c_4c_7}\{-c_2(q^{t-1,1}-q^{t-1,2})+(2c_2+c_3c_4^2)(q^{t1}-q^{t2})-c_2(q^{t+1,1}-q^{t+1,2})\} \\ &\qquad = -1.553\times 0.6638^t+3.494\times 0.6143^t. \end{aligned}$$

A complete survey of the first rows of all relevant submatrices is presented in Table 5.2. They are all of the form $k_1(0.6638)^t+k_2(0.6143)^t$ except that, in a case like $(\mathbf{xx})_{pp}$, the first element may deviate from this pattern.

TABLE 5.2

THE FIRST ROWS OF SOME MATRICES IN THE INFINITE-HORIZON CASE

	First element	*t^{th} element: coefficient of*		*First element*	*t^{th} element: coefficient of*		
		$(0.6638)^t$	$(0.6143)^t$		$(0.6638)^t$	$(0.6143)^t$	
$(\mathbf{xx})_{pp}$	−1.3841	−1.5526	3.4941	−0.00783	0.08016	−0.09935	$(\mathbf{xx})_{qp}$
$(\mathbf{xx})_{pq}$	−0.0078	0.3893	−0.4334	−0.00577	−0.02010	0.01232	$(\mathbf{xx})_{qq}$
$(\mathbf{xy})_{p}$	−1.3841	3.0650	−5.5650	−0.00783	−0.15823	0.15823	$(\mathbf{xy})_{q}$
$(\mathbf{x}\cdot)_{p}$	0.2284	−0.5057	0.9182	0.00129	0.02611	−0.02611	$(\mathbf{x}\cdot)_{q}$

Finally, we have the decision rule itself. This is found by taking the two relevant rows of

$$-\mathbf{K}^{*-1}\mathscr{E}\mathbf{k}^* = -\begin{bmatrix}(\mathbf{xx})_{pp} & (\mathbf{xx})_{pq}\\ (\mathbf{xx})_{qp} & (\mathbf{xx})_{qq}\end{bmatrix}\mathscr{E}\mathbf{k}^*,$$

where $\mathscr{E}\mathbf{k}^*$ takes the following form [see (3.2.18)–(3.2.19)]:

$$\begin{bmatrix}-c_5\\ -c_5\\ \vdots\\ -c_1+c_6+2c_2q_0\\ -c_1+c_6\\ \vdots\end{bmatrix}+\begin{bmatrix}2c_7c_8\mathbf{R}_p'\begin{bmatrix}1\\1\\ \vdots\end{bmatrix}\\ 0\\ 0\\ \vdots\end{bmatrix}+\begin{bmatrix}2c_7\mathbf{R}_p'\mathbf{R}_p\begin{bmatrix}\mathscr{E}v_1-y_0\\ \mathscr{E}v_2\\ \vdots\end{bmatrix}\\ 0\\ 0\\ \vdots\end{bmatrix}.$$

Hence the first-period production decision is the first row of

$$-(\mathbf{xx})_{pp}\left(\begin{bmatrix}-c_5\\-c_5\\ \vdots\end{bmatrix}+2c_7c_8\mathbf{R}_p'\begin{bmatrix}1\\1\\ \vdots\end{bmatrix}+2c_7\mathbf{R}_p'\mathbf{R}_p\begin{bmatrix}\mathscr{E}v_1-y_0\\ \mathscr{E}v_2\\ \vdots\end{bmatrix}\right)$$
$$-(\mathbf{xx})_{pq}\begin{bmatrix}-c_1+c_6+2c_2q_0\\ -c_1+c_6\\ \vdots\end{bmatrix}$$

and the first-period work force decision is the first row of

$$-(\mathbf{xx})_{qp}\left(\begin{bmatrix}-c_5\\-c_5\\ \vdots\end{bmatrix}+2c_7c_8\mathbf{R}_p'\begin{bmatrix}1\\1\\ \vdots\end{bmatrix}+2c_7\mathbf{R}_p'\mathbf{R}_p\begin{bmatrix}\mathscr{E}v_1-y_0\\ \mathscr{E}v_2\\ \vdots\end{bmatrix}\right)$$
$$-(\mathbf{xx})_{qq}\begin{bmatrix}-c_1+c_6+2c_2q_0\\ -c_1+c_6\\ \vdots\end{bmatrix}.$$

Now the first rows of $(\mathbf{xx})_{pp}$, $(\mathbf{xx})_{pq}$, $(\mathbf{xx})_{qp}$, $(\mathbf{xx})_{qq}$ are weighted sums of geometric series. If such a series is postmultiplied by a column of identical elements, the result is simply the sum of this series multiplied by the value of these elements; if the series is postmultiplied by $\mathbf{R}_p'$ or $\mathbf{R}_p'\mathbf{R}_p$, the result is another row whose elements form another geometric series. This is similar to the analysis of 4.2.5 [see (4.2.36)], to which we may therefore refer. The final result in numerical terms is the following pair of linear decision rules in the infinite horizon case:

$$(1.40)\quad \begin{aligned} \tilde{p}_1 &= 153.1+1.007q_0+0.464(\mathscr{E}v_1-y_0) \\ &\quad +\sum_{t=2}^{\infty}\{-0.6626(0.6638)^{t-2}+0.8984(0.6143)^{t-2}\}\mathscr{E}v_t \\ \tilde{q}_1 &= 2.00+0.742q_0+0.00996(\mathscr{E}v_1-y_0) \\ &\quad +\sum_{t=2}^{\infty}\{0.03421(0.6638)^{t-2}-0.02554(0.6143)^{t-2}\}\mathscr{E}v_t, \end{aligned}$$

which corresponds with the appropriate columns of Table 5.1.

5.1.4. First-Period Losses Due to Suboptimal Decisions; Optimal Decision Revisions

We found in Section 4.2 (see Theorem 4.3) that the first-period loss due to any given first-period decision error $\Delta\mathbf{x}_1$ is

$$(1.41)\quad -\tfrac{1}{2}(\Delta\mathbf{x}_1)'(\mathbf{xx})_{11}^{-1}\Delta\mathbf{x}_1.$$

In the present case the interpretation of this first-period loss is the minimum extra costs incurred when the first-period decision error is $\Delta\mathbf{x}_1$. Its computation is straightforward. For the matrix is the inverse of $(\mathbf{xx})_{11}$, apart from the factor $-\frac{1}{2}$, and $(\mathbf{xx})_{11}$ is that part of $(\mathbf{xx})$ that refers to p_1 and q_1. For example, if the horizon is six months, we have from (3.2.17):

$$(\mathbf{xx})_{11} = \frac{-1}{1000}\begin{bmatrix} 1390 & 7.0 \\ 7.0 & 5.91 \end{bmatrix},$$

whence it follows that

$$-\tfrac{1}{2}(\mathbf{xx})_{11}^{-1} = \begin{bmatrix} 0.362 & -0.43 \\ -0.43 & 85.1 \end{bmatrix}.$$

In other words, the first-period loss is then

$$(1.42)\quad 0.362(\Delta p_1)^2+85.1(\Delta q_1)^2-0.86\Delta p_1\Delta q_1,$$

from which we conclude that decision errors Δp_1, Δq_1 of the same sign compensate each other to some extent. This result is similar to that of (3.2.27) in the static analysis, and it seems reasonable to guess that it must be due to the desirability of operating close to capacity. Both this coefficient and the two positive coefficients in (1.42) are closer to zero than the corresponding coefficients in the "static" loss. Thus we have 85.1 for the $(\Delta q_1)^2$-coefficient in (1.42) but 135.0 in (3.2.23); similarly, we have 0.362 for the $(\Delta p_1)^2$-coefficient in (1.42) but 0.695 in (3.2.25). Evidently, these smaller values in the first-period loss are due to the fact that the first-period decision error is assumed to be corrected in later periods as well as possible.

The same analysis can be carried out for other horizons as well. The results are shown in Table 5.3 for $T = 3, 6, 12$, and ∞, which illustrates that in this case (as in that of 5.1.2) a half-year horizon is a satisfactory approximation to the infinite horizon.[1]

TABLE 5.3

THE COEFFICIENTS OF THE FIRST-PERIOD LOSS FOR ALTERNATIVE HORIZONS

Coefficient of	*Horizon (in months)*			
	3	6	12	∞
$(\Delta p_1)^2$	0.359	0.362	0.364	0.364
$(\Delta q_1)^2$	76.5	85.1	87.3	87.3
$\Delta p_1 \Delta q_1$	−1.07	−0.86	−0.98	−0.99

The complement of the loss consequences of a first-period decision error is the set of optimal revisions for later periods. When the horizon is infinite (or when it is finite but applied in the way of a moving horizon), the practical value of such revisions is limited, because all later-period decisions can then be regarded as first-period decisions corresponding with a horizon of the same length, so that there is nothing new. But the structure of the matrix which determines the optimal revisions gives some additional insight into the cost structure and its implications, which is the reason why they are considered here. As follows from Theorem 4.3, this matrix is

$$\begin{bmatrix} (xx)_{21} \\ \vdots \\ (xx)_{T1} \end{bmatrix} (xx)_{11}^{-1}, \tag{1.43}$$

[1] For $T = \infty$ the relevant substitution terms can be read directly from Table 5.2.

where the submatrices $(xx)_{t1}$ contain the substitution terms connecting the production and work force instruments in the tth month with those in the first.

The elements of (1.43) are summarized in Table 5.4 for three alternative horizons ($T = 6, 12, \infty$) and for the second through the sixth month.

TABLE 5.4

OPTIMAL DECISION REVISIONS FOR GIVEN FIRST-PERIOD DECISION ERRORS AND ALTERNATIVE HORIZONS*

Revision in month	*Horizon (in months)* 6	12	∞
	Unit Decision Error in Production ($\Delta p_1 = 1$)		
2	−0.460 −0.0110	−0.464 −0.0100	−0.464 −0.0100
3	−0.259 −0.0149	−0.258 −0.0127	−0.259 −0.0127
4	−0.148 −0.0158	−0.141 −0.0123	−0.141 −0.0122
5	−0.092 −0.0156	−0.075 −0.0106	−0.075 −0.0104
6	−0.074 −0.0154	−0.038 −0.0086	−0.039 −0.0083
	Unit Decision Error in Work Force ($\Delta q_1 = 1$)		
2	0.881 0.776	1.000 0.743	1.007 0.742
3	0.329 0.615	0.275 0.542	0.280 0.541
4	0.228 0.509	−0.057 0.391	−0.053 0.389
5	0.488 0.450	−0.186 0.279	−0.181 0.276
6	1.155 0.428	−0.214 0.199	−0.210 0.194

* In each cell, the upper left-hand element is the coefficient of Δp_t, and the lower right-hand element that of Δq_t, for $t = 2, \ldots, 6$.

We thus find that if there is a unit decision error in production in the first month, then, assuming $T = 6$, the optimal revision implies that 0.460 units are subtracted from the production level which was originally optimal for the second period. The same applies to the third period except that the reduction is now only 0.259 units, and so on; for the second through sixth period as a whole the total reduction is about the same as the original decision error. This implies that the error is "smoothed out" in half a year's time. For $T = 12$ and $T = \infty$ the results are practically identical with those of $T = 6$ except that, obviously, there are now also (minor) revisions for production decisions in the seventh month and later. These are not shown in Table 5.4.

A production decision error implies not only production revisions but also work force revisions. The latter are all negative and hence have the same sign as the accompanying production revisions. This reflects the desire to operate close to capacity. In the case of a six-month horizon the reduction in work force is approximately constant from the third through the sixth month, but when the horizon is larger the reduction diminishes gradually, so that the work force moves back in the direction of the original optimal level. For $T = \infty$ this follows from the fact that the typical submatrix of (1.43) takes the form

$$(xx)_{t1}(xx)_{11}^{-1} = \begin{bmatrix} 1.210(0.6638)^t - 2.642(0.6143)^t & -15.53(0.6638)^t + 20.80(0.6143)^t \\ -0.3033(0.6638)^t + 0.3277(0.6143)^t & 3.894(0.6638)^t - 2.580(0.6143)^t \end{bmatrix}$$

as is easily verified from Table 5.2. The optimal revisions Δp_t, Δq_t $(t = 2, 3, \ldots)$ associated with given first-period decision errors Δp_1, Δq_1 are then:

$$\Delta p_t = \{1.210(0.6638)^t - 2.642(0.6143)^t\}\Delta p_1 + \{-15.53(0.6638)^t + 20.80(0.6143)^t\}\Delta q_1 \tag{1.44}$$

$$\Delta q_t = \{-0.3033(0.6638)^t + 0.3277(0.6143)^t\}\Delta p_1 + \{3.894(0.6638)^t - 2.580(0.6143)^t\}\Delta q_1, \tag{1.45}$$

hence the work force revision, given the production error, has a dominating negative component $(-0.3033 \times 0.6638^t)$ which converges to zero.

Turning to a unit decision error in the work force of the first month, we notice that this leads to a revision of the second-month work force amounting to an addition of about three quarters of a unit to the original optimal level. This implies that in the second month one quarter of the

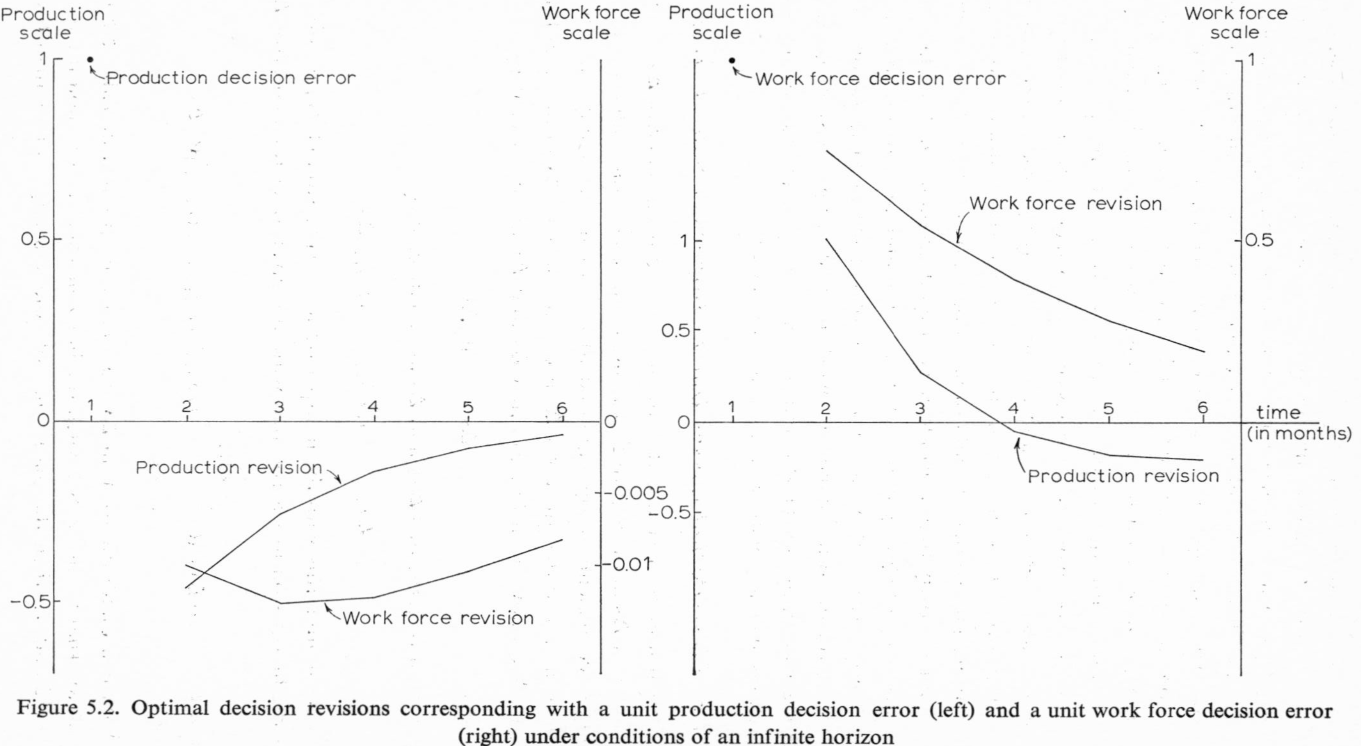

Figure 5.2. Optimal decision revisions corresponding with a unit production decision error (left) and a unit work force decision error (right) under conditions of an infinite horizon

error is removed by layoff. This reduction continues in later months, so that—when the horizon is sufficiently large—only 20 per cent of the first-period error remains in the sixth month. The accompanying production revisions are then positive in the second and third month, which again points to the desire to operate close to capacity. Thereafter, the production revisions are negative, which must be ascribed to the fact that storage costs have to be paid for the additional production of the second and third month. But the situation is different for $T = 6$: the percentage of the first-period work force decision error which remains in the sixth month is about 40, not 20, and the accompanying production revisions are all positive. Evidently, if the horizon is that short, storage costs have a small weight, so that the additional production of the last two months is then less costly than it would have been if account had been taken of the necessity of storing in the seventh month and later. At the same time the work force is then larger in view of capacity considerations. For $T = \infty$, on the other hand, the work force decision revisions decrease with zero as limit, see (1.45), and the accompanying production decision revisions increase with zero as limit, see (1.44).

5.1.5. *First-Period Losses Due to Imperfect Sales Forecasts*

It will now be assumed that the first-period decision error Δx_1 is due to an error $\mathbf{\Delta s}$ in the additive structure of the constraints, all other determining coefficients being supposed to be specified correctly; further, it will be assumed that the error $\mathbf{\Delta s}$ is due to an error $\mathbf{\Delta v}$ in the sales forecasts. We know from (3.2.31) that $\mathbf{\Delta s}$ and $\mathbf{\Delta v}$ are connected by

$$\mathbf{\Delta s} = -\mathbf{R}_p \mathbf{\Delta v}, \tag{1.46}$$

and from (4.2.19) that Δx_1 and $\mathbf{\Delta s}$ are connected by

$$\Delta x_1 = -[(x\cdot)_{11} \ldots (x\cdot)_{1T}]\mathbf{\Delta s}. \tag{1.47}$$

On combining this with the first-period loss expression (1.41) we obtain as the first-period loss associated with any given sales forecast error $\mathbf{\Delta v}$:

$$-\tfrac{1}{2}(\mathbf{\Delta v})' \mathbf{R}_p' \begin{bmatrix} (\cdot x)_{11} \\ \vdots \\ (\cdot x)_{T1} \end{bmatrix} (xx)_{11}^{-1}[(x\cdot)_{11} \ldots (x\cdot)_{1T}]\mathbf{R}_p \mathbf{\Delta v}, \tag{1.48}$$

which is a quadratic form in $\mathbf{\Delta v}$. Its matrix is specified in Table 5.5 for four alternative horizons; when the horizon exceeds six months, as in $T = 12$ and ∞, then the matrix has of course a larger order than 6×6, but only the 6×6 leading submatrix is shown.[1] It is particularly instructive to compare the results for $T = 6$ with the matrix (3.2.33). In both cases we have the matrix of the quadratic form of a loss due to the error $\mathbf{\Delta v}$, and in both cases we have the same horizon and cost structure; but (3.2.33) handles the static approach in which later-period decisions are based on exactly the same error $\mathbf{\Delta v}$ and therefore not revised, whereas the dynamic approach considered by Table 5.5 implies that only

TABLE 5.5

THE MATRIX OF THE QUADRATIC FORM OF THE FIRST-PERIOD LOSS DUE TO SALES FORECAST ERRORS FOR ALTERNATIVE HORIZONS*

	Δv_1	Δv_2	Δv_3	Δv_4	Δv_5	Δv_6
			$T = 3$			
Δv_1	0.0793					
Δv_2	0.0414	0.0228				
Δv_3	0.0180	0.0105	0.0052			
			$T = 6$			
Δv_1	0.0820					
Δv_2	0.0440	0.0250				
Δv_3	0.0228	0.0140	0.0087			
Δv_4	0.0110	0.0077	0.0055	0.0039		
Δv_5	0.0047	0.0041	0.0034	0.0027	0.0020	
Δv_6	0.0015	0.0018	0.0017	0.0015	0.0012	0.0008
			$T = 12$			
Δv_1	0.0825					
Δv_2	0.0442	0.0248				
Δv_3	0.0228	0.0136	0.0081			
Δv_4	0.0112	0.0073	0.0048	0.0031		
Δv_5	0.0049	0.0038	0.0028	0.0021	0.0015	
Δv_6	0.0017	0.0018	0.0017	0.0014	0.0011	0.0008
			$T = \infty$			
Δv_1	0.0825					
Δv_2	0.0442	0.0248				
Δv_3	0.0229	0.0136	0.0081			
Δv_4	0.0112	0.0073	0.0048	0.0031		
Δv_5	0.0050	0.0038	0.0028	0.0021	0.0015	
Δv_6	0.0018	0.0019	0.0016	0.0013	0.0010	0.0008

* Elements above the diagonals are obtained by transposition.

[1] See the Appendix (Section 5.B) for the matrix of (1.48) in the case $T = \infty$.

the first-period decision is affected by $\mathbf{\Delta v}$ and that later-period decisions are revised as well as possible. The differences are quite substantial. For example, the coefficient of $(\Delta v_1)^2$ in the static loss is 0.415 but in the first-period loss 0.0820, i.e., five times less. The relative difference is even larger for the coefficients of $(\Delta v_2)^2$: 0.358 against 0.0250, and *a fortiori*

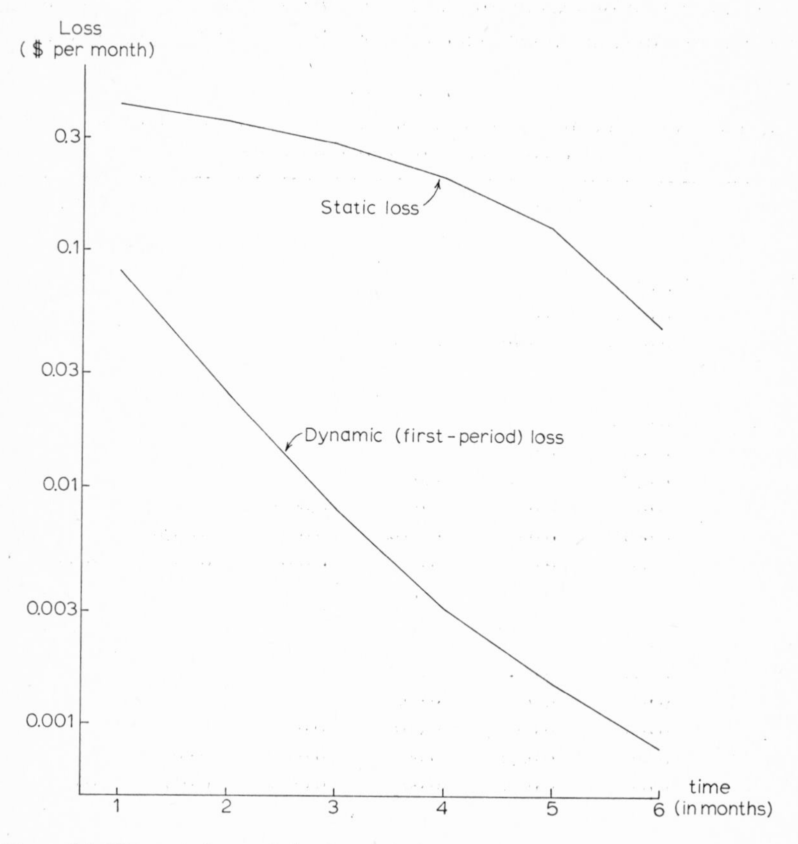

Figure 5.3. The static loss and the first-period loss due to unit sales forecast errors in successive months [the diagonal elements of the matrix (3.2.33) and of Table 5.5 for $T = \infty$]

for $(\Delta v_t)^2$ with $t > 2$. These features illustrate the importance of making appropriate revisions and also the fact that the first-period decision is much more dependent on the sales of the immediate future than on those of later periods. Table 5.5 shows that there is not much difference between the leading 6×6 submatrices for $T = 6$, 12, and ∞. It will further be noticed that the off-diagonal elements, as in the static case (3.2.33), are all positive,[1] which implies that successive forecast errors of opposite sign tend to compensate each other.

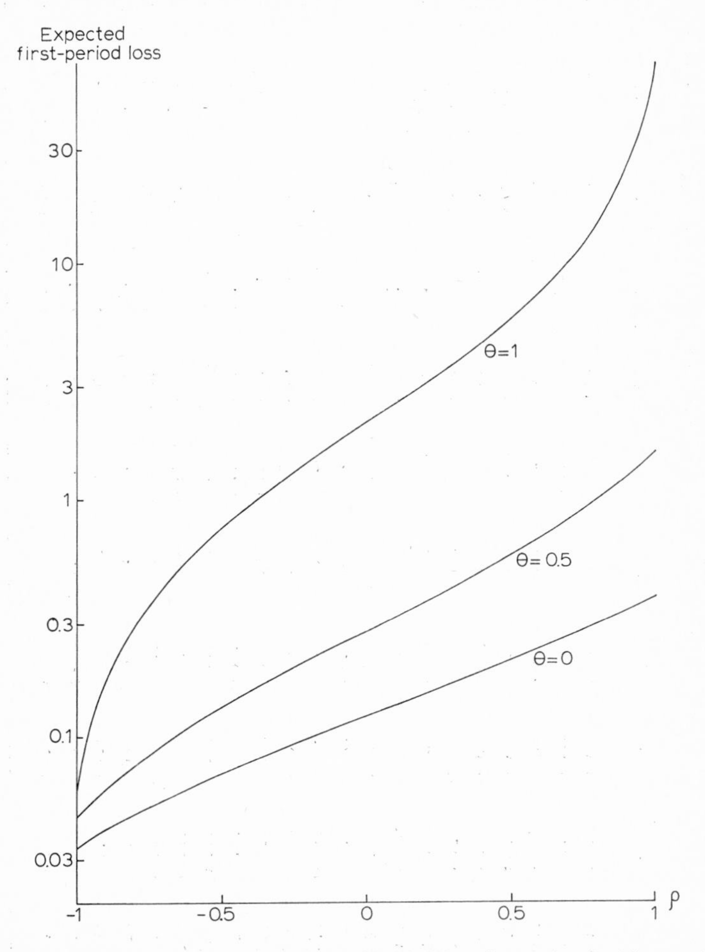

Figure 5.4. The expected first-period loss (divided by σ^2) associated with a statistical forecasting procedure for future sales under conditions (3.2.35)–(3.2.36) as a function of ρ for some values of θ

---

[1] However, it is not true that all off-diagonal elements are positive in the infinite-horizon case. For example, the coefficient of v_1 and v_8 is negative for $T = \infty$ [as can be read from (B.4)–(B.5) of Section 5.B of the Appendix]; but this is only a minor effect numerically.

TABLE 5.6

THE EXPECTED FIRST-PERIOD LOSS ASSOCIATED WITH A STATISTICAL PREDICTION PROCEDURE FOR FUTURE SHIPMENTS*

ρ	θ										
	0	0.1	0.2	0.3	0.4	0.5	0.6	0.7	0.8	0.9	1
−1	0.035	0.037	0.039	0.041	0.043	0.045	0.047	0.048	0.050	0.052	0.053
−0.9	0.041	0.044	0.047	0.051	0.055	0.059	0.065	0.072	0.085	0.108	0.164
−0.8	0.047	0.051	0.056	0.061	0.067	0.075	0.084	0.099	0.123	0.170	0.286
−0.7	0.054	0.059	0.066	0.073	0.081	0.092	0.106	0.128	0.165	0.240	0.423
−0.6	0.061	0.068	0.076	0.085	0.096	0.110	0.130	0.160	0.212	0.317	0.575
−0.5	0.069	0.078	0.088	0.099	0.113	0.131	0.156	0.196	0.265	0.405	0.748
−0.4	0.078	0.088	0.100	0.114	0.132	0.154	0.186	0.236	0.324	0.503	0.945
−0.3	0.087	0.100	0.114	0.131	0.152	0.180	0.219	0.281	0.391	0.616	1.17
−0.2	0.098	0.112	0.129	0.150	0.175	0.209	0.257	0.333	0.469	0.747	1.43
−0.1	0.109	0.126	0.147	0.171	0.201	0.242	0.300	0.393	0.559	0.899	1.74
0	0.122	0.142	0.166	0.194	0.231	0.279	0.350	0.462	0.664	1.08	2.10
0.1	0.136	0.160	0.187	0.221	0.264	0.323	0.408	0.544	0.789	1.29	2.54
0.2	0.152	0.179	0.212	0.252	0.303	0.373	0.476	0.641	0.940	1.56	3.09
0.3	0.170	0.202	0.240	0.288	0.349	0.433	0.558	0.760	1.13	1.89	3.78
0.4	0.190	0.227	0.273	0.329	0.403	0.505	0.657	0.907	1.36	2.31	4.68
0.5	0.213	0.257	0.311	0.378	0.468	0.593	0.782	1.09	1.67	2.88	5.90
0.6	0.239	0.291	0.355	0.437	0.546	0.702	0.940	1.34	2.09	3.67	7.67
0.7	0.270	0.331	0.408	0.507	0.644	0.841	1.15	1.68	2.69	4.86	10.42
0.8	0.305	0.378	0.471	0.594	0.767	1.02	1.44	2.18	3.63	6.85	15.30
0.9	0.345	0.432	0.546	0.699	0.922	1.27	1.87	2.98	5.32	10.86	26.29
1	0.390	0.493	0.629	0.819	1.11	1.60	2.53	4.53	9.39	23.27	72.54

* All figures are to be multiplied by σ_0^2.

It is also interesting to consider the expected first-period loss of a statistical forecasting procedure. This is

$$\sum_{t} \sum_{t'} m_{tt'}^{(1)} \mathscr{E}(\Delta v_t \Delta v_{t'}), \tag{1.49}$$

where $[m_{tt'}^{(1)}]$ is the matrix of the first-period expected loss, e.g., the matrix of Table 5.5 for $T = 6$. This is comparable with (3.2.34). If we make assumptions (3.2.35) and (3.2.36), the expected first-period loss can be tabulated in the same way as we did for the static approach in Table 3.9. The results are shown in Table 5.6 for $T = \infty$; reference is made to Section 5.B of the Appendix for the derivations. A comparison of Tables 5.6 and 3.9 shows that when θ is not too large, the expected first-period loss is much less than its "static" value, particularly when ρ is positive and large. For example, if $0 \leqq \theta \leqq 0.5$ and if $\rho = -1$, Table 5.6 gives values which are about one third of the corresponding values of Table 3.9; if $\rho = 0$, this ratio is less than one tenth; and if $\rho = 1$, it decreases further to slightly more than one twentieth. This feature is due to the fact that in the static case later-period decision errors play a prominent role, especially when ρ is not far below 1, whereas in the dynamic case all attention is concentrated on the first-period decision error. When θ is large (particularly in the lower right-hand corner of Table 5.6), the expected first-period loss takes sizable values. For still larger values of θ the loss would "explode" in a manner which is comparable with the case $\gamma(1+r) \geqq 1$ discussed at the end of 4.2.5 (see also the end of Section 5.B of the Appendix). It will be noticed that this is a situation which can only occur if the horizon is infinite, so that there is no possibility of a direct comparison with Table 3.9, which is based on $T = 6$.

5.1.6. Summary

(1) The first-period decision of the maximizing strategy is identical with the optimal first-period decision which was derived in Section 3.2, except that future shipments are now replaced by their conditional expectations, given the information which is available at the beginning of the first period. Some operations with a permutation matrix are necessary in order to connect the partitioning by variables of Section 3.2 with the partitioning by periods of Chapter 4.

(2, 3) The first-period decision of the maximizing strategy is not very sensitive to the choice of alternative horizons as long as the horizon is six months or longer. For shorter horizons the differences are much more substantial, particularly when one-month and two-month horizons are compared with each other; in the former case the influence of the initial work force is larger and that of the first-period sales smaller than in the latter (two-month) case. When the horizon increases beyond limits, the first-period decision of the maximizing strategy involves a linear combination of expected future sales whose weights are weighted sums of two decreasing exponential functions of time; i.e., the coefficients by which the expected sales in month t are multiplied in the first-period production and work force decisions are of the form $a_1\lambda_1^t + a_2\lambda_2^t$, where a_1 and a_2 are constants (of opposite sign) and λ_1 and λ_2 numbers between 0 and 1. The λ's play a crucial role in the analysis for infinite horizons.

(4) The first-period loss due to a first-period decision error is a weighted sum of the squares and the product of the work force and the production decision errors. The weights are much smaller than those of the "static" loss analyzed in Section 3.2, which illustrates the importance of making appropriate revisions, given the first-period error made. These revisions are such that, if there is a decision error in the work force, the error is gradually removed by hiring or layoff, while production is temporarily increased above the original optimum if the work force error is positive (decreased when it is negative) in view of the desirability to operate close to capacity. Thereafter the production revision works in opposite direction because of storage cost considerations. A first-period production decision error leads to optimal revisions in opposite direction for both instruments.

(5) The first-period loss due to sales forecast errors is a quadratic form in these errors. The matrix of this form has much smaller elements than the corresponding matrix of the static loss analyzed in Section 3.2, which again illustrates the importance of making appropriate revisions. Further, the "weight" of future forecast errors diminishes much more rapidly than in the static case, which reflects the decreasing dependence of the first-period decision on later-period shipments. The expected first-period loss associated with a statistical forecasting procedure for future shipments, when analyzed under the same conditions as those of Section 3.2, is considerably below the corresponding "static" loss, particularly when the second-order cross-moments of the forecast errors are positive and large.

5.2. THE COST IMPLICATIONS OF A MISSPECIFIED COST FUNCTION

5.2.1. Statement of the Problem

It is useful to return to 3.2.1, where the cost function of our paint factory was introduced. For any month t, the costs as defined there consist of the following four components:

$$\text{(2.1)} \qquad \text{Regular payroll costs} = c_1 q_t,$$

$$\text{(2.2)} \qquad \text{Hiring and layoff costs} = c_2(q_t - q_{t-1} - c_{10})^2,$$

$$\text{(2.3)} \qquad \text{Overtime costs} = c_3(p_t - c_4 q_t)^2 + c_5 p_t - c_6 q_t + c_{11} p_t q_t,$$

$$\text{(2.4)} \qquad \text{Inventory connected costs} = c_7[y_t - (c_8 + c_9 v_t)]^2,$$

and the c's have been specified numerically as follows:

$$\text{(2.5)} \qquad \begin{array}{llll} c_1 = 340 & c_4 = 5.67 & c_7 = 0.0825 & c_{10} = 0 \\ c_2 = 64.3 & c_5 = 51.2 & c_8 = 320 & c_{11} = 0. \\ c_3 = 0.20 & c_6 = 281 & c_9 = 0 & \end{array}$$

The purpose of this section is to analyze the decision errors and losses which occur if the factory manager acts as if (2.5) is the correct specification of the cost structure whereas in fact this structure is different; or, what essentially amounts to the same thing, to analyze such consequences if (2.5) is correct but the factory manager proceeds under the assumption of different c's. We shall confine ourselves to the case of an infinite horizon, $T = \infty$.

When we add the four components (2.1)–(2.4) and sum over t from 1 to T, and add a minus sign to obtain a function which is to be maximized, we have the following preference function:

$$\text{(2.6)} \qquad -\sum_{t=1}^{T} \{(c_1 - c_6)q_t + c_2(q_t - q_{t-1} - c_{10})^2 + c_3(p_t - c_4 q_t)^2 + c_5 p_t + c_{11} p_t q_t + c_7[y_t - (c_8 + c_9 v_t)]^2\},$$

which can be simplified in some respects when we apply $c_9 = c_{10} = c_{11} = 0$ in accordance with (2.5). In fact, we used these simplifications when defining the coefficient matrices of the preference function in 3.2.2, but it is obvious that we can no longer do so when the c's are supposed to take values which are different from those of (2.5). It is therefore necessary to remove these simplifications for the purpose of the present section.

The easiest case is that of c_{11}. We see from (2.6) that it is multiplied by $p_t q_t$, so that it contributes to the coefficient matrix of the bilinear instrument part of the preference function. The case of c_{10} is slightly more complicated; but we shall show that this coefficient is completely irrelevant for the purpose of maximizing the preference function, at least when $T = \infty$. It appears from (2.6) that c_{10} occurs only in the following form (disregarding the multiplicative factor $-c_2$):

$$\sum_{t=1}^{T}(q_t - q_{t-1} - c_{10})^2 = 2\sum_{t=1}^{T} q_t^2 - 2\sum_{t=1}^{T} q_t q_{t-1} + (q_0^2 - q_T^2 + 2c_{10}q_0 - 2c_{10}q_T),$$

apart from Tc_{10}^2 (which amounts to constant costs per unit of time). Now the term in brackets behind the equation sign is irrelevant for maximization purposes in the infinite-horizon case, partly because it refers to the past and is therefore a constant in the maximization process (q_0^2 and $2c_{10}q_0$), partly because it represents only a terminal effect ($-q_T^2$ and $-2c_{10}q_T$). Since this term is the only one in which c_{10} enters, we may conclude that this coefficient is indeed irrelevant for $T = \infty$.

The case of c_9 has a different character. It was observed in the third paragraph of 3.2.2 that $c_9 = 0$ implies that the only noncontrolled variables occurring in the preference function (2.6) are the inventory levels (the y's); but if $c_9 \neq 0$, we have the shipments (the v's) too. This leads to several modifications. The vector of noncontrolled variables would then become

$$\mathbf{y}^* = \begin{bmatrix} y_1 \\ y_2 \\ \vdots \\ v_1 \\ v_2 \\ \vdots \end{bmatrix}$$

(where the asterisk indicates partitioning by variables), and the constraints would have to be written as

$$\begin{bmatrix} y_1 \\ y_2 \\ \vdots \\ v_1 \\ v_2 \\ \vdots \end{bmatrix} = \begin{bmatrix} 1 & 0 & \dots & 0 & 0 & \dots \\ 1 & 1 & \dots & 0 & 0 & \dots \\ \vdots & \vdots & & \vdots & \vdots & \\ 0 & 0 & \dots & 0 & 0 & \dots \\ 0 & 0 & \dots & 0 & 0 & \dots \\ \vdots & \vdots & & \vdots & \vdots & \end{bmatrix} \begin{bmatrix} p_1 \\ p_2 \\ \vdots \\ q_1 \\ q_2 \\ \vdots \end{bmatrix} + \begin{bmatrix} -v_1 + y_0 \\ -v_1 - v_2 + y_0 \\ \vdots \\ v_1 \\ v_2 \\ \vdots \end{bmatrix},$$

while similar changes would have to be made in the preference function.

We shall prefer, however, to stay as closely to the original set-up as possible. In fact, it is not difficult to do so because the shipments are completely beyond the manager's control; they cannot even be partly and indirectly controlled like the inventory levels. Let us then consider that part of (2.6) that contains the v's:

$$-c_7\sum_{t=1}^{T}(c_8+c_9v_t)^2+2c_7\sum_{t=1}^{T}(c_8+c_9v_t)y_t.$$

The first sum is beyond the manager's control. It is a random variable if the v's are random; but on the assumption that the distribution of future shipments cannot be affected by the factory manager's actions, it is effectively a constant from the viewpoint of maximization. Hence it can be neglected. The second sum can be regarded as a linear combination of inventory levels, the coefficient of y_t being $2c_7(c_8+c_9v_t)$. These coefficients are obviously not constant, but their distribution is independent of the decision maker's actions as soon as this is true for the v's. Hence the presence of these v's caused by $c_9 \neq 0$ is effectively handled by changing the linear part of the preference function.

Summarizing, the maximization of the function (2.6)—minus the cost function—under the general assumption $c_9,\ c_{10},\ c_{11} \neq 0$ is equivalent to the maximization of the preference function

$$w(\mathbf{x}^*, \mathbf{y}) = \mathbf{a}^{*\prime}\mathbf{x}^*+\mathbf{b}'\mathbf{y}+\tfrac{1}{2}(\mathbf{x}^{*\prime}\mathbf{A}^*\mathbf{x}^*+\mathbf{y}'\mathbf{B}\mathbf{y}), \tag{2.7}$$

which is precisely the same preference function as (1.5) in precisely the same variables. However, two of the coefficient matrices are now different. We have

$$\mathbf{A}_{pq} = \mathbf{A}_{qp} = (2c_3c_4-c_{11})\mathbf{I} \tag{2.8}$$

for the matrix of the bilinear terms in production and work force, $\mathbf{I}$ being the $T\times T$ unit matrix. And we have

$$\mathbf{b} = 2c_7c_8\begin{bmatrix}1\\1\\\vdots\\1\end{bmatrix}+2c_7c_9\begin{bmatrix}v_1\\v_2\\\vdots\\v_T\end{bmatrix}, \tag{2.9}$$

which is the new coefficient vector of the noncontrolled variables in the linear part of the preference function. As noted above, there are no changes due to $c_{10} \neq 0$ if $T = \infty$; this coefficient will therefore be disregarded in the discussion which follows. There are no changes either with respect to the constraints subject to which (2.7) is maximized.

5.2.2. The Effect of Cost Coefficient Errors on the Coefficient Matrices of the Preference Function

Errors in the c's lead to losses which can be derived conveniently by the following steps. First, such c-errors imply certain errors in the coefficient matrices of the preference function. Second, the errors in these matrices lead to first-period decision errors. Third, the decision errors imply a certain first-period loss. We shall consider the first step here, the other two being postponed till 5.2.3 and 5.2.4.

For the first step it is convenient to recapitulate the dependence of the coefficient matrices of the preference function on the cost coefficients. Let us introduce the following three vectors:

$$(2.10) \qquad \boldsymbol{\iota} = \begin{bmatrix} 1 \\ 1 \\ 1 \\ \vdots \end{bmatrix}, \qquad \mathbf{e}_1 = \begin{bmatrix} 1 \\ 0 \\ 0 \\ \vdots \end{bmatrix}, \qquad \mathbf{v} = \begin{bmatrix} v_1 \\ v_2 \\ v_3 \\ \vdots \end{bmatrix},$$

each of which has T elements (where T goes to infinity in the limit). The coefficient matrices involving noncontrolled variables are then

$$(2.11) \qquad \mathbf{b} = 2c_7(c_8\boldsymbol{\iota}+c_9\mathbf{v}), \quad \mathbf{B} = -2c_7\mathbf{I}, \quad \mathbf{C} = \mathbf{0}.$$

Further, the coefficient matrices involving production decisions are

$$(2.12) \qquad \mathbf{a}_p = -c_5\boldsymbol{\iota}, \quad \mathbf{A}_{pp} = -2c_3\mathbf{I}, \quad \mathbf{A}_{pq} = \mathbf{A}_{qp} = (2c_3c_4-c_{11})\mathbf{I},$$

while those involving only work force decisions are

$$(2.13) \qquad \mathbf{a}_q = -(c_1-c_6)\boldsymbol{\iota}+2c_2q_0\mathbf{e}_1, \qquad \mathbf{A}_{qq} = -2(c_3c_4^2\mathbf{I}+c_2\mathbf{R}_p'^{-1}\mathbf{R}_p^{-1}).$$

These expressions follow directly from (2.8) and (2.9) and from the relevant formulas of Section 3.2; see (3.2.9)–(3.2.11) and also (4.2.29) for $\mathbf{R}_p'^{-1}\mathbf{R}_p^{-1}$. Using the same notation, we find that the coefficient matrices of the constraints $\mathbf{y} = \mathbf{R}^*\mathbf{x}^*+\mathbf{s}$ can be written as

$$(2.14) \qquad \mathbf{R}^* = [\mathbf{R}_p \quad \mathbf{0}], \qquad \mathbf{s} = -\mathbf{R}_p(\mathbf{v}-y_0\mathbf{e}_1),$$

see (1.8) and (3.2.12).

A brief inspection of (2.11)–(2.13) shows that the coefficient matrices are all linear functions of the c's [including such bilinearities as c_7c_8 in (2.11)], except that $\mathbf{A}_{qq}$ depends on c_4 in a nonlinear manner. Furthermore, it turns out that the coefficients

$$(2.15) \qquad c_1, \quad c_5, \quad c_6, \quad c_8, \quad c_9$$

enter only into the linear part of the preference function, whereas

$$c_2, \quad c_3, \quad c_4, \quad c_7, \quad c_{11} \tag{2.16}$$

are determining factors of the quadratic part. We recall (see Section 4.2 of Chapter 4) that errors in the coefficient matrices of the linear part of the preference function affect the first-period decision linearly, whereas the effect is nonlinear in the case of errors in the coefficient matrices of the quadratic part. Therefore, and given that the c's of (2.15) affect the coefficient matrices linearly, we know that decision errors caused by errors in these c's are linear functions of these c-errors.[1] This is not true for the c's of (2.16). If there are any errors in the latter c's, the result is a pair of first-period production and work force decision errors which is nonlinear in these c-errors. But we shall linearize in what follows, which implies that our statements on the c's of (2.16) will be approximations that may be rather inaccurate when the cost coefficient errors are large.

The dependence of the coefficient matrices (2.11)–(2.13) on the c's is then evaluated conveniently by computing the corresponding matrices of first-order derivatives. For example, we see from (2.11) that the deriv-

TABLE 5.7

FIRST-ORDER DERIVATIVES OF THE COEFFICIENT MATRICES OF THE PREFERENCE FUNCTION WITH RESPECT TO COST COEFFICIENTS

	Instruments					Noncontrolled variables	
	$\mathbf{a}_p$	$\mathbf{a}_q$	$\mathbf{A}_{pp}$	$\mathbf{A}_{qq}$	$\mathbf{A}_{pq} \equiv \mathbf{A}_{qp}$	$\mathbf{b}$	$\mathbf{B}$
c_1	.	$-\boldsymbol{\iota}$	.	.	.	.	.
c_2	.	$2q_0\mathbf{e}_1$	.	$-2\mathbf{R}_p'^{-1}\mathbf{R}_p^{-1}$	.	.	.
c_3	.	.	$-2\mathbf{I}$	$-2c_4^2\mathbf{I}$	$2c_4\mathbf{I}$	.	.
c_4	.	.	.	$-4c_3c_4\mathbf{I}$	$2c_3\mathbf{I}$	.	.
c_5	$-\boldsymbol{\iota}$	.	.	.	.	.	.
c_6	.	$\boldsymbol{\iota}$	.	.	.	.	.
c_7	.	.	.	.	.	$2(c_8\boldsymbol{\iota}+c_9\mathbf{v})$	$-2\mathbf{I}$
c_8	.	.	.	.	.	$2c_7\boldsymbol{\iota}$	.
c_9	.	.	.	.	.	$2c_7\mathbf{v}$	.
c_{11}	.	.	.	.	$-\mathbf{I}$	.	.

[1] Note that the only place where the coefficients (2.15) enter in bilinear form is in (2.11): c_7c_8 and c_7c_9. Given the coefficients (2.16), in particular given c_7, it therefore remains true that the decision errors are linear in the c's of (2.15) in spite of the bilinearities.

ative of **b** with respect to any of the c's is a zero vector except for the derivatives with respect to c_7, c_8, c_9, which are $2(c_8\boldsymbol{\iota}+c_9\mathbf{v})$, $2c_7\boldsymbol{\iota}$, and $2c_7\mathbf{v}$, respectively. The results are summarized in Table 5.7 (except for the matrix **C** which is always zero and which will therefore be disregarded in the sequel); zero derivatives are indicated by dots in the table.

5.2.3. Derivation of the Effect of Cost Coefficient Errors on the First-Period Decision (1)

We apply the dynamic generalization of Theorem 2.6 to obtain the decision error **dx** caused by the error matrices **da**, **db**, . . . Since $\mathbf{dC} = \mathbf{0}$ the result can be written in the form

$$\mathbf{dx} = -(\mathbf{xx})[\mathbf{da}+(\mathbf{dA})\mathbf{x}^0+\mathbf{R}'(\mathbf{db})+\mathbf{R}'(\mathbf{dB})\mathbf{R}\mathbf{x}^0+\mathbf{R}'(\mathbf{dB})\mathbf{s}],$$

where use is made of $(\mathbf{xy}) = (\mathbf{xx})\mathbf{R}'$, see (4.2.2). If we partition by variables we can write this in the present application as

$$\begin{aligned}\begin{bmatrix}\mathbf{dp}\\ \mathbf{dq}\end{bmatrix} = &-\begin{bmatrix}(\mathbf{xx})_{pp} & (\mathbf{xx})_{pq}\\ (\mathbf{xx})_{qp} & (\mathbf{xx})_{qq}\end{bmatrix}\begin{bmatrix}\mathbf{da}_p\\ \mathbf{da}_q\end{bmatrix}\\ &-\begin{bmatrix}(\mathbf{xx})_{pp}\\ (\mathbf{xx})_{qp}\end{bmatrix}\mathbf{R}_p'[\mathbf{db}-(\mathbf{dB})\mathbf{R}_p(\mathbf{v}-y_0\mathbf{e}_1)]\\ &-\begin{bmatrix}(\mathbf{xx})_{pp} & (\mathbf{xx})_{pq}\\ (\mathbf{xx})_{qp} & (\mathbf{xx})_{qq}\end{bmatrix}\begin{bmatrix}\mathbf{dA}_{pp} & \mathbf{dA}_{pq}\\ \mathbf{dA}_{qp} & \mathbf{dA}_{qq}\end{bmatrix}\begin{bmatrix}\mathbf{p}^0\\ \mathbf{q}^0\end{bmatrix}\\ &-\begin{bmatrix}(\mathbf{xx})_{pp}\\ (\mathbf{xx})_{qp}\end{bmatrix}\mathbf{R}_p'(\mathbf{dB})\mathbf{R}_p\mathbf{p}^0.\end{aligned} \tag{2.17}$$

The first-period decision error is then found by taking the first element of **dp** and the first element of **dq**. It is easily seen that this creates no difficulties as far as the first two terms on the right of (2.17) are concerned. Take, for example, the first term and the first-period production error. This term is obtained by postmultiplying minus the first row of $(\mathbf{xx})_{pp}$ by $\mathbf{da}_p$ and adding to this minus the first row of $(\mathbf{xx})_{pq}$ postmultiplied by $\mathbf{da}_q$. Both first rows have been specified in Table 5.2 for $T = \infty$, so the computations are rather straightforward. In the same way we find that the top element of the second vector on the right of (2.17) is obtained by postmultiplying minus the first row of $(\mathbf{xx})_{pp}$ by

$$\mathbf{R}_p'[\mathbf{db}-(\mathbf{dB})\mathbf{R}_p(\mathbf{v}-y_0\mathbf{e}_1)],$$

which is also straightforward and leads to a linear function of future sales. As a simple example we take the case of an error dc_5 in c_5, which implies an error of $(-dc_5)\boldsymbol{\iota}$ in $\mathbf{a}_p$ according to Table 5.7, all other coefficient matrices remaining unaffected. Then (2.17) specifies that the first-period production error is dc_5 times the sum of all elements of the first row of $(\mathbf{xx})_{pp}$, and that the first-period work force error is the same except that we should take the first row of $(\mathbf{xx})_{qp}$. But the sums of the elements of these rows are both zero as is easily verified from Table 5.2, hence any errors in c_5 do not affect the first-period decision. [This holds both for finite and for infinitesimal errors in c_5 because this coefficient falls in the "linear" group (2.15).] In fact, it is not difficult to understand intuitively that c_5 should have no influence on the first-period decision. The term $c_5 p_t$ in (2.3) has the character of proportional costs, which are unavoidable and fixed for given ordered shipments when we take an infinite horizon, when no discounting of future revenues and costs takes place, and when the costs for delayed deliveries do not depend on the delay. We shall therefore disregard c_5 in the sequel.

The algebraic evaluation of the effect of c-errors on the first-period decision is straightforward and is shown (in terms of first-order derivatives) in Table 5.8. The numerical evaluation is also straightforward as long as only the first two terms in the right-hand side of (2.17) are relevant. The last two terms are more complicated, which can be shown as follows. Take the third; then we have to postmultiply the error matrices $\mathbf{dA}_{pp}$ and $\mathbf{dA}_{qp}$ by $\mathbf{p}^0$, which is the vector of all optimal production decisions —not only the first-period decision. Hence we should evaluate

$$(2.18) \quad \begin{bmatrix} \mathbf{p}^0 \\ \mathbf{q}^0 \end{bmatrix} = -\mathbf{K}^{*-1}\mathbf{k}^*$$

$$= -\begin{bmatrix} (\mathbf{xx})_{pp} & (\mathbf{xx})_{pq} \\ (\mathbf{xx})_{qp} & (\mathbf{xx})_{qq} \end{bmatrix} \begin{bmatrix} -c_5\boldsymbol{\iota} + 2c_7c_8\mathbf{R}_p'\boldsymbol{\iota} + 2c_7\mathbf{R}_p'\mathbf{R}_p(\mathbf{v} - y_0\mathbf{e}_1) \\ -(c_1 - c_6)\boldsymbol{\iota} + c_2 q_0 \mathbf{e}_1 \end{bmatrix},$$

see the end of 5.1.3. It is easy to see that we can now no longer confine ourselves to the first rows of such matrices as $(\mathbf{xx})_{pp}$, $(\mathbf{xx})_{pq}, \ldots$; and hence, going back to (1.29)–(1.33), we need more than just the first two rows and the first two columns of $\mathbf{Q}^{-1}$. It is shown in the Appendix (Section 5.C) that the general $(t, t')^{\text{th}}$ element of $\mathbf{Q}^{-1}$ takes the form

$$(2.19) \quad q^{tt'} = 0.120\lambda_1^{|t-t'|} - 0.100\lambda_2^{|t-t'|} - 0.597\lambda_1^{t+t'} - 0.579\lambda_2^{t+t'} + 0.679\lambda_1^t\lambda_2^{t'} + 0.477\lambda_1^{t'}\lambda_2^t,$$

where λ_1 and λ_2 are the same roots as those of (1.39):

$$(2.20) \quad \lambda_1 = 0.6638, \qquad \lambda_2 = 0.6143.$$

TABLE 5.8

FIRST-ORDER DERIVATIVES OF THE OPTIMAL FIRST-PERIOD DECISION WITH RESPECT TO COST COEFFICIENTS

	Production (p_1)	Work force (q_1)
c_1	$\mathbf{e}_1'(\mathbf{XX})_{pq}\boldsymbol{\iota}$	$\mathbf{e}_1'(\mathbf{XX})_{qq}\boldsymbol{\iota}$
c_2	$2\mathbf{e}_1'(\mathbf{XX})_{pq}(\mathbf{R}_p'^{-1}\mathbf{R}_p^{-1}\mathbf{q}^0-q_0\mathbf{e}_1)$	$2\mathbf{e}_1'(\mathbf{XX})_{qq}(\mathbf{R}_p'^{-1}\mathbf{R}_p^{-1}\mathbf{q}^0-q_0\mathbf{e}_1)$
c_3	$2\mathbf{e}_1'[(\mathbf{XX})_{pp}-c_4(\mathbf{XX})_{pq}](\mathbf{p}^0-c_4\mathbf{q}^0)$	$2\mathbf{e}_1'[(\mathbf{XX})_{qp}-c_4(\mathbf{XX})_{qq}](\mathbf{p}^0-c_4\mathbf{q}^0)$
c_4	$-2c_3\mathbf{e}_1'[(\mathbf{XX})_{pp}\mathbf{q}^0+(\mathbf{XX})_{pq}(\mathbf{p}^0-2c_4\mathbf{q}^0)]$	$-2c_3\mathbf{e}_1'[(\mathbf{XX})_{qp}\mathbf{q}^0+(\mathbf{XX})_{qq}(\mathbf{p}^0-2c_4\mathbf{q}^0)]$
c_5	$\mathbf{e}_1'(\mathbf{XX})_{pp}\boldsymbol{\iota}=0$	$\mathbf{e}_1'(\mathbf{XX})_{qp}\boldsymbol{\iota}=0$
c_6	$-\mathbf{e}_1'(\mathbf{XX})_{pq}\boldsymbol{\iota}$	$-\mathbf{e}_1'(\mathbf{XX})_{qq}\boldsymbol{\iota}$
c_7	$-2\mathbf{e}_1'(\mathbf{XX})_{pp}\mathbf{R}_p'[c_8\boldsymbol{\iota}+c_9\mathbf{v}+\mathbf{R}_p(\mathbf{v}-y_0\mathbf{e}_1-\mathbf{p}^0)]$	$-2\mathbf{e}_1'(\mathbf{XX})_{qp}\mathbf{R}_p'[c_8\boldsymbol{\iota}+c_9\mathbf{v}+\mathbf{R}_p(\mathbf{v}-y_0\mathbf{e}_1-\mathbf{p}^0)]$
c_8	$-2c_7\mathbf{e}_1'(\mathbf{XX})_{pp}\mathbf{R}_p'\boldsymbol{\iota}$	$-2c_7\mathbf{e}_1'(\mathbf{XX})_{qp}\mathbf{R}_p'\boldsymbol{\iota}$
c_9	$-2c_7\mathbf{e}_1'(\mathbf{XX})_{pp}\mathbf{R}_p'\mathbf{v}$	$-2c_7\mathbf{e}_1'(\mathbf{XX})_{qp}\mathbf{R}_p'\mathbf{v}$
c_{11}	$\mathbf{e}_1'[(\mathbf{XX})_{pp}\mathbf{q}^0+(\mathbf{XX})_{pq}\mathbf{p}^0]$	$\mathbf{e}_1'[(\mathbf{XX})_{qp}\mathbf{q}^0+(\mathbf{XX})_{qq}\mathbf{p}^0]$

We can then apply (2.19) and the expressions (1.29–(1.33) to obtain $(\mathbf{xx})_{pp}$, $(\mathbf{xx})_{pq}$, $(\mathbf{xx})_{qp}$ and $(\mathbf{xx})_{qq}$, after which these matrices have to be postmultiplied by the vectors $\boldsymbol{\iota}$, $\mathbf{R}_p'\boldsymbol{\iota}$ and $\mathbf{e}_1$ and by the matrix $\mathbf{R}_p'\mathbf{R}_p$ in accordance with (2.18). For example, it is easily seen from (2.18) that the linear dependence of $\mathbf{q}^0$ on $\mathbf{v}-y_0\mathbf{e}_1$ is measured by the coefficient matrix

$$-(\mathbf{xx})_{qp}(2c_7\mathbf{R}_p'\mathbf{R}_p) = \mathbf{Q}^{-1},$$

see (1.29) and (2.11). After some further computations one finds the optimal work force decision vector of which the tth component is:

$$\begin{aligned}(2.21)\qquad q_t^0 &= 76.28\lambda_1^t - 71.69\lambda_2^t - 4.59 &&\text{(constant term)}\\ &+ (2.585\lambda_1^t - 1.585\lambda_2^t)q_0 &&\text{(effect of initial work force)}\\ &+ [q^{t1}\ \ q^{t2}\ \ \ldots](\mathbf{v}-y_0\mathbf{e}_1) &&\text{(effect of shipments).}\end{aligned}$$

For $t = 1$ this leads to the first-period decision rule formulated at the end of 5.1.3.

In the same way we find for the coefficient matrix of the linear dependence of $\mathbf{p}^0$ on $\mathbf{v}-y_0\mathbf{e}_1$:

$$-(\mathbf{xx})_{pp}(2c_7\mathbf{R}_p'\mathbf{R}_p) = \frac{2}{2c_3c_4-c_{11}}(c_3c_4^2\mathbf{I}+c_2\mathbf{R}_p'^{-1}\mathbf{R}_p^{-1})\mathbf{Q}^{-1},$$

where use is made of (1.33). When evaluated at the values (2.5) this matrix becomes

$$(2.22)\qquad 56.7(0.100\mathbf{I}+\mathbf{R}_p'^{-1}\mathbf{R}_p^{-1})\mathbf{Q}^{-1} = [p^{tt'}],\ \text{say.}$$

It is shown in the Appendix (Section 5.C) that for $t > 1$ the typical element $p^{tt'}$ is

$$\begin{aligned}(2.23)\qquad p^{tt'} &= -0.479\lambda_1^{|t-t'|}+0.805\lambda_2^{|t-t'|}+2.382\lambda_1^{t+t'}+4.665\lambda_2^{t+t'}\\ &\quad -2.706\lambda_1^t\lambda_2^{t'}-3.848\lambda_1^{t'}\lambda_2^t\end{aligned}$$

and the typical element of $\mathbf{p}^0$ is then

$$\begin{aligned}(2.24)\qquad p_t^0 &= -304.2\lambda_1^t+578.0\lambda_2^t &&\text{(constant term)}\\ &+ (-10.31\lambda_1^t+12.78\lambda_2^t)q_0 &&\text{(effect of initial work force)}\\ &+ [p^{t1}\ \ p^{t2}\ \ \ldots](\mathbf{v}-y_0\mathbf{e}_1) &&\text{(effect of shipments),}\end{aligned}$$

provided that $t > 1$. For $t = 1$ the algebraic pattern is different but it can be read directly from (1.40).

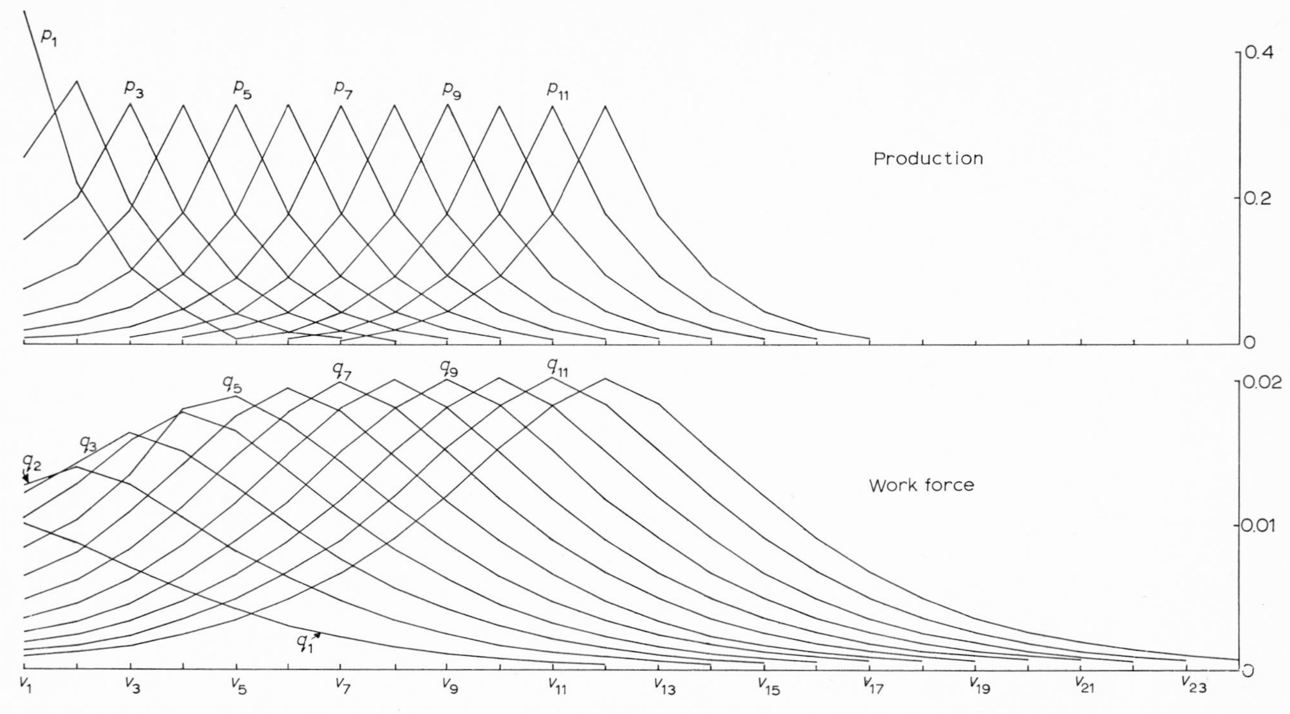

Figure 5.5. The coefficients describing the influence of the expectations of successive sales ($v_1, v_2, \ldots$) on the first-period decision (p_1, q_1) and the predicted later-period decisions ($p_2, p_3, \ldots, q_2, q_3, \ldots$) of the maximizing strategy. The horizon is infinite.

PRODUCTION AND WORK FORCE FORECASTS UP TILL TWELVE MONTHS

Month	Constant term	q_0	v_1-y_0	v_2	v_3	v_4	v_5	v_6	v_7	v_8	v_9	v_{10}	v_{11}	v_{12}	v_{13}	v_{14}	v_{15}	v_{16}	v_{17}	v_{18}	v_{19}	v_{20}	v_{21}	v_{22}	v_{23}	v_{24}
												*Production**														
1	153.1	1.007	464	236	112	47	14	−1	−7	−8	−8	−7	−5	−4	−3	−2	−2	−1	−1	−1	−0	−0	−0	−0	−0	−0
2	84.1	0.280	259	363	191	96	44	18	5	−1	−4	−4	−4	−3	−2	−2	−1	−1	−1	−1	−0	−0	−0	−0	−0	−0
3	45.0	−0.053	141	200	336	180	93	45	20	7	1	−2	−3	−3	−2	−2	−1	−1	−1	−1	−0	−0	−0	−0	−0	−0
4	23.3	−0.181	75	108	184	329	178	93	46	21	8	2	−1	−2	−2	−2	−2	−1	−1	−1	−1	−0	−0	−0	−0	−0
5	11.4	−0.210	39	56	98	179	328	177	93	47	22	9	2	−1	−2	−2	−2	−2	−1	−1	−1	−0	−0	−0	−0	−0
6	5.0	−0.195	19	28	50	95	178	327	177	93	47	22	9	2	−1	−2	−2	−2	−1	−1	−1	−1	−0	−0	−0	−0
7	1.8	−0.163	8	12	24	48	94	177	327	177	93	47	22	9	2	−1	−2	−2	−2	−1	−1	−1	−1	−0	−0	−0
8	0.3	−0.129	3	5	10	23	47	93	177	327	177	93	47	22	9	2	−1	−2	−2	−2	−1	−1	−1	−1	−0	−0
9	−0.4	−0.099	0	1	3	10	22	47	93	177	326	177	93	47	22	9	2	−1	−2	−2	−2	−1	−1	−1	−1	−0
10	−0.6	−0.073	−1	−1	0	3	9	22	47	93	177	326	177	93	47	22	9	2	−1	−2	−2	−2	−1	−1	−1	−1
11	−0.6	−0.054	−1	−1	−1	−0	3	9	22	47	93	177	326	177	93	47	22	9	2	−1	−2	−2	−2	−1	−1	−1
12	−0.6	−0.038	−1	−1	−2	−1	−0	3	9	22	47	93	177	326	177	93	47	22	9	2	−1	−2	−2	−2	−1	−1
												*Work force***														
1	2.00	0.742	100	87	70	54	41	30	22	16	11	8	5	4	3	2	1	1	1	0	0	0	0	0	0	0
2	1.97	0.541	127	140	128	106	83	63	47	34	24	17	12	9	6	4	3	2	1	1	1	0	0	0	0	0
3	1.10	0.389	122	144	164	151	126	100	76	56	41	30	21	15	10	7	5	3	2	2	1	1	1	0	0	0
4	0.01	0.276	104	127	158	179	165	138	109	83	62	45	32	23	16	11	8	5	4	3	2	1	1	1	0	0
5	−1.03	0.194	83	103	135	168	189	173	144	114	87	64	47	34	24	17	12	8	6	4	3	2	1	1	1	0
6	−1.92	0.136	64	80	108	141	175	195	178	148	117	89	66	48	34	24	17	12	8	6	4	3	2	1	1	1
7	−2.62	0.094	48	61	83	112	146	179	199	181	150	118	90	67	49	35	25	17	12	8	6	4	3	2	1	1
8	−3.17	0.065	35	45	62	86	115	149	181	200	182	151	119	90	67	49	35	25	18	12	9	6	4	3	2	1
9	−3.57	0.045	25	32	45	64	88	117	150	182	201	183	152	119	91	67	49	35	25	18	12	9	6	4	3	2
10	−3.87	0.031	18	23	33	47	65	89	118	151	183	202	183	152	120	91	67	49	35	25	18	12	9	6	4	3
11	−4.08	0.021	13	16	23	34	48	66	90	119	152	183	202	184	152	120	91	67	49	35	25	18	12	9	6	4
12	−4.24	0.014	9	12	16	24	34	48	67	90	119	152	184	202	184	152	120	91	67	49	35	25	18	12	9	6

* All shipment coefficients are multiplied by 1,000.

** All shipment coefficients are multiplied by 10,000.

It will be noted that (2.21) and (2.24) can be used—after replacing future shipments by relevant conditional expectations—to obtain decision forecasts in the manner of Table 4.1 of 4.1.7. This is an interesting by-product of the cost coefficient analysis; we shall therefore pay some attention to it. Table 5.9 contains the factors which determine the optimal production and work force decisions of the first twelve months: a constant term, a term in the initial work force, and a number of shipment terms. Twenty-four shipment terms have been considered. The result shows, as could be expected, that the effect of the initial work force decreases gradually when the decision refers to a later period; that decisions of the near future are practically independent of shipments of much later periods; also, that decisions for after a year are practically independent of to-day's shipments. The numerical outcomes are rather close to those of Table 3.7 for the six-month horizon case.

5.2.4. *Derivation of the Effect of Cost Coefficient Errors on the First-Period Decision (2)*

We have now assembled sufficient building blocks to obtain numerical results. Let us start with the "simplest" coefficients (c_1, c_6, c_8, c_9), which according to Table 5.8 do not involve the vectors $\mathbf{p}^0$ and $\mathbf{q}^0$. This table specifies that the effect of a 1 per cent error in c_1 on the first-period production decision is 0.01×340 [see (2.5)] times $\mathbf{e}_1'(\mathbf{xx})_{pq}\boldsymbol{\iota}$, i.e., times the sum of all the elements of the first row of $(\mathbf{xx})_{pq}$. Now Table 5.2 shows that these elements take the form of a weighted sum of two convergent geometric series, hence the sum of the first-row elements is easily determined. The result is that the effect of a 1 per cent c_1-error on the first-period production decision is 0.266 (in gallons per month) as is shown in the first row of Table 5.10. The effect of a 1 per cent c_6-error is $-281/340$ times this value, because the c_6-derivative in Table 5.8 is identical with that of c_1 apart from sign and (2.5) specifies $c_1 = 340$, $c_6 = 281$. The results with respect to the first-period work force decision are derived in the same way except that we should take the first row of $(\mathbf{xx})_{qq}$ instead of $(\mathbf{xx})_{pq}$.

To find the effect of a 1 per cent c_8-error we should consider the first row of $(\mathbf{xx})_{pp}\mathbf{R}_p'$ in the case of production and that of $(\mathbf{xx})_{qp}\mathbf{R}_p'$ in the case of work force. It is easily seen that the $(1, t)^{\text{th}}$ element of $(\mathbf{xx})_{pp}\mathbf{R}_p'$ is the sum of the first t elements of the first row of $(\mathbf{xx})_{pp}$, which is found by taking the sums of a finite number of elements of some geometric series. The result is that the first row of $(\mathbf{xx})_{pp}\mathbf{R}_p'$ itself takes the form of a weighted sum of geometric series,[1] so that $\mathbf{e}_1'(\mathbf{xx})_{pp}\mathbf{R}_p'\boldsymbol{\iota}$—and similarly for the work force term—is then easily determined. Regarding c_9, we find from Table 5.8 that it has the same pair of derivatives as c_8 except that $\boldsymbol{\iota}$ is replaced by $\mathbf{v}$. This means that the effect of any given error in c_9 is a homogeneous linear combination of next month's shipments (v_1), of those in the month thereafter (v_2), and so on. Suppose we consider a 0.01 error in c_9. [For all c's which are nonzero according to (2.5) we consider 1 per cent errors in Table 5.10, but this evidently makes no sense in the case of c_9.] The coefficient of v_t in the linear combination just mentioned is then $0.01 \times (-2c_7)$ times the $(1, t)^{\text{th}}$ element of $(\mathbf{xx})_{pp}\mathbf{R}_p'$ for production and $(\mathbf{xx})_{qp}\mathbf{R}_p'$ for work force. These elements have been discussed above and are given in Table 5.10 for $t = 1, \ldots, 6$. It is to be noted that shipments are measured in this table in units of 550 gallons per month, the initial work force (q_0) in units of 100 employees, and the initial inventory level (y_0) in units of 400 gallons; these units correspond approximately with the means of these variables in the period analyzed by HOLT c.s.[2] The last column of Table 5.10 contains the decision errors in case these "average" conditions materialize. The second-last column (under $\bar{v}$) is the sum of the v_t-coefficients (for all positive integers t). It specifies the decision errors involving all shipment terms when these shipments remain constant at the level mentioned.

The consequences of errors in c_2, c_3, c_4, c_7 and c_{11} involve $\mathbf{p}^0$ and $\mathbf{q}^0$. We shall consider them here except c_2 and c_7 which are more complicated—particularly c_7—and which are therefore considered in the Appendix (Section 5.C). Take c_{11}, the derivatives of which involve the first rows of the matrices $(\mathbf{xx})_{pp}$, $(\mathbf{xx})_{pq}, \ldots$, see Table 5.8. These rows are all weighted sums of geometric series, see Table 5.2. They are to be postmultiplied by $\mathbf{q}^0$ and $\mathbf{p}^0$ which have a similar structure. Consider, for example, $\mathbf{e}_1'(\mathbf{xx})_{qp}\mathbf{q}^0$; then the row $\mathbf{e}_1'(\mathbf{xx})_{qp}$ is of the form $[a_1\lambda_1^t + a_2\lambda_2^t]$, which is postmultiplied by the column of constant terms of $\mathbf{q}^0$, viz., $[76.3\lambda_1^t - 71.7\lambda_2^t - 4.6]$; see (2.21). This amounts to determining sums of infinite geometric series. The row must then be multiplied by the effect of the initial work force, which is q_0 times the column $[2.6\lambda_1^t - 1.6\lambda_2^t]$. This too amounts to adding geometric series. Then the

---

[1] Apart from constant terms which increase indefinitely with the horizon but which cancel out in the final result.

[2] See the illustrations in *Planning Production, Inventories, and Work Force* on pp. 20, 22 and 23.

TA

FIRST-PERIOD DECISION ERRORS DUE

Coefficient error	Constant term	Term in q_0	Term in y_0	v_1	v
$\Delta c_1 = 0.01 c_1$	0.266	·	·	·	·
	−0.0682	·	·	·	·
$\Delta c_2 = 0.01 c_2$	−0.018	−0.201	0.011	−0.015	0.0
	−0.0195	0.1015	0.0302	−0.0415	−0
$\Delta c_3 = 0.01 c_3$	−0.542	0.721	0.661	−0.908	−0.0
	0.0270	−0.0926	−0.0243	0.0334	0
$\Delta c_4 = 0.01 c_4$	−0.011	1.409	−0.021	0.029	−0.0
	0.0307	−0.2030	−0.0205	0.0282	0
$\Delta c_6 = 0.01 c_6$	−0.220	·	·	·	·
	0.0563	·	·	·	
$\Delta c_7 = 0.01 c_7$	0.513	−0.520	−0.671	0.923	0.0
	0.0043	−0.0089	−0.0058	0.0080	0
$\Delta c_8 = 0.01 c_8$	1.485	·	·	·	·
	0.0319	·	·	·	
$\Delta c_9 = 0.01$	·	·	·	1.256	0.6
	·	·	·	0.0071	0
$\Delta c_{11} = 0.01$	−0.008	−0.476	−0.017	0.023	0.0
	−0.0149	−0.0113	0.0180	−0.0247	−0

Notes: (1) In each cell the upper-left element refers to the production decision error and the lower-right element to the work force decision error, zero elements being indicated by dots. (2) The cost coefficient errors are all taken equal to 1 per cent of the values (2.5) except c_9 and c_{11}, for which the errors are 0.01 in the relevant

same row has to be multiplied by the effect of shipments, which is a matter of multiplication by $\mathbf{Q}^{-1}$. The typical element of that inverse matrix is given in (2.19), from which it appears that the effect of shipments in month t' on the first-period decision error involves the computation of such infinite sums as

$$\sum_{t=1}^{\infty} \lambda_1^t \lambda_2^{|t-t'|} = \lambda_2^{t'} \sum_{t=1}^{t'} (\lambda_1/\lambda_2)^t + \lambda_2^{-t'} \sum_{t>t'} (\lambda_1 \lambda_2)^t$$

$$= \lambda_1 \frac{\lambda_1^{t'} - \lambda_2^{t'}}{\lambda_1 - \lambda_2} + \lambda_1^{t'} \frac{\lambda_1 \lambda_2}{1 - \lambda_1 \lambda_2} .$$

Results of this type are then added and the outcomes are shown in Table

T ERRORS IN THE COST COEFFICIENTS

	Shipment terms				Total decision error under average conditions
	v_4	v_5	v_6	$\bar{v}$	
	.	.	.	.	0.266
.	.	.	.	.	−0.0682
57	0.065	0.058	0.044	0.195	−0.013
.0228	−0.0139	−0.0072	−0.0026	−0.0985	0.0137
21	0.127	0.079	0.032	−0.699	0.141
.0213	0.0144	0.0085	0.0041	0.0899	−0.0000
14	−0.130	−0.116	−0.088	−0.390	0.987
.0070	−0.0021	−0.0081	−0.0114	−0.0532	−0.2460
	.	.	.	.	−0.220
.	.	.	.	.	0.0563
78	−0.192	−0.137	−0.076	0.504	−0.174
.0015	−0.0005	−0.0014	−0.0015	0.0086	−0.0018
	.	.	.	.	1.485
.	.	.	.	.	0.0319
57	0.179	0.083	0.034	2.553	2.553
.0087	0.0074	0.0059	0.0046	0.0548	0.0548
06	0.122	0.120	0.107	0.893	0.391
.0169	−0.0126	−0.0090	−0.0062	−0.0993	−0.1075

dimension. (3) "Average conditions" in the last column means $q_0 = y_0 = v_t = 1$ for all t, the units being 100 employees for q_0, 400 gallons for y_0, and 550 gallons per month for v_t. (4) The same unit for v_t applies to the columns under $v_1, \ldots, v_6, \bar{v}$; the $\bar{v}$-column is the sum of all v_t-columns for $t = 1, \ldots, \infty$.

5.10. For c_3 and c_4 the procedure is analogous as will be clear from a glance at their derivatives in Table 5.8.

It is now very simple to determine the first-period loss due to 1 per cent coefficient errors under average conditions. The results are shown in Table 5.11, the diagonal elements representing the isolated loss effects of single cost coefficient errors. Thus, let d_1 be the two-element first-period decision error due to a 1 per cent error in c_1 (consisting of the first two elements of the last column of Table 5.10), then the first-period loss of this c_1-error is $d_1' H d_1$ where $H = -\frac{1}{2}(xx)_{11}^{-1}$, the elements of $(xx)_{11}$ being the leading elements of $(\mathbf{xx})_{pp}$, $(\mathbf{xx})_{pq}$, $(\mathbf{xx})_{qp}$, $(\mathbf{xx})_{qq}$ as specified in Table 5.2. This loss is \$ 0.45 per month, see the leading ele-

TABLE 5.11

FIRST-PERIOD LOSSES DUE TO ONE PERCENT ERRORS IN THE COST COEFFICIENTS UNDER AVERAGE CONDITIONS

	$\Delta c_1=0.01c_1$	$\Delta c_2=0.01c_2$	$\Delta c_3=0.01c_3$	$\Delta c_4=0.01c_4$	$\Delta c_6=0.01c_6$	$\Delta c_7=0.01c_7$	$\Delta c_8=0.01c_8$	$\Delta c_9=0.01$	$\Delta c_{11}=0.01$
				First-Period Losses (in $ per month)					
$\Delta c_1=0.01c_1$	0.4495	−0.1705	0.0373	3.2502	−0.7430	−0.0229	0.0000	0.0000	1.4106
$\Delta c_2=0.01c_2$		0.0167	−0.0034	−0.6159	0.1409	−0.0004	0.0425	0.0731	−0.2684
$\Delta c_3=0.01c_3$			0.0072	0.1371	−0.0308	−0.0175	0.1476	0.2536	0.0558
$\Delta c_4=0.01c_4$				5.8759	−2.6862	−0.0861	0.0278	0.0478	5.0997
$\Delta c_6=0.01c_6$					0.3070	0.0190	−0.0000	−0.0000	−1.1658
$\Delta c_7=0.01c_7$						0.0110	−0.1900	−0.3265	−0.0326
$\Delta c_8=0.01c_8$							0.8448	2.9040	−0.0303
$\Delta c_9=0.01$								2.4956	−0.0520
$\Delta c_{11}=0.01$									1.1070
				Decomposition of Diagonal Elements					
$(\Delta p_1)^2$	0.0258	0.0001	0.0072	0.3544	0.0176	0.0110	0.8029	2.3718	0.0557
$(\Delta q_1)^2$	0.4058	0.0165	0.0000	5.2819	0.2772	0.0003	0.0887	0.2619	1.0099
$\Delta p_1 \Delta q_1$	0.0179	0.0002	0.0000	0.2396	0.0122	−0.0003	−0.0467	−0.1380	0.0415
				Percentage Error Leading to a First-Period Loss of $ 1 per month					
	1.49	7.74	11.78	0.41	1.80	9.55	1.09	0.63	0.95

Notes: (1) The diagonal elements of the upper part of the table specify the first-period loss of a 1 per cent error in one single cost coefficient, the off-diagonal elements specify *double* cross-terms (measuring the interaction effect of errors in two coefficients). (2) The diagonal elements of the upper part are quadratic forms of the type $a(\Delta p_1)^2+b(\Delta q_1)^2+c\Delta p_1\Delta q_1$, the three components of which are specified in the three rows below the upper part. (3) For the meaning of "1 per cent errors" and "average conditions" see notes (2) and (3) of Table 5.10.

ment of Table 5.11. In the same way, we obtain $d_2' H d_2 = \$0.017$ per month for a 1 per cent error in c_2. If both errors are made at the same time, the first-period loss becomes

$$(d_1+d_2)' H(d_1+d_2) = d_1' H d_1 + d_2' H d_2 + 2d_1' H d_2,$$

which shows that we then need twice the cross-term, $2d_1' H d_2$. Such terms are given in the off-diagonal elements of the table. In the present case we have $2d_1' H d_2 = -\$0.17$ per month, which shows that errors in c_1 and c_2 of the same sign tend to compensate each other.

5.2.5. Discussion of the Numerical Results

Before proceeding to a discussion of the results collected in Tables 5.10 and 5.11 we wish to make three preliminary remarks. First, these tables apply to the special case when the errors are 1 per cent of the values given in (2.5), but the results can be easily adjusted for other errors. For example, let there be a simultaneous error of k_1 per cent in c_1 and k_2 per cent in c_2; then the decision error is k_1 times the two-element column vector of first-period decision errors corresponding with a 1 per cent error in c_1 plus k_2 times the similar vector for a 1 per cent error in c_2, apart from the discrepancies of linearization. The first-period loss due to this simultaneous coefficient error is, in the notation used at the end of 5.2.4,

$$k_1^2(d_1' H d_1) + k_2^2(d_2' H d_2) + k_1 k_2(2d_1' H d_2),$$

again apart from the discrepancies just mentioned. Such losses due to error combinations can therefore be easily determined. It is also straightforward to compute the coefficient errors which lead to any given first-period loss. For example, take such a loss of \$1 per month. This is realized by a c_1-error of $1/\sqrt{0.45} = 1.49$ per cent or by a c_2-error of $1/\sqrt{0.017} = 7.74$ per cent. These figures are given in the last row of Table 5.11. The three rows immediately above the last row contain the decomposition of the diagonal elements of the upper part of that table in terms of the squared production error, the squared work force error, and the product of these.

The second remark deals with the use of the outcomes as a guide to research on cost coefficients. It is evidently useful to know the financial consequences of a 1 per cent error in $c_1, c_2, \ldots$; on the other hand, they do not tell the whole story. One should also have some idea about the probable magnitude of such errors and about the financial sacrifices which have to be made if one wishes to improve on the estimates. These topics are beyond the scope of the present chapter, but further progress in this direction will be made in Chapter 6 (see particularly 6.1.5) and Chapter 7 (see 7.1.2). The third point, finally, has to do with an alternative use of the results of Table 5.10. Suppose that the wages and hence the regular payroll costs go up in such a way that c_1 increases by 1 per cent. Then the factory manager's optimal behaviour pattern is changed in a way which can be read directly from Table 5.10: the optimal work force decreases by 0.068 and the optimal production increases by 0.266.[1] In other words, we can use this table to adjust the decision rules when the cost coefficients change.

The results of Tables 5.10 and 5.11 can be discussed conveniently under the following four headings corresponding with the four components of the cost function, (2.1)–(2.4):

(i) *Regular payroll costs* (c_1). Starting from a supposedly "true" value $c_1 = 340$, so that a 1 per cent error amounts to $\Delta c_1 = 3.4$, we find from Table 5.10 a positive first-period production error of slightly more than $\frac{1}{4}$ and a negative first-period work force error of slightly less than 0.07. If we compare these discrepancies with the average production of 550 gallons per month and the average work force of 100 employees, we must conclude that they are relatively small: 0.05 and -0.07 per cent respectively. We may also say that the decision rules are rather insensitive to alternative specifications of and changes in the c_1-coefficient. The first-period loss of a 1 per cent c_1-error is \$ 0.45 per month; or, alternatively, it takes a $1\frac{1}{2}$ per cent error to have a loss of \$ 1 per month, a 15 per cent error for a loss of \$ 100 per month, etc. Note that these loss statements are valid only if the c_1-error is considered in isolation, i.e., if there are no errors in the other c's. When this condition is not satisfied we have to consider the interaction effects of c_1 with $c_2, c_3, \ldots$ (see the off-diagonal elements in the first row of Table 5.11); these effects will be discussed below when the relevant coefficient errors are considered.

(ii) *Hiring and layoff costs* (c_2, c_{10}). We already know that c_{10}-errors have no effects. Regarding c_2, this coefficient unlike c_1 has the property that it leads to decision errors which depend on the initial work force, the initial inventory level, and future shipments. Under average conditions

[1] A wage increase will in general also affect overtime costs, so that other coefficients have then to be adjusted as well. But this is straightforward.

a 1 per cent error in c_2 implies decision errors of opposite sign compared with those of c_1, but the production error is numerically negligible. The work force error is also smaller in absolute value than in the c_1-case and the result of all this is that the loss consequences of a 1 per cent c_2-error are considerably smaller than those of a c_1-error of the same relative size. The interaction term for c_1 and c_2 is negative, which is the natural result of the opposite signs of the decision errors.

These numerical statements apply only to average conditions. When conditions are not "average" we cannot confine ourselves to the last elements of the c_2-rows in Table 5.10; instead, we should analyze the dependence of the production and work force decision errors on q_0, y_0 and v_t. Suppose then that the factory is 50 per cent larger than average in the sense that $q_0 = y_0 = v_t = 1.5$ for all t. Given the constant term of -0.018 and the total error of -0.013 under average conditions we find that the production decision error under the new condition is

$$-0.018+1.5(-0.013+0.018) = -0.011.$$

In this way one can compute easily the first-period decision errors due to any given c_2-error under any other set of conditions in which v_t is the same for all t. If v_t changes over time one needs the columns under v_1, v_2, . . . in Table 5.10. This table shows that as far as c_2 and the production decision are concerned, an increase in the coefficient value leads to a reduced dependence of the first-period decision on first-period shipments and an increased dependence on later shipments. For work force this dependence is reduced as far as the v's are shown in the table; the effect is opposite but of minor numerical importance for shipments farther ahead than half a year.

(iii) *Overtime costs* (c_3, c_4, c_5, c_6, c_{11}). Errors in c_5 have been found to have no effect on decisions and losses. The coefficient c_6 plays a role which is completely analogous to that of c_1 apart from sign, see, e.g., Table 5.7 .The result is that as in the case of c_1 the decision errors caused by a 1 percent c_6-error consist only of a constant term, but they have signs opposite to those of a 1 per cent c_1-error. We should therefore expect that the interaction term in the first-period loss of (c_1, c_6) is negative and that of (c_2, c_6) positive, and Table 5.11 shows that this is indeed the case. As the c_6-value of (2.5) is almost 20 per cent below that of c_1, the loss consequences are reduced accordingly.

Regarding c_3, we find that a 1 per cent error in this coefficient has only minor consequences, at least under average conditions. The effect on the first-period work force decision is practically nil and that on production about half of the effect of a 1 per cent c_1-error. The result is that a 12 per cent error in c_3 is needed to produce a loss of \$ 1 per month. For c_4 the situation is different. It will be remembered that this coefficient measures the capacity per employee. If it is overestimated by 1 per cent, there is under average conditions a production decision error of almost 1 accompanied by a negative work force error of almost $\frac{1}{4}$. These figures are higher than any of the values discussed so far; the result is that a 0.4 per cent error is sufficient for a \$ 1 per month first-period loss. That the work force decision error is negative is intuitively plausible. For suppose that there is an actual increase in the capacity per employee; then fewer men are necessary, which leads to a layoff. But there is the quadratic hiring and layoff cost function, which implies a considerable penalty on a large layoff. Thus it is also intuitively plausible that the increase in capacity leads to a rather small layoff in the first month and hence to an increased rate of production in that month.

Finally, we have c_{11}, which is the coefficient of the bilinear term $p_t q_t$ in the overtime cost function and which vanishes according to (2.5). If that is the correct specification and if a positive value is actually applied, the result under average conditions is a positive production error and a negative work force error. Table 5.10 shows that the shipment part of the former error increases in importance from v_1 till v_4, after which it decreases gradually.

(iv) *Inventory connected costs* (c_7, c_8, c_9). The coefficients considered up till now have all in common that if they are specified erroneously, they lead to decision errors in production and work force which are of opposite sign under average conditions. This feature as such is not favourable, because the first-period loss is a quadratic form whose 2×2 matrix, $-\frac{1}{2}(xx)_{11}^{-1}$, has negative off-diagonal elements; hence decision errors of opposite sign re-inforce each other, which is illustrated by the positive $\Delta p_1 \Delta q_1$-terms of Table 5.11. The opposite holds for the coefficients of the inventory cost function: their errors lead to decision errors which are either both positive or both negative, so that the $\Delta p_1 \Delta q_1$-terms are now negative. Another difference with most of the previous coefficients is that the loss consequences of their erroneous specification are here mainly due to the effect on the production decision. One of the present coefficients, c_7, has however only minor effects under average conditions. A 10 per cent error is necessary to lead to a \$ 1 loss per month, so that it is comparable with c_3 in this respect. Errors in c_8 are more serious: a 1 per cent error leads to a production decision error of almost $1\frac{1}{2}$, which exceeds all production errors considered so far. The positive sign of this decision error is plausible: we recall that c_8 stands for the optimal inventory level and hence, when this level is overstated, it stands to reason that too much will be produced to obtain that larger inventory. Regarding c_9, finally, this coefficient is the only one which leads to decision errors in the form of a homogeneous linear combination of future shipments. It describes the dependence of the optimal inventory level on the shipments of the same period and its value is zero according to (2.5). A positive specification error has qualitatively the same consequences as a positive error in c_8, as could be guessed: it leads to a positive production decision error and also to a positive work force error.

5.2.6. Summary

(1) The problem of this section is to analyze the first-period decision and loss consequences of imperfect specifications of the coefficients of the cost function in the infinite-horizon case. The original specification contains zero values for some of the coefficients, which necessitates a (minor) reformulation of the cost function compared with that of Section 5.1.

(2, 3, 4) The procedure adopted consists of the following steps. First, the effect of given cost coefficient errors on the coefficient matrices of the preference function is analyzed. Second, one has to trace the effect of these coefficient matrices on the first-period production and work force decisions. Finally, the first-period loss of these decision errors has to be computed. It turns out (i) that errors in certain cost coefficients have no consequences whatsoever on the first-period decision, (ii) that errors in certain other coefficients lead to decision errors whose size depends on the development of future shipments, and (iii) that it is necessary to evaluate algebraically the optimal production and work force decision for all future periods, not only for the first period as was done in Section 5.1. [The derivations mentioned under (iii) are not only useful for tracing the effects of cost coefficient errors but also for the formulation of predictions of the future behaviour according to the maximizing strategy.]

(5) On the whole it turns out that cost coefficient errors do not lead to very large losses or, what amounts to the same thing, that the decision rules for production and work force are not very sensitive to cost coefficient changes. Coefficient errors dealing with regular payroll costs, hiring

and layoff costs, and overtime costs lead to production and work force decision errors of opposite sign, at least when the level of shipments is equal to the average level during the period for which the cost function was fitted; furthermore, the work force error is dominant in the sense that it is responsible for the greater part of the first-period loss. In contrast to this the coefficients of the inventory cost function, if erroneously specified, lead to production and work force errors of the same sign and the former decision error dominates the latter. If we consider 1 per cent errors in the various cost coefficients, it turns out that the largest first-period loss is made by an error in the coefficient which measures the output capacity per employee. The coefficient by which the square of the discrepancy between actual and capacity output is multiplied and the similar discrepancy coefficients of the inventory cost function and the hiring and layoff cost function lead to the smallest losses.

Appendix to Chapter 5

5.A. THE INVERSION OF AN INFINITE BAND MATRIX (1)

The first two rows and columns of the inverse of an infinite band matrix like **Q** as defined in (1.38) can be derived as follows. Let us write $q^{tt'}$ for the typical element of $\mathbf{Q}^{-1}$. Then we postmultiply the successive rows of **Q** by the first column of $\mathbf{Q}^{-1}$, which leads to the following system of an infinite number of linear equations:

$$\text{(A.1)} \qquad \begin{aligned} &a'q^{11}+b'q^{21}+cq^{31} &&= 1 \\ &bq^{11}+aq^{21}+bq^{31}+cq^{41} &&= 0 \\ &cq^{11}+bq^{21}+aq^{31}+bq^{41}+cq^{51} &&= 0 \\ &cq^{21}+bq^{31}+aq^{41}+bq^{51}+cq^{61} &&= 0 \\ &cq^{31}+bq^{41}+aq^{51}+bq^{61}+cq^{71} &&= 0 \\ &\ldots\ldots\ldots\ldots\ldots\ldots \end{aligned}$$

Hence we have

$$\text{(A.2)} \qquad cq^{t1}+bq^{t+1,1}+aq^{t+2,1}+bq^{t+3,1}+cq^{t+4,1} = 0 \quad \text{for } t > 0,$$

which can be regarded as an ordinary difference equation with the following characteristic equation:

$$\text{(A.3)} \qquad c\lambda^4+b\lambda^3+a\lambda^2+b\lambda+c = 0.$$

Since $c \neq 0$, there is no solution $\lambda = 0$, so that we can define

$$\text{(A.4)} \qquad \lambda' = \lambda+\frac{1}{\lambda}.$$

On substituting this in (A.3), we find that this characteristic equation can be simplified to

$$\text{(A.5)} \qquad c\lambda'^2+b\lambda'+(a-2c) = 0.$$

This is an ordinary quadratic equation, the roots of which are

$$\text{(A.6)} \qquad \lambda' = \frac{-b\pm\sqrt{b^2-4c(a-2c)}}{2c};$$

given each solution λ', we can find two solutions for λ from (A.4), which is also a quadratic equation (in λ):

$$\lambda = \frac{\lambda' \pm \sqrt{\lambda'^2 - 4}}{2}. \tag{A.7}$$

We thus find four solutions of the characteristic equation (A.3), two of which are positive and smaller than 1:

$$\lambda_1 = 0.6637615, \quad \lambda_2 = 0.614298, \tag{A.8}$$

while the two other roots are larger than 1:

$$\lambda_3 = 1.5065655, \quad \lambda_4 = 1.627875. \tag{A.9}$$

It is easily seen that $\lambda_1 \lambda_3 = \lambda_2 \lambda_4 = 1$ and that, more generally, the four solutions of (A.3) must be pairwise reciprocal to each other, because if some λ satisfies (A.4), so must $1/\lambda$. In deriving (A.8) and (A.9), use has been made of the *a*, *b*, and *c*-specifications given in the text below equation (1.38).

The general solution of the difference equation (A.2) is therefore

$$q^{t1} = A_1 \lambda_1^t + A_2 \lambda_2^t + A_3 \lambda_3^t + A_4 \lambda_4^t, \tag{A.10}$$

where the λ's are given in (A.8)–(A.9) and the A's are constants to be determined. It is obvious that A_3 and A_4 should be zero, because otherwise the successive elements of the first column of $\mathbf{Q}^{-1}$ would increase beyond limits (so that the first-period decision of the maximizing strategy would "explode," its dependence on future sales increasing with time).[1] Furthermore, A_1 and A_2 can be found by substituting (A.10) in the first two equations of (A.1):

$$\begin{aligned} &a'(A_1\lambda_1 + A_2\lambda_2) + b'(A_1\lambda_1^2 + A_2\lambda_2^2) + c(A_1\lambda_1^3 + A_2\lambda_2^3) = 1 \\ &b(A_1\lambda_1 + A_2\lambda_2) + a(A_1\lambda_1^2 + A_2\lambda_2^2) + b(A_1\lambda_1^3 + A_2\lambda_2^3) \\ &\qquad + c(A_1\lambda_1^4 + A_2\lambda_2^4) = 0, \end{aligned} \tag{A.11}$$

[1] That A_3 and A_4 should be zero can also be proved directly along the following lines. Supposing that we consider a finite horizon consisting of T months, then (A.1) is a T-equation system whose last two equations are

$$\begin{aligned} cq^{T-3,1} + bq^{T-2,1} + aq^{T-1,1} + b'q^{T1} &= 0 \\ cq^{T-2,1} + bq^{T-1,1} + a''q^{T1} &= 0, \end{aligned}$$

where $a'' = (3c_2c_3 + c_2c_7 + c_3c_4^2c_7)/c_3c_4c_7 = 474.7$. Then we can solve the four A's of (A.10) by substitution in these two equations and in the first two equations of (A.1). On taking the limit for $T \to \infty$ we find $A_3 = A_4 = 0$. See C. VAN DE PANNE and G. J. AEYELTS AVERINK, "Imperfect Management Decisions and Predictions and Their Financial Implications in Dynamic Quadratic Cost Minimization," *Statistica Neerlandica*, Vol. 15 (1961), pp. 293–318, particularly Appendix B.

which gives

$$A_1 = -A_2 = 0.20131921$$

in accordance with (1.39).

For the elements of the first row of $\mathbf{Q}^{-1}$ one can proceed in precisely the same way except that one should multiply this row by the successive columns of $\mathbf{Q}$, rather than multiply the successive rows of $\mathbf{Q}$ by the first column of $\mathbf{Q}^{-1}$ as we did in the beginning of this section. For the elements of the second row and column, too, the procedure is identical, except that in the two-equation system (A.11) the right-hand 1 is now placed in the second equation. The result is that the tth element is a weighted sum of λ_1^t and λ_2^t with the following weights:

first row: 0.07764922 and −0.06769126
second row: 0.18958862 and −0.18413664
second column: 0.26555888 and −0.27283376.

5.B. EXPECTED FIRST-PERIOD LOSSES DUE TO SALES FORECAST ERRORS IN THE INFINITE-HORIZON CASE

We shall consider the matrix

$$(\text{B.1}) \qquad -\tfrac{1}{2}\mathbf{R}_p' \begin{bmatrix} (\cdot x)_{11} \\ \vdots \\ (\cdot x)_{T1} \end{bmatrix} (xx)_{11}^{-1}[(x\cdot)_{11} \;\ldots\; (x\cdot)_{1T}]\mathbf{R}_p$$

of the first-period loss associated with a sales forecast error $\Delta\mathbf{v}$ for the limiting case in which T increases beyond limits. An inspection of Table 5.2 shows that we should multiply $-\frac{1}{2}$ by

$$(\text{B.2}) \quad \mathbf{R}_p' \begin{bmatrix} (\cdot x)_{11} \\ (\cdot x)_{21} \\ \vdots \end{bmatrix} = \begin{bmatrix} 1 & 1 & 1 & \ldots \\ 0 & 1 & 1 & \ldots \\ 0 & 0 & 1 & \ldots \\ \vdots & \vdots & \vdots & \end{bmatrix} \begin{bmatrix} a_1\lambda_1 + a_2\lambda_2 & b_1\lambda_1 + b_2\lambda_2 \\ a_1\lambda_1^2 + a_2\lambda_2^2 & b_1\lambda_1^2 + b_2\lambda_2^2 \\ \vdots & \vdots \end{bmatrix}$$

$$= \begin{bmatrix} \dfrac{a_1\lambda_1}{1-\lambda_1} + \dfrac{a_2\lambda_2}{1-\lambda_2} & \dfrac{b_1\lambda_1}{1-\lambda_1} + \dfrac{b_2\lambda_2}{1-\lambda_2} \\ \dfrac{a_1\lambda_1^2}{1-\lambda_1} + \dfrac{a_2\lambda_2^2}{1-\lambda_2} & \dfrac{b_1\lambda_1^2}{1-\lambda_1} + \dfrac{b_2\lambda_2^2}{1-\lambda_2} \\ \vdots & \vdots \end{bmatrix},$$

where λ_1 and λ_2 are given in (A.8) and $a_1 = 0.5057$, $a_2 = -0.9182$,

$b_1 = -0.02611$, $b_2 = 0.02611$. We should then postmultiply by $(xx)_{11}^{-1}$, which is a 2×2 matrix of known coefficients (see Table 5.2), after which the result is to be postmultiplied by the transpose of the matrix (B.2). It follows that (B.1) is of the form

$$\text{(B.3)} \qquad \begin{bmatrix} d_1\lambda_1 + d_2\lambda_2 & d_3\lambda_1 + d_4\lambda_2 \\ d_1\lambda_1^2 + d_2\lambda_2^2 & d_3\lambda_1^2 + d_4\lambda_2^2 \\ \vdots & \vdots \end{bmatrix} \begin{bmatrix} e_{11} & e_{12} \\ e_{21} & e_{22} \end{bmatrix}$$

$$\times \begin{bmatrix} d_1\lambda_1 + d_2\lambda_2 & d_1\lambda_1^2 + d_2\lambda_2^2 & \dots \\ d_3\lambda_1 + d_4\lambda_2 & d_3\lambda_1^2 + d_4\lambda_2^2 & \dots \end{bmatrix},$$

where $d_1 = a_1/(1-\lambda_1)$, e_{11} is the leading element of $-\frac{1}{2}(xx)_{11}^{-1}$, and so on. The typical $(t, t')^{\text{th}}$ element of (B.1) [and of (B.3)] is then

$$\text{(B.4)} \qquad A\lambda_1^{t+t'} + B\lambda_2^{t+t'} - C(\lambda_1^t\lambda_2^{t'} + \lambda_1^{t'}\lambda_2^t),$$

where

$$\text{(B.5)} \qquad A = 1.4654, \qquad B = 2.6225, \qquad C = 1.9041.$$

The expected first-period loss associated with a sales forecast procedure which satisfies assumptions (3.2.35)–(3.2.36) can then be written as the sum of

$$\text{(B.6)} \qquad \sigma_0^2 \sum_{t=1}^{\infty} (A\lambda_1^{2t} + B\lambda_2^{2t} - 2C\lambda_1^t\lambda_2^t)(1+\theta)^t$$

and

$$\text{(B.7)} \quad 2\sigma_0^2 \sum_{t=1}^{\infty} \sum_{\substack{t'=1 \\ t<t'}}^{\infty} [A\lambda_1^{t+t'} + B\lambda_2^{t+t'} - C(\lambda_1^t\lambda_2^{t'} + \lambda_1^{t'}\lambda_2^t)]\rho^{t'-t}(1+\theta)^{\frac{1}{2}(t+t')}.$$

These are sums of geometric series, the evaluation of which is straightforward. Applying the numerical specifications (A.8) and (B.5), we obtain for (B.6):

$$\text{(B.8)} \ \sigma_0^2(1+\theta)\left[\frac{0.6456}{1-0.4406(1+\theta)} + \frac{0.9896}{1-0.3774(1+\theta)} - \frac{1.5527}{1-0.4077(1+\theta)}\right],$$

which is the expected first-period loss in case $\rho = 0$. For $\rho \neq 0$ we have to add (B.7), which can be written as $\sigma_0^2(1+\theta)^{1\frac{1}{2}}\rho$ times the sum of the following four terms:

$$\text{(B.9)} \quad \frac{0.8571}{1-0.6638(1+\theta)^{\frac{1}{2}}/\rho}\left[\frac{1}{1-0.6638(1+\theta)^{\frac{1}{2}}\rho} - \frac{0.6638(1+\theta)^{\frac{1}{2}}}{\rho - 0.4406(1+\theta)\rho}\right]$$

$$\text{(B.10)} \quad \frac{1.2158}{1-0.6143(1+\theta)^{\frac{1}{2}}/\rho}\left[\frac{1}{1-0.6143(1+\theta)^{\frac{1}{2}}\rho} - \frac{0.6143(1+\theta)^{\frac{1}{2}}}{\rho - 0.3774(1+\theta)\rho}\right]$$

$$\text{(B.11)}\quad \frac{-1.0307}{1-0.6143(1+\theta)^{\frac{1}{2}}/\rho}\left[\frac{1}{1-0.6638(1+\theta)^{\frac{1}{2}}\rho}-\frac{0.6143(1+\theta)^{\frac{1}{2}}}{\rho-0.4077(1+\theta)\rho}\right]$$

$$\text{(B.12)}\quad \frac{-0.9539}{1-0.6638(1+\theta)^{\frac{1}{2}}/\rho}\left[\frac{1}{1-0.6143(1+\theta)^{\frac{1}{2}}\rho}-\frac{0.6638(1+\theta)^{\frac{1}{2}}}{\rho-0.4077(1+\theta)\rho}\right].$$

These are the expressions on which Table 5.6 is based. It is to be noted that the convergence of the sums (B.6)–(B.7) requires that the square of the largest root ($\lambda_1^2 = 0.4406$) be smaller than the reciprocal of $1+\theta$. This is satisfied by Table 5.6, since $\theta \leqq 1$.

5.C. THE INVERSION OF AN INFINITE BAND MATRIX (2)

5.C.1. Q as the Product of Four Simpler Matrices

To obtain all elements $q^{tt'}$ of $\mathbf{Q}^{-1}$ we can in principle proceed along the lines of Section 5.A, but we are then faced with a difficulty of the following kind. Suppose that we wish to derive the fourth column, say, of $\mathbf{Q}^{-1}$. Then the right-hand unit which appears in the first equation of (A.1) and (A.11) is replaced by a zero, and the unit reappears in the fourth equation. It is then no longer true that a difference equation of the type (A.2) holds for all $t > 0$. To avoid this complication we shall follow a different approach: $\mathbf{Q}$ will be written as the product of four matrices, each of which is relatively easy to invert. First, we write $\mathbf{Q}$ as a positive scalar (d_1^2) times the product of two triangular matrices $\mathbf{D}_1$ and $\mathbf{D}_2$ with units on the diagonal (apart from the leading element of $\mathbf{D}_1$):

$$\text{(C.1)}\qquad \mathbf{Q} = \begin{bmatrix} a' & b' & c & 0 & 0 & \cdots \\ b & a & b & c & 0 & \cdots \\ c & b & a & b & c & \cdots \\ 0 & c & b & a & b & \cdots \\ 0 & 0 & c & b & a & \cdots \\ \vdots & \vdots & \vdots & \vdots & \vdots & \end{bmatrix} = d_1^2 \mathbf{D}_1 \mathbf{D}_2,$$

where

$$\text{(C.2)}\quad \mathbf{D}_1 = \begin{bmatrix} d' & d_2' & d_3 & 0 & 0 & \cdots \\ 0 & 1 & d_2 & d_3 & 0 & \cdots \\ 0 & 0 & 1 & d_2 & d_3 & \cdots \\ 0 & 0 & 0 & 1 & d_2 & \cdots \\ 0 & 0 & 0 & 0 & 1 & \cdots \\ \vdots & \vdots & \vdots & \vdots & \vdots & \end{bmatrix}, \qquad \mathbf{D}_2 = \begin{bmatrix} 1 & 0 & 0 & 0 & 0 & \cdots \\ d_2 & 1 & 0 & 0 & 0 & \cdots \\ d_3 & d_2 & 1 & 0 & 0 & \cdots \\ 0 & d_3 & d_2 & 1 & 0 & \cdots \\ 0 & 0 & d_3 & d_2 & 1 & \cdots \\ \vdots & \vdots & \vdots & \vdots & \vdots & \end{bmatrix}.$$

The d's are to be found from the following equations:

$$d_1^2(1+d_2^2+d_3^2) = a \tag{C.3}$$

$$d_1^2(d_2+d_2 d_3) = b \tag{C.4}$$

$$d_1^2 d_3 = c \tag{C.5}$$

$$d_1^2(d'+d_2' d_2+d_3^2) = a' \tag{C.6}$$

$$d_1^2(d_2'+d_2 d_3) = b'. \tag{C.7}$$

Equations (C.3)–(C.5) enable us to obtain solutions for d_1, d_2, d_3.[1] By adding twice (C.4) and twice (C.5) to (C.3) we obtain the square of $d_1(1+d_2+d_3)$ which equals $a+2b+2c$; by subtracting twice (C.4) and adding twice (C.5) we obtain the square of $d_1(1-d_2+d_3)$ which equals $a-2b+2c$. If we take square roots and subtract we obtain

$$2d_1 d_2 = \sqrt{a+2b+2c}-\sqrt{a-2b+2c} \tag{C.8}$$

and similarly by adding instead of subtracting:

$$2d_1(1+d_3) = \sqrt{a+2b+2c}+\sqrt{a-2b+2c}. \tag{C.9}$$

From (C.5) we have $d_1\sqrt{d_3} = \sqrt{c}$, which together with (C.9) specifies $2(1+d_3)/\sqrt{d_3}$ in terms of a, b and c. This is a quadratic equation from which d_3 can be solved. We can then find d_1 from (C.5), d_2 from (C.8), d_2' from (C.7), and d' from (C.6). In numerical terms the result is as follows:

$$\begin{array}{llll} d_1 = & 18.36080 & d' = & 0.29788 \\ d_2 = & -1.27806 & d_2' = & -0.87031. \\ d_3 = & 0.40775 & & \end{array} \tag{C.10}$$

The next step implies that we write each of the triangular matrices $\mathbf{D}_1$ and $\mathbf{D}_2$ as the product of two other triangular matrices of simpler form:

$$\mathbf{D}_1 = \mathbf{D}_3\mathbf{D}_4 \quad \text{and} \quad \mathbf{D}_2 = \mathbf{D}_5\mathbf{D}_6, \tag{C.11}$$

where

$$\mathbf{D}_3 = \begin{bmatrix} d''-\lambda_1 & 0 & 0 & \dots \\ 0 & 1 & -\lambda_1 & 0 & \dots \\ 0 & 0 & 1 & -\lambda_1 & \dots \\ 0 & 0 & 0 & 1 & \dots \\ \vdots & \vdots & \vdots & \vdots & \end{bmatrix}, \quad \mathbf{D}_4 = \begin{bmatrix} d'''-\lambda_2 & 0 & 0 & \dots \\ 0 & 1 & -\lambda_2 & 0 & \dots \\ 0 & 0 & 1 & -\lambda_2 & \dots \\ 0 & 0 & 0 & 1 & \dots \\ \vdots & \vdots & \vdots & \vdots & \end{bmatrix}; \tag{C.12}$$

[1] Note that these solutions are not unique. If d_1, d_2, d_3 is one solution, then $d_1^* = d_1 d_3$, $d_2^* = d_2/d_3$, $d_3^* = 1/d_3$ is also a solution.

$$\text{(C.13)}\quad \mathbf{D}_5 = \begin{bmatrix} 1 & 0 & 0 & 0 \dots \\ -\lambda_1 & 1 & 0 & 0 \dots \\ 0 & -\lambda_1 & 1 & 0 \dots \\ 0 & 0 & -\lambda_1 & 1 \dots \\ \vdots & \vdots & \vdots & \vdots \end{bmatrix}, \mathbf{D}_6 = \begin{bmatrix} 1 & 0 & 0 & 0 \dots \\ -\lambda_2 & 1 & 0 & 0 \dots \\ 0 & -\lambda_2 & 1 & 0 \dots \\ 0 & 0 & -\lambda_2 & 1 \dots \\ \vdots & \vdots & \vdots & \vdots \end{bmatrix}.$$

These four matrices involve four parameters, d'', d''', λ_1 and λ_2, of which the last two take the values (A.8). The first two are

$$\text{(C.14)}\quad d'' = \frac{-d_2' - \lambda_1}{\lambda_2} = 0.33624, \quad d''' = \frac{-d'\lambda_2}{d_2' + \lambda_1} = 0.88593.$$

5.C.2. The Inversion

On combining (C.1) and (C.11) we find

$$\text{(C.15)}\qquad \mathbf{Q}^{-1} = (d_1^2 \mathbf{D}_3 \mathbf{D}_4 \mathbf{D}_5 \mathbf{D}_6)^{-1} = \frac{1}{d_1^2} \mathbf{D}_6^{-1} \mathbf{D}_5^{-1} \mathbf{D}_4^{-1} \mathbf{D}_3^{-1}.$$

The simplest inverses are those of $\mathbf{D}_5$ and $\mathbf{D}_6$. We have

$$\text{(C.16)}\qquad \mathbf{D}_5^{-1} = \begin{bmatrix} 1 & 0 & 0 & 0 & \dots \\ \lambda_1 & 1 & 0 & 0 & \dots \\ \lambda_1^2 & \lambda_1 & 1 & 0 & \dots \\ \lambda_1^3 & \lambda_1^2 & \lambda_1 & 1 & \dots \\ \vdots & \vdots & \vdots & \vdots & \end{bmatrix}$$

and similarly for $\mathbf{D}_6^{-1}$ in terms of λ_2. Their product takes the form:

$$\text{(C.17)}\quad \mathbf{D}_6^{-1}\mathbf{D}_5^{-1} = \frac{1}{\lambda_1 - \lambda_2} \begin{bmatrix} \lambda_1 - \lambda_2 & 0 & 0 & 0 & \dots \\ \lambda_1^2 - \lambda_2^2 & \lambda_1 - \lambda_2 & 0 & 0 & \dots \\ \lambda_1^3 - \lambda_2^3 & \lambda_1^2 - \lambda_2^2 & \lambda_1 - \lambda_2 & 0 & \dots \\ \lambda_1^4 - \lambda_2^4 & \lambda_1^3 - \lambda_2^3 & \lambda_1^2 - \lambda_2^2 & \lambda_1 - \lambda_2 & \dots \\ \vdots & \vdots & \vdots & \vdots & \end{bmatrix}.$$

To find $\mathbf{D}_3^{-1}$ we notice first that $\mathbf{D}_3$ can be easily expressed in terms of $\mathbf{D}_5$:

$$\text{(C.18)}\qquad \mathbf{D}_3 = \mathbf{D}_5' \begin{bmatrix} d'' & 0 & 0 & 0 & \dots \\ 0 & 1 & 0 & 0 & \dots \\ 0 & 0 & 1 & 0 & \dots \\ 0 & 0 & 0 & 1 & \dots \\ \vdots & \vdots & \vdots & \vdots & \end{bmatrix},$$

so that $\mathbf{D}_3^{-1}$ is obtained by transposing $\mathbf{D}_5^{-1}$ as specified in (C.16) and multiplying the first row by $1/d''$:

$$\text{(C.19)} \qquad \mathbf{D}_3^{-1} = \begin{bmatrix} 1/d'' & \lambda_1/d'' & \lambda_1^2/d'' & \lambda_1^3/d'' & \dots \\ 0 & 1 & \lambda_1 & \lambda_1^2 & \dots \\ 0 & 0 & 1 & \lambda_1 & \dots \\ 0 & 0 & 0 & 1 & \dots \\ \vdots & \vdots & \vdots & \vdots & \end{bmatrix}.$$

$\mathbf{D}_4^{-1}$ is similar except that λ_1 and d'' are replaced by λ_2 and d''' respectively. Their product is

$$\text{(C.20)} \quad \mathbf{D}_4^{-1}\mathbf{D}_3^{-1} =$$

$$\frac{1}{\lambda_1-\lambda_2}\begin{bmatrix} d_4\lambda_1-d_5\lambda_2 & d_4\lambda_1^2-d_5\lambda_2^2 & d_4\lambda_1^3-d_5\lambda_2^3 & d_4\lambda_1^4-d_5\lambda_1^4 & \dots \\ 0 & \lambda_1-\lambda_2 & \lambda_1^2-\lambda_2^2 & \lambda_1^3-\lambda_2^3 & \dots \\ 0 & 0 & \lambda_1-\lambda_2 & \lambda_1^2-\lambda_2^2 & \dots \\ 0 & 0 & 0 & \lambda_1-\lambda_2 & \dots \\ \vdots & \vdots & \vdots & \vdots & \end{bmatrix},$$

where

$$\text{(C.21)} \qquad d_4 = \frac{1}{d'''}\{1-(1-1/d'')(1-\lambda_2/\lambda_1)\} = 1.2948$$

$$\text{(C.22)} \qquad d_5 = 1/d''' = 1.1288.$$

On combining (C.15), (C.17) and (C.20) we find that $q^{tt'}$ is the reciprocal of $d_1^2(\lambda_1-\lambda_2)^2$ times the product of the row

$$[\lambda_1^t-\lambda_2^t \quad \lambda_1^{t-1}-\lambda_2^{t-1} \quad \dots \quad \lambda_1-\lambda_2 \quad 0 \quad 0 \quad \dots]$$

and the column

$$\{d_4\lambda_1^{t'}-d_5\lambda_2^{t'} \quad \lambda_1^{t'-1}-\lambda_2^{t'-1} \quad \dots \quad \lambda_1-\lambda_2 \quad 0 \quad 0 \quad \dots\},$$

in other words:

$$\text{(C.23)} \qquad q^{tt'} = \frac{1}{d_1^2(\lambda_1-\lambda_2)^2}\{(\lambda_1^t-\lambda_2^t)(d_4\lambda_1^{t'}-d_5\lambda_2^{t'}) + \sum_{i=1}^{\mathrm{Min}\,(t,t')}(\lambda_1^{t-i}-\lambda_2^{t-i})(\lambda_1^{t'-i}-\lambda_2^{t'-i})\}.$$

The first expression in curled brackets leads to terms in $\lambda_1^{t+t'}$, $\lambda_2^{t+t'}$, $\lambda_1^t\lambda_2^{t'}$ and $\lambda_1^{t'}\lambda_2^t$. To evaluate the second term we write $p = \mathrm{Min}\,(t, t')$:

$$\sum_1^p \lambda_1^{t+t'-2i} + \sum_1^p \lambda_2^{t+t'-2i} - (\lambda_1^t \lambda_2^{t'} + \lambda_1^{t'} \lambda_2^t) \sum_1^p (\lambda_1 \lambda_2)^{-i}$$

$$= \frac{\lambda_1^{t+t'-2p} - \lambda_1^{t+t'}}{1-\lambda_1^2} + \frac{\lambda_2^{t+t'-2p} - \lambda_2^{t+t'}}{1-\lambda_2^2} - \frac{\lambda_1^{t-p}\lambda_2^{t'-p} + \lambda_1^{t'-p}\lambda_2^{t-p} - (\lambda_1^t \lambda_2^{t'} + \lambda_1^{t'} \lambda_2^t)}{1-\lambda_1\lambda_2}.$$

Now $t-p = 0$ if $t \leqq t'$ and $t-t'$ if $t \geqq t'$. Similarly $t'-p = t'-t$ if $t \leqq t'$ and 0 if $t \geqq t'$. Hence $t+t'-2p = |t-t'|$ and also,

$$\lambda_1^{t-p}\lambda_2^{t'-p} + \lambda_1^{t'-p}\lambda_2^{t-p} = \lambda_1^{|t-t'|} + \lambda_2^{|t-t'|}.$$

It follows that the second term in curled brackets of (C.23) can be written as

$$\frac{\lambda_1^{|t-t'|} - \lambda_1^{t+t'}}{1-\lambda_1^2} + \frac{\lambda_2^{|t-t'|} - \lambda_2^{t+t'}}{1-\lambda_2^2} - \frac{\lambda_1^{|t-t'|} + \lambda_2^{|t-t'|} - \lambda_1^t \lambda_2^{t'} - \lambda_1^{t'} \lambda_2^t}{1-\lambda_1\lambda_2}.$$

On combining these results we obtain $q^{tt'}$ as specified in (2.19).

5.C.3. *Some Further Computations* (*1*)

For the derivations which follow it is useful to recognize that

$$\text{(C.24)} \qquad \mathbf{R}_p^{-1}\boldsymbol{\iota} = \mathbf{e}_1, \quad \mathbf{R}_p'^{-1}\boldsymbol{\iota} = \mathbf{0}, \quad \mathbf{R}_p^{-1}\mathbf{R}_p'^{-1}\mathbf{e}_1 = \mathbf{e}_1 - \mathbf{e}_2,$$

where $\mathbf{e}_2$ is the second unit vector (containing infinitely many zeros except for a 1 on the second place). Consider then (2.18) and write $(\mathbf{xx})_{pp}$, $(\mathbf{xx})_{pq}$, ... in terms of the c's, $\mathbf{R}_p$, $\mathbf{Q}$, etc.; see (1.29)–(1.33) and (2.11)–(2.13). For $\mathbf{p}^0$ we then have

$$\mathbf{p}^0 = \frac{1}{2c_3c_4c_7}(c_3c_4^2\mathbf{I} + c_2\mathbf{R}_p'^{-1}\mathbf{R}_p^{-1})\mathbf{Q}^{-1}\mathbf{R}_p^{-1}\mathbf{R}_p'^{-1}$$
$$\times [-c_5\boldsymbol{\iota} + 2c_7c_8\mathbf{R}_p'\boldsymbol{\iota} + 2c_7\mathbf{R}_p'\mathbf{R}_p(\mathbf{v} - y_0\mathbf{e}_1)]$$
$$+ \frac{1}{2c_7}\mathbf{R}_p^{-1}\mathbf{R}_p'^{-1}\mathbf{Q}'^{-1}[-(c_1-c_6)\boldsymbol{\iota} + 2c_2q_0\mathbf{e}_1],$$

where use has been made of $c_9 = c_{10} = c_{11} = 0$ [because we wish to evaluate $\mathbf{p}^0$ and $\mathbf{q}^0$ at the values (2.5)]. Using (C.24), we can simplify this to

$$\text{(C.25)}\quad \mathbf{p}^0 = \frac{c_8}{c_3 c_4}(c_3 c_4^2 \mathbf{I} + c_2 \mathbf{R}_p'^{-1}\mathbf{R}_p^{-1})\mathbf{Q}^{-1}\mathbf{e}_1 + \frac{1}{c_3 c_4}(c_3 c_4^2 \mathbf{I} + c_2 \mathbf{R}_p'^{-1}\mathbf{R}_p^{-1})\mathbf{Q}^{-1}(\mathbf{v} - y_0 \mathbf{e}_1) - \frac{c_1 - c_6}{2c_7}\mathbf{R}_p^{-1}\mathbf{R}_p'^{-1}\mathbf{Q}'^{-1}\boldsymbol{\iota} + \frac{c_2}{c_7} q_0 \mathbf{R}_p^{-1}\mathbf{R}_p'^{-1}\mathbf{Q}'^{-1}\mathbf{e}_1 .$$

In exactly the same way we obtain

$$\text{(C.26)}\quad \mathbf{q}^0 = c_8 \mathbf{Q}^{-1}\mathbf{e}_1 + \mathbf{Q}^{-1}(\mathbf{v} - y_0 \mathbf{e}_1) - \frac{c_1 - c_6}{2c_3 c_4}\mathbf{Q}^{-1}\boldsymbol{\iota} + \frac{c_2}{c_3 c_4} q_0 \mathbf{Q}^{-1}\mathbf{e}_1 + \frac{c_2}{c_4 c_7} q_0 \mathbf{Q}^{-1}(\mathbf{e}_1 - \mathbf{e}_2).$$

These expressions involve $\mathbf{Q}^{-1}\mathbf{e}_1$, $\mathbf{Q}^{-1}\mathbf{e}_2$, $\mathbf{Q}'^{-1}\mathbf{e}_1$, $\mathbf{Q}^{-1}\boldsymbol{\iota}$ and $\mathbf{Q}'^{-1}\boldsymbol{\iota}$. The first three of these vectors are given in (1.39). In what follows it will prove useful to use the vector

$$\text{(C.27)}\quad \mathbf{r}_1 = \begin{bmatrix} \lambda_1 \\ \lambda_1^2 \\ \lambda_1^3 \\ \vdots \end{bmatrix} = \sum_{t=1}^{\infty} \lambda_1^t \mathbf{e}_t$$

(and similarly $\mathbf{r}_2$ as a function of λ_2), $\mathbf{e}_t$ being the tth unit vector. We can then write (1.39) in the form:

$$\text{(C.28)}\quad \begin{aligned} \mathbf{Q}^{-1}\mathbf{e}_1 &= 0.2013\mathbf{r}_1 - 0.2013\mathbf{r}_2 \\ \mathbf{Q}^{-1}\mathbf{e}_2 &= 0.2656\mathbf{r}_1 - 0.2728\mathbf{r}_2 \\ \mathbf{Q}'^{-1}\mathbf{e}_1 &= 0.0776\mathbf{r}_1 - 0.0677\mathbf{r}_2 . \end{aligned}$$

To obtain the tth element of $\mathbf{Q}^{-1}\boldsymbol{\iota}$, we have to sum $q^{tt'}$ as defined in (2.19) over all t' from 1 to ∞. Similarly, the t'^{th} element of $\mathbf{Q}'^{-1}\boldsymbol{\iota}$ is obtained by summing $q^{tt'}$ over all t. In both cases this is a matter of adding the components of geometric series and the result is

$$\text{(C.29)}\quad \begin{aligned} \mathbf{Q}^{-1}\boldsymbol{\iota} &= 0.1764\boldsymbol{\iota} - 0.4559\mathbf{r}_1 + 0.2795\mathbf{r}_2 \\ \mathbf{Q}'^{-1}\boldsymbol{\iota} &= 0.1764\boldsymbol{\iota} - 0.7765\mathbf{r}_1 + 0.6770\mathbf{r}_2 . \end{aligned}$$

On combining (C.26)–(C.29), we conclude that $\mathbf{q}^0$ can be regarded as the sum of three expressions, one of which is a constant term [the first plus the third on the right of (C.26)] and which is a homogeneous linear combination of $\boldsymbol{\iota}$, $\mathbf{r}_1$ and $\mathbf{r}_2$; the second is a homogeneous linear expression in shipments with the understanding that initial inventories are to be subtracted from first-period shipments, the matrix of this linear expression being $\mathbf{Q}^{-1}$; and the third is a homogeneous linear function of the initial work force [the fourth plus the fifth term on the right of (C.26)] whose weights are homogeneous linear functions of $\mathbf{r}_1$ and $\mathbf{r}_2$. The numerical results based on the c-values of (2.5) are given in (2.21).

For $\mathbf{p}^0$ we still need $\mathbf{R}_p'^{-1}\mathbf{R}_p^{-1}$ postmultiplied by $\mathbf{Q}^{-1}$ and $\mathbf{Q}^{-1}\mathbf{e}_1$ as well as $\mathbf{R}_p^{-1}\mathbf{R}_p'^{-1}$ postmultiplied by $\mathbf{Q}'^{-1}\boldsymbol{\iota}$ and $\mathbf{Q}'^{-1}\mathbf{e}_1$, see the right-hand side of (C.25). Now $\mathbf{Q}^{-1}\mathbf{e}_1$ is a linear combination of $\mathbf{r}_1$ and $\mathbf{r}_2$, see (C.28), hence we need

$$\text{(C.30)}\quad \mathbf{R}_p'^{-1}\mathbf{R}_p^{-1}\mathbf{r}_1 = \begin{bmatrix} 2 & -1 & 0 & \cdots \\ -1 & 2 & -1 & \cdots \\ 0 & -1 & 2 & \cdots \\ \vdots & \vdots & \vdots & \end{bmatrix} \begin{bmatrix} \lambda_1 \\ \lambda_1^2 \\ \lambda_1^3 \\ \vdots \end{bmatrix} = \mathbf{e}_1 - \frac{(1-\lambda_1)^2}{\lambda_1}\mathbf{r}_1 .$$

In the same way $\mathbf{Q}'^{-1}\boldsymbol{\iota}$ and $\mathbf{Q}'^{-1}\mathbf{e}_1$ are linear combinations of $\boldsymbol{\iota}$, $\mathbf{r}_1$ and $\mathbf{r}_2$, hence we need $\mathbf{R}_p^{-1}\mathbf{R}_p'^{-1}\boldsymbol{\iota} = \mathbf{0}$ [see (C.24)] and

$$\text{(C.31)}\quad \mathbf{R}_p^{-1}\mathbf{R}_p'^{-1}\mathbf{r}_1 = \begin{bmatrix} 1 & -1 & 0 & \cdots \\ -1 & 2 & -1 & \cdots \\ 0 & -1 & 2 & \cdots \\ \vdots & \vdots & \vdots & \end{bmatrix} \begin{bmatrix} \lambda_1 \\ \lambda_1^2 \\ \lambda_1^3 \\ \vdots \end{bmatrix} = (1-\lambda_1)\mathbf{e}_1 - \frac{(1-\lambda_1)^2}{\lambda_1}\mathbf{r}_1 .$$

It follows that the constant term in $\mathbf{p}^0$ [the first plus the third term on the right of (C.25)] is a homogeneous linear combination of $\mathbf{e}_1$, $\mathbf{r}_1$ and $\mathbf{r}_2$. The same applies to the term in q_0 [the fourth of (C.25)]. It will be observed that the $\mathbf{e}_1$-terms disappear when we disregard the first-period decision, p_1^0, as we did in (2.24). Finally, we have $\mathbf{R}_p'^{-1}\mathbf{R}_p^{-1}\mathbf{Q}^{-1}$, which is part of the coefficient matrix of the shipment term. Its typical element is

$$-q^{t-1,t'} + 2q^{tt'} - q^{t+1,t'},$$

provided that $t > 1$. This typical element can be easily derived from (2.19). After multiplication by c_2/c_3c_4 and adding $c_4q^{tt'}$ we obtain $p^{tt'}$ as given in (2.23).

5.C.4. Some Further Computations (2)

We can now easily derive the c_2-results of Tables 5.10 and 5.11. The derivatives of the first-period production and work force decisions with respect to this coefficient are, according to Table 5.8, twice the first rows of $(\mathbf{xx})_{pq}$ and $(\mathbf{xx})_{qq}$, respectively, postmultiplied by $\mathbf{R}_p'^{-1}\mathbf{R}_p^{-1}\mathbf{q}^0 - q_0\mathbf{e}_1$. It follows from Table 5.2 that these first rows are linear combinations of $\mathbf{r}_1'$ and $\mathbf{r}_2'$. Hence we must evaluate $\mathbf{r}_1'\mathbf{R}_p'^{-1}\mathbf{R}_p^{-1}$, which is the transpose of $\mathbf{R}_p'^{-1}\mathbf{R}_p^{-1}\mathbf{r}_1$ and thus given in (C.30). Therefore, the $\mathbf{q}^0$-part of these derivatives is a linear combination of $\mathbf{e}_1'\mathbf{q}^0$, $\mathbf{r}_1'\mathbf{q}^0$ and $\mathbf{r}_2'\mathbf{q}^0$, which can be evaluated in a straightforward manner with the aid of (2.21).

The case of c_7 is more complicated. We notice first that the $c_9\mathbf{v}$-terms in the derivatives of Table 5.8 can be disregarded, because these derivatives are evaluated at the values (2.5) which specify $c_9 = 0$. Next we consider the $c_8\boldsymbol{\iota}$-terms. This requires that we take the first row of $(\mathbf{xx})_{pp}$ in the case of production and of $(\mathbf{xx})_{qp}$ in that of work force, postmultiplied by $\mathbf{R}_p'\boldsymbol{\iota}$ (in both cases apart from the multiplicative factor $-2c_8$). Now the first row of $(\mathbf{xx})_{pp}$ is a linear combination of $\mathbf{e}_1$, $\mathbf{r}_1$ and $\mathbf{r}_2$, that of $(\mathbf{xx})_{qp}$ is linear in $\mathbf{r}_1$ and $\mathbf{r}_2$ only. When this is postmultiplied by $\mathbf{R}_p'$ we obtain a row whose t^{th} element consists of a constant part (independent of t) plus the elements of certain converging geometric series. This row must then be postmultiplied by $\boldsymbol{\iota}$, i.e., we have to take the sum of all the elements of that row. This sum consists of a certain multiple of T (the horizon) plus the sums of the geometric series just mentioned. It appears that the multiple of T cancels against other such multiples, which is as it should be. The remaining part (the sums of the geometric series) supplies part of the constant term of the c_7-derivatives.

We proceed to consider the $\mathbf{p}^0$-part of the derivatives, i.e., twice the first row of $(\mathbf{xx})_{pp}$ or $(\mathbf{xx})_{qp}$ postmultiplied by $\mathbf{R}_p'\mathbf{R}_p\mathbf{p}^0$. This means that we have to postmultiply $\mathbf{e}_1'$, $\mathbf{r}_1'$ and $\mathbf{r}_2'$ by $\mathbf{R}_p'\mathbf{R}_p$ and then by $\mathbf{p}^0$. Now $\mathbf{p}^0$ is the sum of (i) a constant term which takes the form of a linear combination of $\mathbf{r}_1$ and $\mathbf{r}_2$, (ii) a term in the initial work force whose coefficient vector is a linear combination of $\mathbf{r}_1$ and $\mathbf{r}_2$, and (iii) a term in $\mathbf{v} - y_0\mathbf{e}_1$ whose coefficient matrix is a linear combination of $\mathbf{Q}^{-1}$ and $\mathbf{R}_p'^{-1}\mathbf{R}_p^{-1}\mathbf{Q}^{-1}$. For (i) and (ii) we therefore need such scalar expressions as $\mathbf{r}_1'\mathbf{R}_p'\mathbf{R}_p\mathbf{r}_1$, which turn out to be fixed numbers plus certain multiples of T; as in the case of the preceding paragraph such multiples cancel against each other. The fixed numbers of (i) contribute to the constant term of the c_7-derivatives, those of (ii) to the part which is linear in q_0. There are no further expressions in q_0.

Component (iii) of the $\mathbf{p}^0$-part requires such rows as $\mathbf{r}_1'\mathbf{R}_p'\mathbf{R}_p\mathbf{Q}^{-1}$ and $\mathbf{r}_1'\mathbf{R}_p'\mathbf{R}_p\mathbf{R}_p'^{-1}\mathbf{R}_p^{-1}\mathbf{Q}^{-1}$. Apart from terms in T which cancel, both rows are multiples of $\mathbf{r}_1'\mathbf{Q}^{-1}$. Thus the coefficient vector by which $\mathbf{v} - y_0\mathbf{e}_1$

is multiplied in this component involves $\mathbf{r}_1'\mathbf{Q}^{-1}$ and $\mathbf{r}_2'\mathbf{Q}^{-1}$ linearly; the result is that the transpose of this vector is a linear combination of $\mathbf{r}_1$, of $\mathbf{r}_2$, of

$$\mathbf{r}_1^* = \begin{bmatrix} \lambda_1 \\ 2\lambda_1^2 \\ 3\lambda_1^3 \\ \vdots \end{bmatrix} = \sum_{t=1}^{\infty} t\lambda_1^t \mathbf{e}_t, \tag{C.32}$$

and of $\mathbf{r}_2^*$ as a similar function of λ_2. This component is of course not the only place where $\mathbf{v} - y_0\mathbf{e}_1$ enters into the c_7-derivatives; we also have the $\mathbf{R}_p(\mathbf{v}-y_0\mathbf{e}_1)$ expressions inside the square brackets of Table 5.8. This leads to a coefficient vector which is a linear combination of $\mathbf{r}_1'$ and $\mathbf{r}_2'$. On combining this with component (iii) we find that the c_7-derivative of production contains the following linear expression in $\mathbf{v}-y_0\mathbf{e}_1$:

$$(359.6\mathbf{r}_1 - 352.6\mathbf{r}_2 - 8.73\mathbf{r}_1^* - 23.24\mathbf{r}_2^*)'(\mathbf{v} - y_0\mathbf{e}_1) \tag{C.33}$$

and for work force:

$$(-14.12\mathbf{r}_1 + 14.14\mathbf{r}_2 + 0.4509\mathbf{r}_1^* + 0.6608\mathbf{r}_2^*)'(\mathbf{v} - y_0\mathbf{e}_1). \tag{C.34}$$

CHAPTER 6

Macrodynamic Decision Rules

6.1. A FOUR-YEAR STRATEGY FOR THE UNITED STATES IN THE NINETEEN-THIRTIES [1]

6.1.1. Statement of the Dynamic Problem; Constraints in Final Form

The purpose of this chapter is to apply the dynamic theory of Chapter 4 to macroeconomic decision problems. In the present section we shall dynamize the anti-depression policy of Section 3.1, after which the remainder of the chapter will be devoted to a more extensive application to conditions in The Netherlands in the period 1957–1959.

Let us return to 3.1.2, where the objective was formulated as the minimization of the sum of squares of the following deviations between desired and actual values:

$(W_2)_{32+t}-(W_2^*)_{32+t}$	(government wage bill)
$\bar{T}_{32+t}-\bar{T}^*_{32+t}$	(indirect taxes less subsidies)
$G_{32+t}-G^*_{32+t}$	(government expenditure on goods and services)
$C_{32+t}-C^*_{32+t}$	(consumption)
$I_{32+t}-I^*_{32+t}$	(investment)
$D_{32+t}-D^*_{32+t}$	(distribution variable, $W_1-2\Pi$),

[1] It is advised to re-read Section 3.1 before reading this section. The results of this section are mainly based on the following articles: P. J. M. VAN DEN BOGAARD and H. THEIL, "Macrodynamic Policy-Making: An Application of Strategy and Certainty Equivalence Concepts to the Economy of the United States, 1933–1936," *Metroeconomica*, Vol. 11 (1959), pp. 149–167; H. THEIL and E. KAPTEIN, "The Effect of Forecasting Errors on Optimal Programming of Production-Inventory and Anti-Depression Policies," Report 5906 of the Econometric Institute of the Netherlands School of Economics (1959) [this paper is partly published in *Management Sciences, Models and Techniques*, edited by C. W. CHURCHMAN and M. VERHULST (London 1960), Vol. 1, pp. 295–323]; H. THEIL and T. KLOEK, "The Operational Implications of Imperfect Models," in: *Mathematical Methods in the Social Sciences, 1959*, edited by K. J. ARROW, S. KARLIN and P. SUPPES (Stanford 1960).

where $t = 1, 2, 3, 4$, i.e., such that the six variables refer to the four-year period 1933–36. In other words, the objective takes the form of the maximization of the simple preference function

$$w(\mathbf{x}, \mathbf{y}) = -\tfrac{1}{2}(\mathbf{x}'\mathbf{x}+\mathbf{y}'\mathbf{y}), \tag{1.1}$$

where $\mathbf{x}$ and $\mathbf{y}$ are vectors of instruments and of noncontrolled variables, respectively, each containing 12 elements partitioned by years in accordance with the procedure of Chapter 4:

$$\mathbf{x} = \begin{bmatrix} x_1 \\ x_2 \\ x_3 \\ x_4 \end{bmatrix}, \quad x_t = \begin{bmatrix} (W_2)_{32+t}-(W_2^*)_{32+t} \\ \overline{T}_{32+t}-\overline{T}_{32+t}^* \\ G_{32+t}-G_{32+t}^* \end{bmatrix}, \tag{1.2}$$

$$\mathbf{y} = \begin{bmatrix} y_1 \\ y_2 \\ y_3 \\ y_4 \end{bmatrix}, \quad y_t = \begin{bmatrix} C_{32+t}-C_{32+t}^* \\ I_{32+t}-I_{32+t}^* \\ D_{32+t}-D_{32+t}^* \end{bmatrix}.$$

This is completely in line with the static preference function (3.1.10) and it implies, just as there, that the coefficient vectors **a** and **b** of the linear part of the preference function are **0**, that the matrix of the bilinear part, **C**, is also **0**, and that the matrices of the quadratic forms, **A** and **B**, are both $-\mathbf{I}$. The only difference is that the orders of these matrices are now larger due to the fact that the present problem refers to a four-year period, which is also reflected by the use of the bold-face roman type for **x, y, a, b, A, B** and **C**.

We proceed to the constraints, which are to be written in the form $\mathbf{y} = \mathbf{R}\mathbf{x}+\mathbf{s}$, or, more extensively, as

$$\begin{bmatrix} y_1 \\ y_2 \\ y_3 \\ y_4 \end{bmatrix} = \begin{bmatrix} R_{11} & \mathbf{0} & \mathbf{0} & \mathbf{0} \\ R_{21} & R_{22} & \mathbf{0} & \mathbf{0} \\ R_{31} & R_{32} & R_{33} & \mathbf{0} \\ R_{41} & R_{42} & R_{43} & R_{44} \end{bmatrix} \begin{bmatrix} x_1 \\ x_2 \\ x_3 \\ x_4 \end{bmatrix} + \begin{bmatrix} s_1 \\ s_2 \\ s_3 \\ s_4 \end{bmatrix}, \tag{1.3}$$

where $R_{tt'}$ measures the effectiveness of the instruments in t' with respect to the noncontrolled variables in t, while s_t specifies the additive structure of the constraints for t.

Our task is now to specify the coefficient matrices of (1.3) in terms of the coefficients of the equation system (3.1.1)–(3.1.4). It was observed in 3.1.4 that this system is not in required form, since it contains noncontrolled variables both on the left and on the right of the equation signs. This was remedied by taking the reduced form, which describes each of the system's jointly dependent variables linearly in terms of predetermined variables (exogenous and lagged endogenous variables) and structural disturbances. The result was shown in Table 3.4; for consumption, e.g., we have the following reduced-form relation:

$$\begin{aligned}C = {} & 41.816+0.666W_2-0.188\overline{T}+0.671G \\ & + 0.155(t-1931)-0.189(W_2)_{-1}+0.189\overline{T}_{-1} \\ & + 0.743\Pi_{-1}+0.189Y_{-1}-0.098K_{-1} \\ & + 1.671u_C+0.671u_I+1.148u_W .\end{aligned} \tag{1.4}$$

The coefficients of the three instruments W_2, $\overline{T}$, G are 0.666, -0.188, 0.671, respectively, which means that they form the C-row of the multiplicative structure of the constraints; the remaining part of the reduced-form relation is exogenous or lagged endogenous and hence taken as given in the static case, so that it can be put into the additive structure of the constraints. After repeating this for the two other noncontrolled variables (I and D) the problem of formulating the constraints is solved, at least in the static case; but not in the dynamic four-year case. We must then realize that, in an equation like (1.4), the consumption of 1934 is expressed in profits (Π), national income (Y) and capital stock (K) of 1933. These values are not known at the beginning of the four-year strategy period 1933–36, and they are not exogenous either.

This problem is solved as follows. Let us write g for the vector of values taken by the exogenous variables in any given year, and h for the corresponding endogenous vector. Suppose that the system is linear; also, that lags are confined to one year. The reduced form can then be written as

$$h = P_1 h_{-1} + P_2 g + P_3 g_{-1} + P_4 u, \tag{1.5}$$

where u is the vector of structural disturbances in the appropriate year and the P's are reduced-form coefficient matrices of appropriate order, P_1 being necessarily square. For example, for Klein's Model I we have

$$h = \begin{bmatrix} C \\ \Pi \\ W_1 \\ I \\ Y \\ K \end{bmatrix}, \quad g = \begin{bmatrix} W_2 \\ \overline{T} \\ G \\ t-1931 \end{bmatrix}, \quad u = \begin{bmatrix} u_C \\ u_I \\ u_W \end{bmatrix}$$

(the constant terms being disregarded); further, Table 3.4 specifies:

$$P_1 = \begin{bmatrix} 0 & 0.743 & 0 & 0 & 0.189 & -0.098 \\ 0 & 0.863 & 0 & 0 & -0.063 & -0.164 \\ 0 & 0.626 & 0 & 0 & 0.237 & -0.119 \\ 0 & 0.746 & 0 & 0 & -0.015 & -0.184 \\ 0 & 1.489 & 0 & 0 & 0.174 & -0.283 \\ 0 & 0.746 & 0 & 0 & -0.015 & 0.816 \end{bmatrix},$$

$$P_2 = \begin{bmatrix} 0.666 & -0.188 & 0.671 & 0.155 \\ -0.224 & -1.281 & 1.119 & -0.052 \\ -0.162 & -0.204 & 0.811 & 0.195 \\ -0.052 & -0.296 & 0.259 & -0.012 \\ 0.614 & -1.484 & 1.930 & 0.143 \\ -0.052 & -0.296 & 0.259 & -0.012 \end{bmatrix},$$

$$P_3 = \begin{bmatrix} -0.189 & 0.189 & 0 & 0 \\ 0.063 & -0.063 & 0 & 0 \\ -0.237 & 0.237 & 0 & 0 \\ 0.015 & -0.015 & 0 & 0 \\ -0.174 & 0.174 & 0 & 0 \\ 0.015 & -0.015 & 0 & 0 \end{bmatrix}, \qquad P_4 = \begin{bmatrix} 1.671 & 0.671 & 1.148 \\ 1.119 & 1.119 & -0.386 \\ 0.811 & 0.811 & 1.445 \\ 0.259 & 1.259 & -0.089 \\ 1.930 & 1.930 & 1.059 \\ 0.259 & 1.259 & -0.089 \end{bmatrix}.$$

Now the problem is the following. Although (1.5) specifies—in terms of the matrix P_2—the influence of the exogenous variables on the endogenous variables in the same year, it does not specify this influence on the endogenous variables one year later; at least, it does not do so explicitly. But since we assume that the coefficients of the equation system are constant over time, we can write

$$\begin{aligned} h &= P_1(P_1 h_{-2} + P_2 g_{-1} + P_3 g_{-2} + P_4 u_{-1}) + P_2 g + P_3 g_{-1} + P_4 u \\ &= P_1^2 h_{-2} + P_2 g + (P_1 P_2 + P_3) g_{-1} + P_1 P_3 g_{-2} + P_4 u + P_1 P_4 u_{-1}, \end{aligned}$$

which shows that the influence of the exogenous variables on the endogenous variables one year later is measured by the matrix $P_1 P_2 + P_3$. When continuing in this way, we obtain for any positive integer t:

$$(1.6) \qquad \begin{aligned} h = {} & P_1^{t+1} h_{-t-1} + P_2 g + \sum_{\tau=1}^{t} P_1^{\tau-1}(P_1 P_2 + P_3) g_{-\tau} \\ & + P_1^t P_3 g_{-t-1} + P_4 u + \ldots + P_1^t P_4 u_{-t}, \end{aligned}$$

which is the so-called final form of the equation system.[1] Its successive coefficient matrices

(1.7) $$P_2, \quad P_1P_2+P_3, \quad P_1(P_1P_2+P_3), \quad P_1^2(P_1P_2+P_3), \ \ldots$$

measure the influence of the exogenous variables on the endogenous variables of the same year, on those of the next year, and so on. In particular, the first three elements of the first row of P_2 (0.666, -0.188, 0.671) describe the effectiveness of the three instruments W_2, $\bar{T}$, G with respect to the noncontrolled variable C in the same year; similarly, the first three elements of the first row of $P_1P_2+P_3$ describe the effectiveness of W_2, $\bar{T}$, G with respect to the consumption level one year later, and so on. In precisely the same way, the fourth rows of P_2, $P_1P_2+P_3, \ldots$ supply the coefficients measuring the effectiveness of the instruments with respect to investment, while those referring to the distribution variable $D = W_1 - 2\Pi$ are obtained by subtracting twice the second row from the third. It will be noticed that these coefficients are all constant over time [which is ultimately due to the fact that the coefficients of the structural system (3.1.1)–(3.1.4) are constant over time]. This implies that the coefficient matrices R_{11}, R_{22}, R_{33}, R_{44} of (1.3), which measure the effectiveness of instruments with respect to current noncontrolled variables, are all equal; in fact, they are equal to the static R-matrix defined in (3.1.13) as is easily verified. In the same way, the matrices R_{21}, R_{32}, R_{43} are all equal; they specify the effectiveness of the instruments with respect to noncontrolled variables one year later. And so on. It follows that the multiplicative structure of the present constraints can be partitioned in a particularly simple manner:

(1.8) $$\mathbf{R} = \begin{bmatrix} R_1 & 0 & 0 & 0 \\ R_2 & R_1 & 0 & 0 \\ R_3 & R_2 & R_1 & 0 \\ R_4 & R_3 & R_2 & R_1 \end{bmatrix},$$

where R_1 describes the "current" effectiveness of the instruments, R_2 that of one year later, etc. A survey of these submatrices based on the above-mentioned P-matrices is given in Table 6.1. For example, the coefficient measuring the effect of $\bar{T}$ on C is -0.188 in the current year, -1.014 one year later, -1.006 two years later, and -0.543 three years later; evidently Klein's Model I has strong dynamic characteristics.

[1] For more details, see H. THEIL and J. C. G. BOOT, "The Final Form of Econometric Equation Systems," *Review of the International Statistical Institute*, Vol. 30 (1962), pp. 136–152.

TABLE 6.1

SUBMATRICES OF THE MULTIPLICATIVE AND THE ADDITIVE STRUCTURE OF THE CONSTRAINTS

	W_2	$\bar{T}$	G	Constant term	u_C	u_I	u_W
		$\mathbf{R}_1$		$\boldsymbol{\sigma}_1$		$\mathbf{S}_1$	
C	0.666	−0.188	0.671	−5.393	1.671	0.671	1.148
I	−0.052	−0.296	0.259	−3.704	0.259	1.259	−0.089
D	0.285	2.358	−1.427	−0.729	−1.427	−1.427	2.217
		$\mathbf{R}_2$		$\boldsymbol{\sigma}_2$		$\mathbf{S}_2$	
C	−0.234	−1.014	1.170	−7.554	1.170	1.071	−0.078
I	−0.152	−0.894	0.759	−4.524	0.759	0.574	−0.287
D	0.095	1.172	−0.475	−0.062	−0.475	−0.266	0.792
		$\mathbf{R}_3$		$\boldsymbol{\sigma}_3$		$\mathbf{S}_3$	
C	−0.172	−1.006	0.859	−8.034	0.859	0.604	−0.318
I	−0.076	−0.518	0.382	−5.030	0.382	0.113	−0.213
D	−0.007	0.186	0.033	1.998	0.033	0.281	0.213
		$\mathbf{R}_4$		$\boldsymbol{\sigma}_4$		$\mathbf{S}_4$	
C	−0.079	−0.543	0.396	−8.228	0.396	0.052	−0.227
I	−0.005	−0.088	0.024	−5.892	0.024	−0.261	−0.069
D	−0.060	−0.285	0.301	5.106	0.301	0.508	−0.044

The additive structure of the constraints has a similar form. It is easily seen that the first term on the right of (1.6) implies the presence of 1932 values of endogenous variables (1932 being the year preceding the strategy period); further, that the g-terms imply the presence of non-instrumental exogenous variables (of which there is only one in the present case: time, t) during the strategy period; also, that there are 1932 values of the exogenous variables, see the first term on the second line of (1.6); finally, that there is a linear combination of structural disturbances. Now the first three categories can be represented by known numbers at the beginning of 1933, at least when data on past events are available sufficiently rapidly; for the first and third group consist of 1932 values while the second deals with the variable t whose behaviour over time is perfectly predictable. Regarding the linear combination of disturbances, their coefficients are constant over time as in the case of the multiplicative structure. Therefore, the additive structure takes the form

$$\mathbf{s} = \boldsymbol{\sigma} + \mathbf{S}\mathbf{u}, \tag{1.9}$$

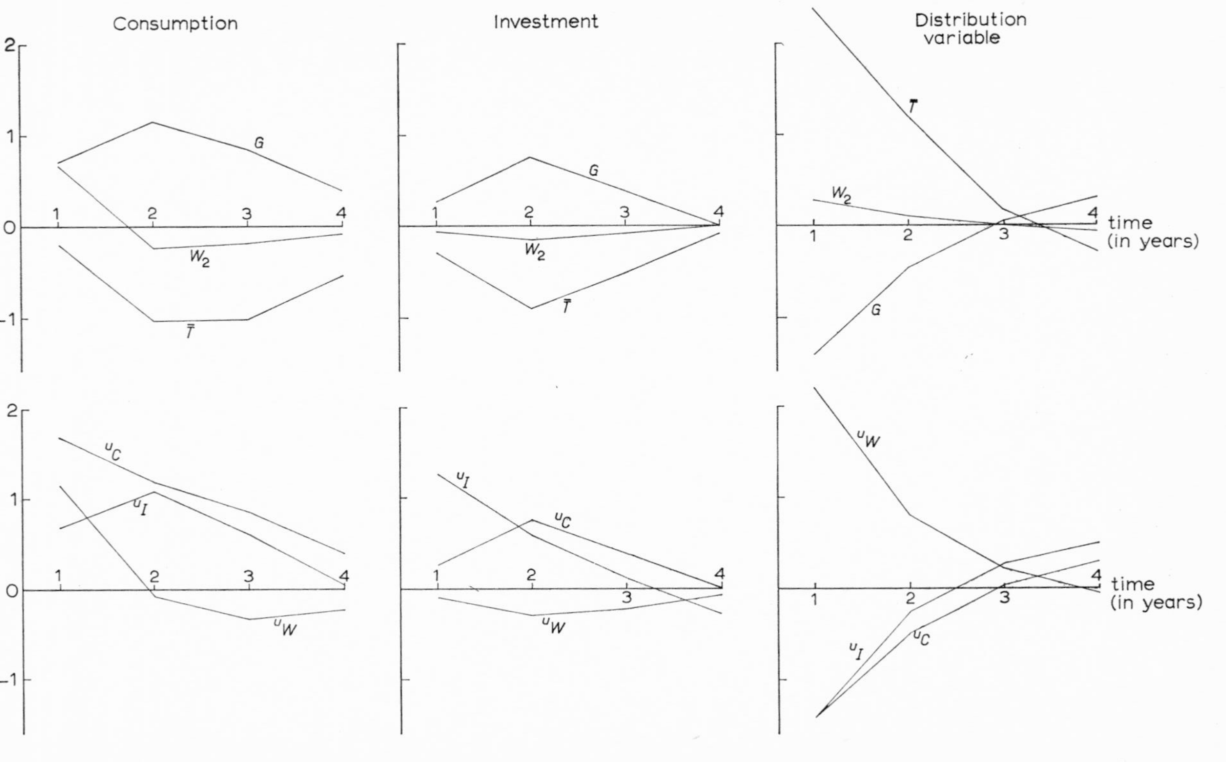

Figure 6.1. The effect of instrument changes and structural disturbances on the noncontrolled variables in successive years

where

$$(1.10) \qquad \boldsymbol{\sigma} = \begin{bmatrix} \sigma_1 \\ \sigma_2 \\ \sigma_3 \\ \sigma_4 \end{bmatrix}, \qquad \mathbf{S} = \begin{bmatrix} S_1 & 0 & 0 & 0 \\ S_2 & S_1 & 0 & 0 \\ S_3 & S_2 & S_1 & 0 \\ S_4 & S_3 & S_2 & S_1 \end{bmatrix}, \qquad \mathbf{u} = \begin{bmatrix} u_1 \\ u_2 \\ u_3 \\ u_4 \end{bmatrix},$$

$\boldsymbol{\sigma}_t$ being a three-element column vector consisting of the fixed numbers discussed above, $u_1, \ldots, u_4$ the structural disturbance vectors in the four strategy years, and $S_1, \ldots, S_4$ coefficient matrices of order 3×3. It follows from (1.6) that S_t is obtained from $P_1^{t-1} P_4$ by taking successively the first row (for C), the fourth row (for I), and the third row minus twice the second (for D). The $\boldsymbol{\sigma}$'s and S's are specified in Table 6.1; for the derivation of the $\boldsymbol{\sigma}$'s it must be remembered that some adjustments are necessary because instruments and noncontrolled variables are both measured as deviations from desired values in a way similar to that of 3.1.4.

6.1.2. The Maximizing Strategy Compared with Actual Development

The problem as formulated in 6.1.1 amounts to the maximization of the preference function (1.1) subject to $\mathbf{y} = \mathbf{Rx}+\mathbf{s}$ where $\mathbf{R}$ and $\mathbf{s}$ are specified in (1.8), (1.9), (1.10) and Table 6.1; or, given that $\mathbf{s}$ is stochastic, to the derivation of the strategy which maximizes expected utility subject to these constraints. We apply the first-period certainty equivalence theorem to find this maximizing strategy, so that we have to compute the first $m = 3$ components of $\mathscr{E}\tilde{\mathbf{x}} = -\mathbf{K}^{-1}\mathscr{E}\mathbf{k}$, see (4.1.18). Hence we need

$$(1.11) \qquad \mathbf{K} = -(\mathbf{I}+\mathbf{R}'\mathbf{R}),$$

where use is made of $\mathbf{A} = \mathbf{B} = -\mathbf{I}$, $\mathbf{C} = \mathbf{0}$, see (1.1) and (4.1.11). On applying (1.8) and Table 6.1, we find for $\mathbf{K}$ the 12×12 matrix which is given in Table 6.2. We also need

$$(1.12) \qquad \mathbf{K}^{-1} = (\mathbf{xx}) = -(\mathbf{I}+\mathbf{R}'\mathbf{R})^{-1},$$

the substitution matrix of the 12 instruments, which is also specified in Table 6.2. Finally, we need

$$(1.13) \qquad \mathbf{k} = -\mathbf{R}'\mathbf{s},$$

use being made of $\mathbf{a} = \mathbf{b} = \mathbf{0}$, $\mathbf{C} = \mathbf{0}$, $\mathbf{B} = -\mathbf{I}$, see (1.1) and (4.1.11).

TABLE 6.2

THE MATRICES **K** AND $\mathbf{K}^{-1} = (\mathbf{xx})$ FOR HORIZONS OF FOUR, THREE, AND TWO YEARS*

		First year			Second year			Third year			Fourth year		
		W_2	$\bar{T}$	G	W_2	$\bar{T}$	G	W_2	$\bar{T}$	G	W_2	$\bar{T}$	G
							K						
First year	W_2	−1.659	−1.318	0.634	0.055	−0.618	0.659	−0.099	−0.053	0.193	0.070	0.126	−0.032
	$\bar{T}$		−11.583	7.346	−0.139	−5.459	4.751	0.476	−1.079	1.642	0.438	0.543	−0.019
	G			−6.855	−0.277	3.092	−3.296	−0.494	0.266	−0.966	−0.348	−0.629	0.158
Second year	W_2				−1.650	−1.258	0.584	0.070	−0.547	0.587	0.112	−0.039	0.126
	$\bar{T}$					−11.199	7.044	−0.037	−4.920	4.241	0.590	−0.783	1.075
	G						−6.607	−0.349	2.738	−2.937	−0.562	0.197	−0.628
Third year	W_2							−1.614	−1.047	0.407	0.121	−0.313	0.332
	$\bar{T}$								−9.884	5.988	0.295	−3.219	2.583
	G									−5.722	−0.604	1.565	−1.658
Fourth year	W_2										−1.527	−0.563	−0.026
	$\bar{T}$											−6.684	3.568
	G												−3.553
						$\mathbf{K}^{-1} = (\mathbf{xx})$ *for a four-year horizon*							
First year	W_2	−0.682	0.121	0.086	−0.049	−0.025	−0.052	−0.018	−0.011	−0.013	−0.006	−0.006	−0.000
	$\bar{T}$		−0.333	−0.320	0.039	0.072	0.004	0.012	0.000	0.018	0.005	0.002	0.004
	G			−0.516	0.110	0.067	0.110	0.040	0.023	0.031	0.014	0.013	0.001
Second year	W_2				−0.715	0.114	0.044	−0.062	−0.034	−0.059	−0.024	−0.014	−0.010
	$\bar{T}$					−0.349	−0.319	0.038	0.072	−0.002	0.013	−0.001	0.013
	G						−0.578	0.095	0.054	0.100	0.039	0.013	0.026
Third year	W_2							−0.723	0.112	0.047	−0.073	−0.031	−0.044
	$\bar{T}$								−0.353	−0.325	0.044	0.069	−0.014
	G									−0.590	0.112	0.046	0.070
Fourth	W_2										−0.757	0.124	0.100

year	$\bar{T}$		−0.333	−0.320	0.040	0.072	0.002	0.014	−0.001	0.014
	G			−0.517	0.112	0.066	0.108	0.044	0.020	0.025
Second year	W_2				−0.718	0.116	0.050	−0.072	−0.029	−0.044
	$\bar{T}$					−0.351	−0.324	0.045	0.070	−0.014
	G						−0.588	0.113	0.047	0.070
Third year	W_2							−0.756	0.125	0.100
	$\bar{T}$								−0.365	−0.345
	G									−0.676

$\mathbf{K}^{-1} = (\mathbf{xx})$ *for a two-year horizon*

First year	W_2	−0.684	0.123	0.091	−0.058	−0.021	−0.038
	$\bar{T}$		−0.335	−0.325	0.048	0.070	−0.011
	G			−0.528	0.131	0.058	0.077
Second year	W_2				−0.751	0.128	0.103
	$\bar{T}$					−0.363	−0.344
	G						−0.675

* Elements below the diagonal are obtained by transposition.

The inverse (1.12) should then be postmultiplied by the expectation of (1.13), given the information which is available at the end of 1932. Since we take **R** as fixed and given, the random variability of **k** is confined to that of **s**; and since the subvectors s_t are, according to (1.9) and (1.10), equal to $\boldsymbol{\sigma}_t$ plus a linear combination of disturbances whose conditional means (given the information at the end of 1932) are all zero,[1] we have

$$\mathscr{E}\tilde{\mathbf{x}} = -(\mathbf{I}+\mathbf{R}'\mathbf{R})^{-1}\mathbf{R}'\boldsymbol{\sigma}. \tag{1.14}$$

The first three elements of the vector (1.14) are

$$\tilde{x}_1 = \begin{bmatrix} (\tilde{W}_2)_{33}-(W_2^*)_{33} \\ \tilde{T}_{33}-T_{33}^* \\ \tilde{G}_{33}-G_{33}^* \end{bmatrix} = \begin{bmatrix} 1.10 \\ 1.22 \\ 3.83 \end{bmatrix}, \tag{1.15}$$

which is the first-period decision of the maximizing strategy. On combining this with the desired values of Table 3.3 we obtain:

$$(\tilde{W}_2)_{33} = 6.13, \quad \tilde{T}_{33} = 8.62, \quad \tilde{G}_{33} = 14.26. \tag{1.16}$$

For the second year, 1934, we take the 1933 values $\tilde{x}_1$ and u_1 as given and proceed as if 1934 is the first year of a three-year strategy period 1934–36. The constraints then take the form:

$$\begin{bmatrix} y_2 \\ y_3 \\ y_4 \end{bmatrix} = \begin{bmatrix} R_1 & \mathbf{0} & \mathbf{0} \\ R_2 & R_1 & \mathbf{0} \\ R_3 & R_2 & R_1 \end{bmatrix} \begin{bmatrix} x_2 \\ x_3 \\ x_4 \end{bmatrix} + \begin{bmatrix} s_2+R_2\tilde{x}_1 \\ s_3+R_3\tilde{x}_1 \\ s_4+R_4\tilde{x}_1 \end{bmatrix}, \tag{1.17}$$

hence the multiplicative structure of the constraints is now

$$\mathbf{R}_* = \begin{bmatrix} R_1 & \mathbf{0} & \mathbf{0} \\ R_2 & R_1 & \mathbf{0} \\ R_3 & R_2 & R_1 \end{bmatrix}, \tag{1.18}$$

a 9×9 matrix. The new **K**-matrix is then $-(\mathbf{I}+\mathbf{R}_*'\mathbf{R}_*)$, where the order of $\mathbf{I}$ $(= -\mathbf{A})$ is also reduced because the 1933 instruments are deleted from the preference function. This new **K**-matrix is simply the lower right-hand 9×9 submatrix of the old **K**; its inverse is also given in Table 6.2. The inverse has then to be postmultiplied by the conditional expectation of the new **k**, which is $\mathbf{R}_*'$ times the new **s**.[2] This new **s** is the second

---

[1] On the assumption that the disturbances are uncorrelated over time.

[2] Note that this is only true because the preference function contains no bilinear terms which connect first-period variables with later-period variables. If this would not be true, i.e., if $\mathbf{A}_{t1}$, $\mathbf{B}_{t1}$, $\mathbf{C}_{t1}$, $\mathbf{C}_{1t}$ would not be all zero, the preference function which is relevant at the beginning of the second period would contain a linear part; see (4.1.20).

right-hand column vector in (1.17). When deriving its conditional expectation, we should take account of the fact that the relevant information is now that of the beginning of 1934. On comparing this with (1.9) and (1.10), we obtain the following conditional expectation of the new **s**:

$$\boldsymbol{\sigma}_* = \begin{bmatrix} \sigma_2 + S_2 u_1 + R_2 \tilde{x}_1 \\ \sigma_3 + S_3 u_1 + R_3 \tilde{x}_1 \\ \sigma_4 + S_4 u_1 + R_4 \tilde{x}_1 \end{bmatrix}. \tag{1.19}$$

The second-period decision of the maximizing strategy is then the top three-element subvector of $-(\mathbf{I}+\mathbf{R}'_* \mathbf{R}_*)^{-1}\mathbf{R}'_* \boldsymbol{\sigma}_*$, viz.:

$$\tilde{x}_2 = \begin{bmatrix} (\tilde{\tilde{W}}_2)_{34} - (W_2^*)_{34} \\ \tilde{\tilde{T}}_{34} - T_{34}^* \\ \tilde{G}_{34} - G_{34}^* \end{bmatrix} = \begin{bmatrix} 0.38 \\ 0.70 \\ 2.33 \end{bmatrix}, \tag{1.20}$$

which, when combined with the desired values of Table 3.3, gives

$$(\tilde{\tilde{W}}_2)_{34} = 5.64, \quad \tilde{\tilde{T}}_{34} = 8.34, \quad \tilde{G}_{34} = 13.20. \tag{1.21}$$

The further derivations for $\tilde{x}_3$ and $\tilde{x}_4$ are now straightforward. Each time when the strategy period is reduced by one year, a subvector x_t is no longer free but fixed at the level $\tilde{x}_t$, and a disturbance vector u_t becomes past and known. This leads to a series of **K**-matrices, the first of which is—as we saw above—of order 12×12, and the second is 9×9, the third 6×6, and the fourth 3×3. For $\tilde{x}_3$ we have a 6×6 matrix whose inverse is given in Table 6.2 along with the larger matrices; for $\tilde{x}_4$ this is no longer necessary because it deals with the last year, so that it is essentially a static decision whose K and K^{-1} have already been derived in (3.1.18) and (3.1.24), respectively. The results are gathered in Table 6.3. It contains the behaviour according to the maximizing strategy, $\tilde{x}_1, \ldots, \tilde{x}_4$, together with the corresponding noncontrolled values, arranged in the S-columns (S = results of the maximizing strategy). The latter values are found by substituting $\tilde{x}_1, \ldots, \tilde{x}_4$ and the realized values of the structural disturbances into the constraints.[1] For comparison purposes

---

[1] The disturbance values have been taken from L. R. Klein, *Economic Fluctuations in the United States, 1921–1941* (New York–London 1950), p. 69, and are as follows:

	1933	1934	1935	1936
u_C	0.63	−0.13	0.03	2.05
u_I	1.04	−0.16	0.11	1.56
u_W	0.40	0.30	0.04	−0.76

TABLE 6.3

THE RESULTS OF THE MAXIMIZING STRATEGY, 1933-1936

	A	S	D	A	S	D	A	S	D	A	S	D
	Instruments											
	W_2			$\bar{T}$			G					
1932	5.3			8.3			10.2					
1933	5.6	6.13	5.04	5.4	8.62	7.40	9.3	14.26	10.44			
1934	6.0	5.64	5.25	6.8	8.34	7.64	10.0	13.20	10.87			
1935	6.1	6.05	5.47	7.2	7.37	7.87	10.5	13.83	11.30			
1936	7.4	6.28	5.68	8.3	6.91	8.11	10.3	13.31	11.73			
	Noncontrolled variables											
	C			I			D			Y		
1932	45.6			−6.2			15.0			41.3		
1933	46.5	49.57	49.69	−5.1	−4.80	−3.10	6.1	6.76	11.25	45.3	50.42	49.63
1934	48.7	52.74	53.78	−3.0	−1.81	0.00	6.0	6.41	7.50	48.9	55.80	57.02
1935	51.3	56.69	57.88	−1.3	0.81	3.10	5.2	1.83	3.75	53.3	63.97	64.40
1936	57.7	64.43	61.97	2.1	6.03	6.20	1.6	−6.76	0.00	61.8	76.86	71.78

Note: A = actual development, S = results of the maximizing strategy, D = desired values.

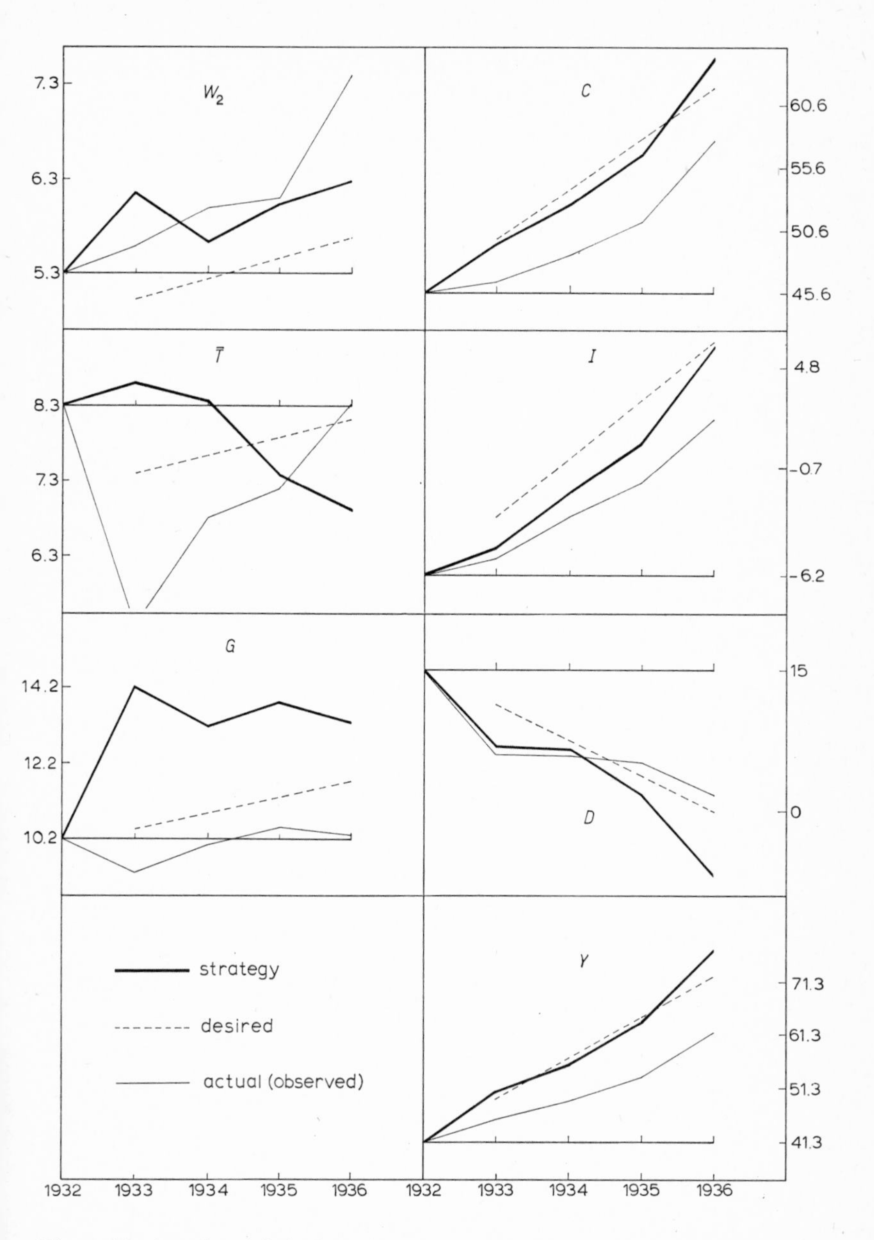

Figure 6.2. Actual and desired development of instruments and noncontrolled variables and their behaviour according to the maximizing strategy

the actual development realized during President Roosevelt's administration is also given, as well as the desired values taken from Tables 3.2 and 3.3. The table contains also the results for national income (Y); its desired values have been derived by substituting those of C, I, G and $\overline{T}$ in the first of the three definitional equations (3.1.4).

The results show rather stable values for the government wage bill and for government expenditure on goods and services; the strategy values of the latter instrument are considerably above those of the actual realizations. These two expenditure instruments are consistently above their desired level, which is of course in accordance with generally accepted ideas about anti-depression policies. Indirect taxes decrease gradually from 8.62 billions in 1933 to 6.91 billions in 1936; measured as a percentage of national income the decline is even larger. The development of the latter variable is indeed impressive. The strategy value which it takes in 1936 is far above the value which was actually realized in that year; in fact, it exceeds all Y-values of the interwar period. Regarding the noncontrolled variables C and I, we observe that the strategy values are below the desires in three years out of four, which is also in accordance with a depression situation.

6.1.3. Predicting Future Actions and Their Consequences

When computing the first-period decision of the maximizing strategy, we considered only the first m components of the mT-element vector $-\mathbf{K}^{-1}\mathscr{E}\mathbf{k}$. But we know from 4.1.7 that the other $m(T-1)$ components are forecasts of later decisions and that these are revised period after period (year after year in this case). Table 6.4 gives a complete picture of all forecasts and realizations of the instrument values of the maximizing strategy (compare also Table 4.1).

The table shows that at the beginning of 1933 the W_2-decision for that year is calculated as 6.13 billions per year; that at this same moment a forecast of 6.26 billions is made of the 1934 decision for that variable, which turns out to overstate the actual 1934 decision (which amounts to 5.64 billions); that at the same time also a 6.20 billion forecast of the 1935 decision is made, which is revised to a new forecast of 5.96 billions at the beginning of 1934, and which turns out to be realized as 6.05 billions; and so on. Viewed as a whole, the forecasts are rather accurate.

There are only few cases in which no-change extrapolation would lead to smaller prediction errors; an example of such a case is the 1933 forecast of the 1934 realization of W_2, which amounts to an increase whereas the actual change (from 6.13 to 5.64) is a decrease. There are 18 predictions (three for 1934, six for 1935, and nine for 1936) and hence also 18 prediction errors; their median—disregarding signs—is less than

TABLE 6.4

FORECASTS AND REALIZATIONS OF THE INSTRUMENT VALUES OF THE MAXIMIZING STRATEGY

Computations made at the beginning of	1933	1934	1935	1936
		W_2		
1933	*6.13*	6.26	6.20	6.36
1934		*5.64*	5.96	6.30
1935			*6.05*	6.34
1936				*6.28*
		T		
1933	*8.62*	8.45	7.64	6.99
1934		*8.34*	7.43	6.87
1935			*7.37*	6.92
1936				*6.91*
		G		
1933	*14.26*	13.92	13.71	13.30
1934		*13.20*	13.66	13.36
1935			*13.83*	13.36
1936				*13.31*

Note: Figures printed in italics are realizations, all others are forecasts.

0.1 billions of dollars, whereas the median of the absolute values of the nine successive differences of the realizations in Table 6.4 is about five times larger. We also note that the 9 forecast revisions make the forecast more accurate than its predecessor in 5 cases, less accurate in 3, one case being a zero revision up to two decimal places.

Table 6.5 completes the picture of Table 4.1 for the noncontrolled variables. Their 1933 values are found by applying $\tilde{y}_1 = R_1\tilde{x}_1 + s_1$, but since s_1 is unknown at the beginning of 1933 we replace s_1 by $\mathscr{E}_0 s_1$, its conditional expectation given the available information at that point of time. For consumption this leads to a forecast of 47.36 billions, and one year later—when s_1 is known—it appears that the actual value is 49.57 billions. At the beginning of 1933 there is also a forecast of $\tilde{y}_2 = R_2 \tilde{x}_1 + R_1 \tilde{x}_2 + s_2$, which is obtained by replacing $\tilde{x}_2$ and s_2 by $\mathscr{E}_0 \tilde{x}_2$ and $\mathscr{E}_0 s_2$ respectively, and which implies a 51.77 billion forecast of

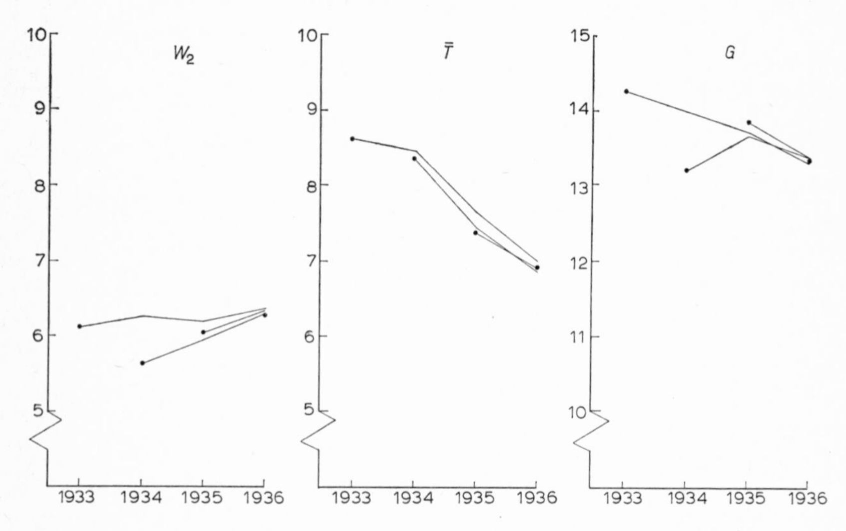

Figure 6.3. Forecasts, revisions of forecasts, and realizations (indicated by heavy dots) of the instrument values of the maximizing strategy

consumption in 1934. At the beginning of 1934 we replace $\mathscr{E}_0 \tilde{x}_2$ by $\tilde{x}_2$ and $\mathscr{E}_0 s_2$ by $\mathscr{E}_1 s_2$, implying a revised forecast of 52.72 billions; one year later it turns out that the actual value is 52.74 billions. And so on. For an appraisal of these forecasts it is useful to make a distinction between the first three years and the last (1936). There are 18 prediction errors for the three noncontrolled variables in the first category, and the median of their absolute values is less than 0.3 billions, which is much smaller than the median of the absolute values of the first differences of the realizations. There are 9 forecast revisions in this group; in 6 cases they make the prediction more accurate, in 3 less accurate. For national income (Y) the picture is roughly similar.

The forecasts for 1936 are all far worse, which must be ascribed to the large structural disturbances of that year. The revisions of these forecasts are of minor importance, their size being less than 10 per cent of the error of the revised forecast in all cases. The instrument forecasts of Table

6.4 were not characterized by this feature, because the maximizing strategy is unable to take account of the 1936 disturbances when the horizon consists of only four years; but these disturbances would surely have affected the quality of the 1937 instrument forecasts if we had decided

TABLE 6.5

FORECASTS AND REALIZATIONS OF THE NONCONTROLLED VALUES (AND NATIONAL INCOME) OF THE MAXIMIZING STRATEGY

Computations made at the beginning of	1933	1934	1935	1936
			C	
1933	47.36	51.77	56.37	60.73
1934	(*49.57*)	52.72	56.68	60.79
1935		(*52.74*)	56.52	60.75
1936			(*56.69*)	60.83
				(*64.43*)
			I	
1933	−6.23	−2.38	0.90	3.59
1934	(*−4.80*)	−1.54	0.89	3.38
1935		(*−1.81*)	0.67	3.40
1936			(*0.81*)	3.47
				(*6.03*)
			D	
1933	8.25	5.02	1.91	0.05
1934	(*6.76*)	5.34	1.95	0.08
1935		(*6.41*)	1.94	0.06
1936			(*1.83*)	0.08
				(*−6.76*)
			Y	
1933	46.78	54.85	63.34	70.33
1934	(*50.42*)	56.04	63.81	70.66
1935		(*55.80*)	63.66	70.59
1936			(*63.97*)	70.70
				(*76.86*)

Note: The figures in brackets and printed in italics are realizations, all others are forecasts.

to choose a five-year strategy ending in 1937. The question arises, therefore, whether the rather unfavourable picture of the forecasts of the 1936 noncontrolled values must be considered as "normal"—given the model used and the preference function chosen—, or the much more favourable picture of the earlier years. The answer is that the "normal" picture probably lies between these two limits. The forecast errors are due to the fact

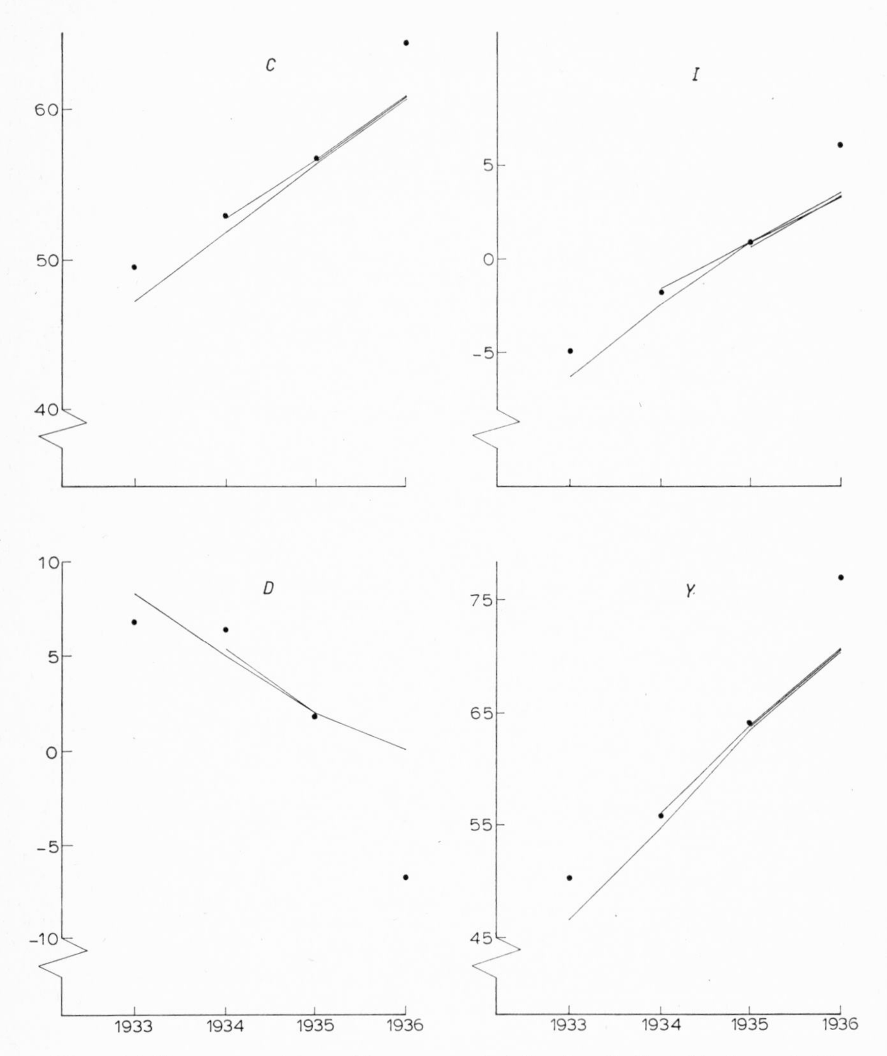

Figure 6.4. Forecasts, revisions of forecasts, and realizations (indicated by heavy dots) of the noncontrolled values of the maximizing strategy

that the disturbances deviate from their expectations (zero). Now in the first three years the disturbances are all small—to be precise, less than their estimated standard deviations [1]—, whereas in 1936 the ratios of the realized disturbances to the corresponding estimated standard deviations are 1.8, 1.3 and -1.0. If we add the squares of these figures (and assume normality and independence), we arrive at a χ^2-value of almost 6, which is just above the 10 per cent significance level with three degrees of freedom. This means that discrepancies of the kind which we observed for 1936 will occur two or three times in twenty years on the average.

6.1.4. The Expected First-Period Loss Due to the Random Variation of the Disturbances

We shall now go somewhat deeper into statistical considerations of the kind just mentioned. Since the random variation of the structural disturbances is the only source of uncertainty in our problem — under our assumptions at least! —, it is worthwhile to see whether we can measure their shares in the loss to which they lead. The argument, comparable with that of 3.1.6, is as follows.

The first-period loss associated with a first-period decision error $x_1 - x_1^0$ is the quadratic form $-\frac{1}{2}(x_1 - x_1^0)'(xx)_{11}^{-1}(x_1 - x_1^0)$, see (4.2.8). Here $(xx)_{11}$ is the substitution matrix of the first-period instruments, which in our case is the leading 3×3 submatrix of $\mathbf{K}^{-1} = (\mathbf{xx})$ as specified in Table 6.2. If we take $T = 4$ and use 1933 as the first year, the relevant leading submatrix of Table 6.2 is the one corresponding with a four-year horizon. Its negative inverse is

$$
\begin{array}{cc}
 & \begin{array}{ccc} (W_2) & (\bar{T}) & (G) \end{array} \\
-(xx)_{11}^{-1} = & \begin{bmatrix} 1.58 & 0.79 & -0.23 \\ 0.79 & 7.84 & -4.73 \\ -0.23 & -4.73 & 4.83 \end{bmatrix} \begin{array}{c} (W_2) \\ (\bar{T}) \\ (G) \end{array}
\end{array} \tag{1.22}
$$

whence it follows that the squared decision error $(W_2 - W_2^0)^2$ is multiplied by $\frac{1}{2} \times 1.58$ in the first-period loss, the squared error $(\bar{T} - \bar{T}^0)^2$ by $\frac{1}{2} \times 7.84$, the error product $(W_2 - W_2^0)(\bar{T} - \bar{T}^0)$ by 0.79, etc. (We delete the time subscript here, because 1933 is the only year which enters into the picture.) On comparing the matrix (1.22) with the static matrix $K = (xx)^{-1}$ of (3.1.18) we observe that they resemble each other very much. Just as we could conclude from (3.1.18) that a unit decision error in taxes is about four or five times more serious than a unit decision

[1] These estimated standard deviations are 1.14 (for u_C), 1.19 (for u_I), and 0.78 (for u_W), see KLEIN, *loc. cit.*, p. 69. See also the footnote on p. 235.

error in the government wage bill, and almost twice as serious as a unit error in government expenditure on goods and services, in just the same way can we draw similar conclusions from (1.22) with respect to first-period losses.

The disturbances lead to first-period decision errors via their effect on the additive structure of the constraints. Accordingly we should consider the first $m = 3$ elements of $\mathbf{x}-\mathbf{x}^0 = -(\mathbf{x}\cdot)(\mathbf{s}_e-\mathbf{s})$, or, in other words, the first three rows of

$$-(\mathbf{x}\cdot) = -(\mathbf{xx})(\mathbf{C}+\mathbf{R}'\mathbf{B}) = (\mathbf{xx})\mathbf{R}',$$

given that $\mathbf{C} = \mathbf{0}$ and $\mathbf{B} = -\mathbf{I}$ [see also (4.2.2)]. Now the first three rows of $(\mathbf{xx})\mathbf{R}'$ are

$$[(xx)_{11} \quad (xx)_{12} \quad (xx)_{13} \quad (xx)_{14}]\mathbf{R}',$$

whence it follows that the first-period decision error caused by a prediction error $\mathbf{s}_e-\mathbf{s}$ is

$$(1.23) \qquad x_1-x_1^0 = [(xx)_{11} \quad (xx)_{12} \quad (xx)_{13} \quad (xx)_{14}]\mathbf{R}'(\mathbf{s}_e-\mathbf{s}).$$

On combining this with the expression $-\frac{1}{2}(x_1-x_1^0)'(xx)_{11}^{-1}(x_1-x_1^0)$, where $(xx)_{11}^{-1}$ is a specified in (1.22), we obtain the first-period loss associated with the error $\mathbf{s}_e-\mathbf{s}$. The matrices $(xx)_{1t}$ are supplied by the first three rows of $\mathbf{K}^{-1}$ of Table 6.2 for $T = 4$.

Now it follows from (1.9) that if $\mathbf{s}_e$ is the same function of $\mathscr{E}\mathbf{u} = \mathbf{0}$ as $\mathbf{s}$ is of $\mathbf{u}$, we have $\mathbf{s}_e-\mathbf{s} = -\mathbf{S}\mathbf{u}$, the submatrices of $\mathbf{S}$ being given in Table 6.1. Hence the first-period decision error which is due to the application of the first-period certainty equivalence theorem is

$$(1.24) \qquad \tilde{x}_1-x_1^0 = -[(xx)_{11} \quad (xx)_{12} \quad (xx)_{13} \quad (xx)_{14}]\mathbf{R}'\mathbf{S}\mathbf{u}$$

and the corresponding first-period loss is $\frac{1}{2}\mathbf{u}'\mathbf{M}\mathbf{u}$ where

$$(1.25) \qquad \mathbf{M} = -\mathbf{S}'\mathbf{R}\begin{bmatrix}(xx)_{11}\\ \vdots \\ (xx)_{41}\end{bmatrix}(xx)_{11}^{-1}[(xx)_{11} \ldots (xx)_{14}]\mathbf{R}'\mathbf{S}.$$

The expected first-period loss is then $\frac{1}{2}\mathscr{E}(\mathbf{u}'\mathbf{M}\mathbf{u})$, which is a linear combination of the variances and covariances of the disturbances of the consumption function (u_C), the investment function (u_I) and the demand-for-labour function (u_W) in the four years 1933–1936, the weights of this combination being the elements of $\mathbf{M}$. This matrix is presented in Table 6.6, which shows that its successive diagonal elements decrease

TABLE 6.6

THE MATRIX **M** OF THE FIRST-PERIOD LOSS DUE TO THE NEGLECT OF STRUCTURAL DISTURBANCES*

		First year			Second year			Third year			Fourth year		
		u_C	u_I	u_W	u_C	u_I	u_W	u_C	u_I	u_W	u_C	u_I	u_W
First year	u_C	4.650	3.870	−2.405	0.917	1.016	0.807	0.200	0.080	0.297	0.027	−0.072	0.084
	u_I		3.506	−2.882	0.845	0.960	0.708	0.176	0.063	0.267	0.022	−0.070	0.074
	u_W			4.186	−0.600	−0.797	−0.324	−0.086	0.008	−0.156	−0.001	0.071	−0.041
Second year	u_C				0.278	0.280	0.289	0.070	0.037	0.098	0.012	−0.017	0.028
	u_I					0.297	0.266	0.065	0.030	0.094	0.010	−0.020	0.027
	u_W						0.336	0.081	0.050	0.109	0.015	−0.013	0.032
Third year	u_C							0.020	0.012	0.026	0.004	−0.003	0.008
	u_I								0.008	0.015	0.002	−0.001	0.005
	u_W									0.036	0.005	−0.005	0.011
Fourth year	u_C										0.001	−0.000	0.001
	u_I											0.002	−0.001
	u_W												0.003

* Elements below the diagonal are obtained by transposition.

rapidly (so that the harm done by later-period variances is much less than that of the immediate future). On the assumption that the disturbances are uncorrelated over time and have variances and covariances which are constant over time, we can disregard the off-diagonal blocks of **M**. If the disturbances are also uncorrelated in the same year, so that the above-mentioned covariances vanish, the expected loss is further simplified:

$$(1.26)\quad \tfrac{1}{2}\mathscr{E}(\mathbf{u}'\mathbf{M}\mathbf{u}) = \tfrac{1}{2}\sum_{i=0}^{3} m_{1+3i} \text{ var } u_C + \tfrac{1}{2}\sum_{i=0}^{3} m_{2+3i} \text{ var } u_I + \tfrac{1}{2}\sum_{i=0}^{3} m_{3+3i} \text{ var } u_W ,$$

where m_i stands for the ith diagonal element of **M**. After applying the m_i-values of Table 6.6 and the estimated values of the variances,[1] we obtain the following shares of the three disturbances in the expected first-period loss:

$$(1.27)\qquad 0.44 \quad 0.37 \quad 0.19.$$

This shows that the disturbed character of the consumption function is slightly more serious than that of the investment function and much more serious than that of the demand-for-labour function. These results are in qualitative accordance with the corresponding static outcomes obtained in 3.1.6.[2]

6.1.5. The Expected First-Period Loss Due to the Sampling Errors of the Consumption Function Coefficients [3]

It was assumed up till now that the coefficients of the equation system which underlies the constraints coincide with the "true" parameters. But this is not true. For example, the consumption function is postulated

---

[1] These estimated values are 1.30 (for u_C), 1.42 (for u_I), 0.61 (for u_W); see KLEIN, *loc. cit.*, p. 69.

[2] If we do not assume that the disturbances are uncorrelated in the same year but apply the estimated correlations (0.32 for u_C and u_I, -0.51 for u_C and u_W, 0.30 for u_I and u_W, see KLEIN, *loc. cit.*, p. 71), the shares (1.27) are reduced to 0.34, 0.29, 0.15, which do not add up to 1 because of the covariance terms. The share of the covariance of u_C and u_I in the expected first-period loss is then 0.19, that of the covariance of u_C and u_W is 0.10, and that of the covariance of u_I and u_W is -0.08.

[3] In this subsection we shall formulate our problem in terms of fixed but unknown parameters, estimates of these parameters, sampling distributions, and so on. It will therefore be clear that the analysis is of the classical, non-Bayesian variety.

to be of the general form

$$C = \alpha_0 + \alpha_1 \Pi + \alpha_2 \Pi_{-1} + \alpha_3 (W_1 + W_2) + u_C, \tag{1.28}$$

and the coefficients are not known but are estimated by

$$\begin{aligned} a_0 &= 16.786 \\ a_1 &= 0.020 \\ a_2 &= 0.225 \\ a_3 &= 0.800. \end{aligned} \tag{1.29}$$

To what extent the a's and α's differ is unknown. But if we shift our attention from estimates to estimators we can compute the expected first-period loss associated with the statistical procedure by which the estimates have been derived, at least approximately. Now the estimates (1.29) are (asymptotically) unbiased and have the following (asymptotic) covariance matrix: [1]

$$V = \begin{array}{c} \begin{matrix} (\alpha_1) & (\alpha_2) & (\alpha_3) & (\alpha_0) \end{matrix} \\ \begin{bmatrix} 0.0099 & -0.0061 & -0.0014 & -0.0085 \\ -0.0061 & 0.0083 & -0.0004 & -0.0146 \\ -0.0014 & -0.0004 & 0.0014 & -0.0292 \\ -0.0085 & -0.0146 & -0.0292 & 1.6454 \end{bmatrix} \end{array} \begin{matrix} (\alpha_1) \\ (\alpha_2) \\ (\alpha_3) \\ (\alpha_0) \end{matrix}. \tag{1.30}$$

The objective of the analysis will be a breakdown of the expected first-period loss according to sampling variances and covariances. It is possible to extend the analysis to the coefficients of the two other behavioural equations (the investment and the demand-for-labour equation), but this will not be pursued here.

Ultimately, the first-period loss is due to a first-period error, which in this case (like that of 6.1.4) is due to a specification error in the constraints. The constraint coefficient matrices **R** and **s** are derived from the final form of the equation system, which in turn is derived from the reduced form; and the latter, finally, is derived from the structural equations of which the consumption function is one.

Accordingly, the first step is the computation of the effect of given changes in the α's on the reduced-form coefficients. The effect is not linear for α_1 and α_3, which are coefficients of jointly dependent variables. We

[1] The matrix (1.30) is the estimated asymptotic covariance matrix of the linearized maximum-likelihood (LML) estimates derived by T. ROTHENBERG and C. T. LEENDERS in "Efficient Estimation of Simultaneous Equation Systems," Report 6216 of the Econometric Institute of the Netherlands School of Economics.

TABLE 6.7

THE REDUCED-FORM COEFFICIENTS OF KLEIN'S MODEL I AND THE EFFECT ON THESE OF CHANGES IN THE COEFFICIENTS OF THE CONSUMPTION FUNCTION*

Current endogenous variables	Lagged endogenous variables			Instruments			Lagged instruments		Noninstrumental exogenous	Constant term (including disturbance)			
	Π_{-1}	Y_{-1}	K_{-1}	W_2	$\bar{T}$	G	$(W_2)_{-1}$	$\bar{T}_{-1}$	$t-1931$	1933	1934	1935	1936
	Reduced-form coefficients												
C	0.743	0.189	−0.098	0.666	−0.188	0.671	−0.189	0.189	0.155	44.03	41.83	41.97	45.42
Π	0.863	−0.063	−0.164	−0.224	−1.281	1.119	0.063	−0.063	−0.052	39.78	37.62	38.20	42.39
W_1	0.626	0.237	−0.119	−0.162	−0.204	0.811	−0.237	0.237	0.195	32.27	30.54	30.50	32.17
I	0.746	−0.015	−0.184	−0.052	−0.296	0.259	0.015	−0.015	−0.012	28.02	26.32	26.72	29.14
Y	1.489	0.174	−0.283	0.614	−1.484	1.930	−0.174	0.174	0.143	72.05	68.16	68.69	74.56
K	0.746	−0.015	0.816	−0.052	−0.296	0.259	0.015	−0.015	−0.012	28.02	26.32	26.72	29.14
	Effect of a 0.01 *increase of* α_1 $(\times 10^4)$												
C	144	−11	−27	−37	−214	187	11	−11	− 9	6 646	6 286	6 382	7 083
Π	97	− 7	−18	−25	−143	125	7	− 7	− 6	4 450	4 209	4 273	4 742
W_1	70	− 5	−13	−18	−104	91	5	− 5	− 4	3 225	3 050	3 097	3 437
I	[illegible]	[illegible]	[illegible]	[illegible]	[illegible]	[illegible]	[illegible]	[illegible]	[illegible]	[illegible]	[illegible]	[illegible]	[illegible]

Π	112												
W_1	81												
I	26												
Y	193												
K	26												
	Effect of a 0.01 increase of α_3 $(\times 10^4)$												
C	105	40	−20	140	−34	135	−40	40	33	5 393	5 103	5 096	5 375
Π	70	27	−13	94	−23	91	−27	27	22	3 611	3 417	3 412	3 599
W_1	51	19	−10	68	−17	66	−19	19	16	2 617	2 476	2 473	2 608
I	16	6	− 3	22	− 5	21	− 6	6	5	835	790	789	832
Y	121	46	−23	162	−39	156	−46	46	38	6 227	5 893	5 885	6 207
K	16	6	− 3	22	− 5	21	− 6	6	5	835	790	789	832
	*Effect of a unit increase*** *of* α_0 $(\times 10^3)$												
C										1 671	1 671	1 671	1 671
Π										1 119	1 119	1 119	1 119
W_1										811	811	811	811
I										259	259	259	259
Y										1 930	1 930	1 930	1 930
K										259	259	259	259

* Zeros are indicated by blank cells.

** Unit increase = increase of 1 billion dollars per year.

therefore linearize and consider the impact of small changes (an increase of 0.01 in the multiplicative coefficients) on the reduced-form coefficients. The results are shown in Table 6.7 and should be read as follows: the Π_{-1}-coefficient of the reduced-form equation for C is 0.743 on the basis of the values (1.29), and if α_1 increases by 0.01, the Π_{-1}-coefficient is raised by 0.0144; and so on. The table shows that α_1 and α_3-changes affect all reduced-form coefficients, whereas α_2 affects only the Π_{-1}-coefficients. The latter feature is due to the fact that α_2 is the coefficient of the predetermined variable Π_{-1}. In exactly the same way, changes in the constant term α_0 affect only the constant terms of the reduced-form equations. These constant terms have been specified separately for each of the four years of the strategy period, since they are taken here as including the disturbances which were actually realized.

The second step consists of the computation of the effect of given α-changes on the coefficients of the final form and on **R** and **s**. Now we found in 6.1.1 that the first rows of the submatrices

$$R_1, \quad R_2, \quad R_3, \quad R_4,$$

which measure the effectiveness of the instruments with respect to consumption in the successive years, are the first three elements of the first rows of

$$P_2, \quad P_1 P_2 + P_3, \quad P_1(P_1 P_2 + P_3), \quad P_1^2(P_1 P_2 + P_3),$$

the P's being the reduced-form coefficient matrices of (1.5). Similar results apply to the R-elements which refer to the other noncontrolled variables. Consequently, since we have obtained the effect of α-changes on the P-matrices, we can find their effect on the R-matrices easily after appropriate linearizations. For the additive structure **s** we can proceed in the same manner. Its four submatrices $\mathbf{s}_t$ consist of a vector of fixed elements, $\boldsymbol{\sigma}_t$, plus a linear combination of disturbances with $S_1, \ldots, S_4$ as coefficient matrices; see (1.9)–(1.10). When the α's change, these determining factors are changed too. The linearized effects are given in Table 6.8. The results for R_1 can of course be read directly from Table 6.7 (because the rows of R_1 refer directly to appropriate rows of P_2), but those of R_2, R_3 and R_4 are new. We find, for example, that if α_2 increases by 0.01, the effectiveness of taxes with respect to consumption is changed from -1.014 to $-1.014-0.0214$. This example illustrates that α_2-changes affect the instrumental effectiveness after a year, whereas they do not affect the current effectiveness; a feature which is due to the fact that α_2 is the coefficient of a lagged endogenous variable.

CONSUMPTION FUNCTION*

Non-controlled variables	W_2	$\bar{T}$	G	W_2	$\bar{T}$	G	W_2	$\bar{T}$	G	W_2	$\bar{T}$	G	Additive structure			
	R_1			R_2			R_3			R_4			s_1	s_2	s_3	s_4
							Coefficient values									
C	0.666	−0.188	0.671	−0.234	−1.014	1.170	−0.172	−1.006	0.859	−0.079	−0.543	0.396	37.55	35.18	36.55	42.84
I	−0.052	−0.296	0.259	−0.152	−0.894	0.759	−0.076	−0.518	0.382	−0.005	−0.088	0.024	−5.62	−4.64	−2.49	2.11
D	0.285	2.358	−1.427	0.095	1.172	−0.475	−0.007	0.186	0.033	−0.060	−0.285	0.301	5.04	0.08	−3.61	−11.91
							Effect of a 0.01 *increase of* α_1 ($\times 10^4$)									
C	−37	−214	187	−53	−323	266	−52	−329	260	−34	−229	170	1498	2757	4084	5907
I	−6	−33	29	−21	−124	106	−23	−143	115	−13	−90	66	232	945	1446	1867
D	32	183	−160	34	209	−169	19	128	−94	−2	4	10	−1279	−1885	−2264	−3023
							Effect of a 0.01 *increase of* α_2 ($\times 10^4$)									
C				−37	−214	187	−53	−324	267	−52	−331	262	1170	2330	3382	4394
I				−6	−33	29	−21	−124	106	−23	−143	115	181	765	1220	1475
D				32	183	−160	34	209	−169	19	130	−95	−100	−1623	−1877	−2071
							Effect of a 0.01 *increase of* α_3 ($\times 10^4$)									
C	140	−34	135	62	−171	285	19	−282	346	−17	−286	297	3838	6136	8052	9677
I	22	−5	21	58	−38	91	11	−100	139	−21	−121	121	594	2276	3010	3193
D	−120	29	−116	−9	136	−201	36	179	−174	43	113	−70	−3277	−4036	−4033	−4064
							Effect of a unit increase of α_0 ($\times 10^3$)									
C													1671	2841	3700	4095
I													259	1017	1399	1423
D													−1427	−1902	−1868	−1567

* See the footnotes below Table 6.7.

The third step is the computation of the first-period decision errors and the corresponding loss. It will prove instructive to split up the decision error according to a constant-term effect and a substitution effect. These are:

$$\mathbf{e}_o = -(\mathbf{I}+\mathbf{R}'\mathbf{R})^{-1}\mathbf{R}'[-(\mathbf{dR})(\mathbf{I}+\mathbf{R}'\mathbf{R})^{-1}\mathbf{R}'\mathbf{s}+\mathbf{ds}] \tag{1.31}$$

$$\mathbf{e}_u = -(\mathbf{I}+\mathbf{R}'\mathbf{R})^{-1}(\mathbf{dR})'[\mathbf{I}-\mathbf{R}(\mathbf{I}+\mathbf{R}'\mathbf{R})^{-1}\mathbf{R}']\mathbf{s}, \tag{1.32}$$

where **dR**, **ds** are the error matrices which result from the errors $d\alpha_i$; the expressions (1.31)–(1.32) are easily derived from (2.1.37) in the appropriate dynamic interpretation. The constant-term component of the first-period loss is then

$$L_o = -\tfrac{1}{2}(\mathbf{e}_o)_1'(xx)_{11}^{-1}(\mathbf{e}_o)_1, \tag{1.33}$$

where $(\mathbf{e}_o)_1$ stands for the first-period subvector of $\mathbf{e}_o$. The substitution and the mixed component are

$$L_u = -\tfrac{1}{2}(\mathbf{e}_u)_1'(xx)_{11}^{-1}(\mathbf{e}_u)_1 \tag{1.34}$$

$$L_m = -(\mathbf{e}_o)_1'(xx)_{11}^{-1}(\mathbf{e}_u)_1, \tag{1.35}$$

respectively. The results are gathered in Table 6.9 and show that the constant-term component of the first-period decision error dominates the substitution component in all cases: the latter is about 40 per cent of the former for W_2 in case of an α_2-change, in all other cases it is 25 per cent or less.[1] At the loss level the difference is even larger because of the quadratic effect. The substitution effect of α_0-changes vanishes for obvious reasons.

The results of Table 6.9 show that a 0.01 error in the specification of the workers' marginal propensity to consume (α_3) is far more serious than the same error with respect to the capitalists' marginal propensity to consume, either current or lagged (α_1 or α_2). However, before concluding that future research efforts should primarily be concentrated on a better specification of α_3 it is worthwhile to glance at the covariance matrix (1.30), which shows that the standard error of the α_3-estimate is far below those of α_1 and α_2. To obtain the expected first-period loss

[1] Table 6.9 differs slightly from the corresponding Tables 5 and 6 of "The Operational Implications of Imperfect Models," quoted above, owing to a small computing error in the latter tables. Further, in the present section a different V-matrix [see (1.30)] is used, which affects Table 6.10 below.

associated with the sampling errors we note that the upper half of Table 6.9 specifies for the first-period decision error:

$$x_1 - x_1^0 = D(d\alpha) \tag{1.36}$$

(apart from linearization errors), where

$$D = 100 \begin{bmatrix} -0.0354 & -0.0193 & -0.0925 & -0.3312 \\ 0.0109 & 0.0029 & 0.0534 & 0.1459 \\ -0.1282 & -0.0863 & -0.4032 & -1.0956 \end{bmatrix}; \quad d\alpha = \begin{bmatrix} d\alpha_1 \\ d\alpha_2 \\ d\alpha_3 \\ d\alpha_0 \end{bmatrix}. \tag{1.37}$$

TABLE 6.9

FIRST-YEAR DECISION ERRORS AND FIRST-YEAR LOSSES DUE TO THE USE OF ERRONEOUS CONSUMPTION FUNCTION COEFFICIENTS

	0.01 error in α_1	0.01 error in α_2	0.01 error in α_3	unit error in α_0
	Decision error components			
W_2: constant-term effect	−0.0294	−0.0137	−0.1103	−0.3312
substitution effect	−0.0060	−0.0055	0.0178	0
total	−0.0354	−0.0193	−0.0925	−0.3312
$\bar{T}$: constant-term effect	0.0109	0.0037	0.0459	0.1459
substitution effect	0.0001	−0.0008	0.0075	0
total	0.0109	0.0029	0.0534	0.1459
G: constant-term effect	−0.1408	−0.0977	−0.4231	−1.0956
substitution effect	0.0126	0.0114	0.0199	0
total	−0.1282	−0.0863	−0.4032	−1.0956
	Loss components			
Constant-term component	0.0550	0.0246	0.5273	3.703
Substitution component	0.0004	0.0004	0.0007	0
Mixed component	−0.0091	−0.0059	−0.0282	0
Total	0.0464	0.0191	0.4998	3.703

The first-period loss given $d\alpha$ is then $-\frac{1}{2}(d\alpha)' D'(xx)_{11}^{-1} D(d\alpha)$, and the expected first-period loss:

$$-\tfrac{1}{2}\mathscr{E}[(d\alpha)' D'(xx)_{11}^{-1} D(d\alpha)] = \sum_{r=0}^{4} \sum_{s=0}^{4} g_{rs} \operatorname{cov}(d\alpha_r, d\alpha_s), \tag{1.38}$$

where

$$[g_{rs}] = -\tfrac{1}{2} D'(xx)_{11}^{-1} D. \tag{1.39}$$

In other words, g_{rr} var $(d\alpha_r)$ is the contribution of the sampling variance of the α_r-estimator to the expected first-period loss, and

$$g_{rs} \text{ cov } (d\alpha_r, d\alpha_s) + g_{sr} \text{ cov } (d\alpha_s, d\alpha_r) \tag{1.40}$$

is the contribution of the sampling covariance of the α_r and the α_s-estimators. This breakdown (normalized such that the largest variance contribution is 1) is shown in Table 6.10. The result reveals that the α_3-estimator leads indeed to the largest expected loss as far as its variance is concerned, but the difference with α_1 is not nearly as large as was suggested by the lower half of Table 6.9. The result shows also that the variance contribution of the constant term is rather sizable; furthermore, that several covariance contributions are of considerable importance.[1] For example, if we combine α_1 and α_2 and hence consider the capitalists' multiplicative consumption pattern as a whole, the aggregate expected loss is only 0.35, which is due to the negative covariance contribution. In the same way, the combined expected loss of the α_3 and α_0-errors is about 0.75, and that of the α_1 and α_3-errors slightly more than 1. The three covariance contributions involved are so large that it is evidently of great importance to take them into account.

TABLE 6.10

BREAKDOWN OF THE EXPECTED FIRST-YEAR LOSS DUE TO THE SAMPLING ERRORS OF THE CONSUMPTION FUNCTION COEFFICIENTS

	α_1	α_2	α_3	α_0
α_1	0.63	−0.50	−0.59	−0.10
α_2		0.22	−0.12	−0.11
α_3			1	−1.10
α_0				0.84

6.1.6. Summary

(1) The objective of this section is the maximizing strategy based on the preference function and the constraints of Section 3.1 for the four-year period 1933–1936. For this purpose the econometric model which underlies the constraints has to be formulated in final form, which means that

[1] In Table 6.10 the covariance contributions are given above the diagonal and counted twice in accordance with (1.40).

all lagged endogenous variables are eliminated successively by expressing them in terms of exogenous variables, disturbances, and 1932 values.

(2) The maximizing strategy implies a much higher level of government expenditure on goods and services than was actually realized in 1933–1936. It also leads to a higher level of indirect taxes except in the last year, and to roughly the same development of the government wage bill. The maximizing strategy leads to higher levels of consumption, investment, and national income. When its results are compared with the desired development of these variables, we find that the development of consumption, investment and national income is below the desired path in most of the years, whereas the converse is true for the government wage bill and for government expenditure on goods and services.

(3) The—conditionally unbiased—forecasts of future instrument values are rather accurate on the average, most of them being far better than no-change extrapolation. The same applies to the forecasts of future noncontrolled values with the exception of the last year, which was characterized by unusually large disturbances of the structural equations which underlie the constraints. A majority of the forecast revisions brought the prediction closer to the corresponding realized value.

(4) Given the preference function chosen and given the assumption that the coefficients of the model are specified correctly (and given that there are no noninstrumental exogenous variables except time), the only source of uncertainty is the disturbed character of the behavioural equations. It turns out—under appropriate assumptions regarding vanishing correlations—that the disturbances of the consumption function are responsible for slightly more than 40 per cent of the expected first-period loss, those of the investment function for slightly less, and those of the demand-for-labour function for only 20 per cent.

(5) If we assume that the coefficients of the behavioural equations do not coincide with the "true" parameters but are random drawings from a sampling distribution, we can derive their expected first-period loss. This procedure, when applied to the coefficients of the consumption function, shows that under our preference conditions the sampling errors in the workers' marginal propensity to consume cause the largest loss. Next is the sampling variance of the constant term, third that of the capitalists' current marginal propensity to consume. The covariance contributions to the loss are all negative and some of them are sizable.

6.2. CONSTRAINTS AND PREFERENCE FUNCTIONS FOR THE NETHERLANDS IN 1957–1959 [1]

6.2.1. Introduction; The Choice of Instruments and Noncontrolled Variables

This section and its successor are similar to Section 6.1 in that they attempt to design dynamic decision rules with respect to an economy as a whole. They differ from their predecessor as to the degree of realism which can be claimed with respect to the formulation of preference function and constraints. This formulation has indeed more pretensions, since the quadratic part of the preference function is far from the unit form while moreover the constraints are derived from a much larger model. Also, we shall not confine ourselves to just one quadratic preference function but consider three alternative sets of preferences; and we shall not make the unrealistic assumption that everything is known as soon as it belongs to the past. The present section will be devoted to the formulation of preferences and constraints, after which the result of the maximizing strategies in various forms will follow in Section 6.3.

The first problem that will be considered is the period to be chosen and the specification of instruments and noncontrolled variables. Now in 1956 there was over-employment in The Netherlands and also a considerable deficit on the balance of payments. The government asked the advice of the Social and Economic Council (*Sociaal-Economische Raad*); in fact, it has become customary for the government to take the advice of this Council as one of the bases for designing the economic policy to be followed. In November, 1956 the Council's *Advies inzake de bestedingen* (Advice on National Expenditure) became available, in which the goals for the economic policy in the next few years were formulated as follows:

(i) maximization of national income and full employment of all factors of production, particularly labour;

(ii) promotion of a stable price level;

(iii) an "acceptable" distribution of national income among relevant groups of the population;

(iv) equilibrium in the balance of payments;

---

[1] This section and Section 6.3 are largely based on P. J. M. VAN DEN BOGAARD and A. P. BARTEN, "Optimal Macroeconomic Decision Rules for The Netherlands, 1957–1959," Report 5915 of the Econometric Institute of the Netherlands School of Economics.

(v) a level of investment in fixed capital which enables an improvement of the standard of living of the growing population.

On the basis of this advice a policy of curtailing public expenditure was followed, which implied the prospect of a temporary decline of real wages (since money wages were expected to increase by less than the price level). It is clearly interesting to compare this policy with the strategy approach, and accordingly 1957 is chosen as the first year. Since the greater part of the analysis was completed in 1959, we shall have a three-year strategy period 1957–1959. Furthermore, as to the five goals which are specified above, we shall choose four noncontrolled variables which are directly related to four of these goals. The first is the annual percentage change in private (non-governmental) employment, to be denoted by n^p. The second is p^c, which is the annual percentage change in the price level of private consumption; the adjective "private" implies that consumption by the government, such as military expenditure, is excluded. The third noncontrolled variable is Δq^w, which is the annual change in the percentage share of wages in national income; more precisely, it is the annual change in the ratio ($\times 100$) of private wages per head of the total active wage-earning labour force to national product at factor costs per head of the total active working population, where "active" stands for "not unemployed." The fourth noncontrolled variable, finally, is the annual surplus on the balance of payments, to be written B. These variables, together with the instruments which will be considered below, are summarized in Table 6.11. The fifth goal specified by the Council (investment in fixed assets) has not been taken into explicit account, partly because of a desire not to overburden the analysis with numerous variables, partly because of its long-run character compared with our three-year period.

In the Advice which was quoted above the following instruments of economic policy were suggested:

(i) the general wage rate;

(ii) indirect taxes and subsidies;

(iii) direct taxes;

(iv) government expenditure on commodities;

(v) instruments which are specifically monetary, such as a restrictive credit policy or changes in the rate of interest.

The instruments which have actually been chosen for the analysis which follows are in accordance with these suggestions and are listed in Table 6.11. That the general wage rate is a variable controlled by the government may seem surprising, but in fact this is true in the sense that government consent for wage increases was required; wage cuts are of course unplausible. Regarding the three "autonomous change" tax instruments of Table 6.11, these can be explained as follows. In general, taxes ($\overline{T}$) are levied on something, say on income (Y). This means that the amount of taxes received can be written as a certain function of income; e.g., we may want to approximate linearly and write $\overline{T} = \alpha + \beta Y$, where β stands for the average value of the marginal tax rates in the relevant area. Now the way in which tax rates are changed in The Netherlands is usually such that the marginal rates are only slightly affected; hence after such a change the new linearized function becomes $\overline{T} = \alpha' + \beta Y$, at least approximately. The result of the change is then measured by $\alpha' - \alpha$, which is called the autonomous change (in T^{ia}, T^{wa} or T^{oa}, as the case may be) and which represents an attempt to transform tax rate changes into value changes. The fifth instrument is government expenditure on commodities, G. As to monetary instruments, finally, these have not been taken into consideration because of the considerable uncertainty as to their quantitative impact.

TABLE 6.11

SURVEY OF INSTRUMENTS AND NONCONTROLLED VARIABLES

Symbol	*Description*	*Unit**
	Instruments	
w	Percentage change in the general wage rate	% per year
ΔT^{ia}	Autonomous change in indirect taxes minus subsidies	10^9 guilders per year
ΔT^{wa}	Autonomous change in direct taxes on wage income	10^9 guilders per year
ΔT^{oa}	Autonomous change in direct taxes on nonwage income	10^9 guilders per year
ΔG	Change in government expenditure on commodities	10^9 guilders per year
	Noncontrolled variables	
n^p	Percentage change in private employment	% per year
p^c	Percentage change in the price level of private consumption	% per year
Δq^w	Change in the percentage share of wages in national income	% per year
B	Surplus on the balance of payments	10^9 guilders per year

* Guilders are current (not deflated).

Summarizing, the vectors of instruments and noncontrolled variables can be partitioned according to the three years 1957, 1958, 1959:

$$\mathbf{x} = \begin{bmatrix} x_1 \\ x_2 \\ x_3 \end{bmatrix}, \quad \mathbf{y} = \begin{bmatrix} y_1 \\ y_2 \\ y_3 \end{bmatrix}, \tag{2.1}$$

and each of the subvectors consists of 5 or 4 components:

$$x_t = \begin{bmatrix} w_t \\ \Delta T_t^{ia} \\ \Delta T_t^{wa} \\ \Delta T_t^{oa} \\ \Delta G_t \end{bmatrix}, \quad y_t = \begin{bmatrix} n_t^p \\ p_t^c \\ \Delta q_t^w \\ B_t \end{bmatrix} \quad \text{for } t = 1, 2, 3. \tag{2.2}$$

6.2.2. Three Sets of Desired Values

The Social and Economic Council consists of representatives of trade unions and employers' organizations as well as of members appointed by the Crown whose position with respect to the employer-employee distinction is supposed to be neutral. Our objective will be to formulate a quadratic preference function for each of these groups; more precisely, to select a "typical" individual from each group and to measure his preferences by a quadratic function. These individuals are no real persons; an attempt has been made to formulate the preference functions in such a way that they can be regarded as satisfactory approximations to the ideas which they are supposed to represent.[1] The result can be explained conveniently in terms of the following three steps: first, the desired values for all 9 variables and all 3 years will be formulated, for each of the three sets of preferences; second, the relative intensity of these desires will be measured by the diagonal elements of the square matrices of the quadratic part of the preference functions; finally, two amendments will be made.

For the sake of convenience, we shall denote the preferences of the labour group by "L", those of the Crown members by "C", and those of the employers by "E". Considering the desired values of noncontrolled variables first, in all three cases there is a desire to raise the level of employment in each of the three years. However, this as such means only

[1] This was done by Mr. A. P. BARTEN in discussions with Messrs. C. A. VAN DEN BELD, C. J. VAN EIJK, F. HARTOG, H. KRIJNSE LOCKER, H. M. DE LANGE, J. LIPS, G. PODT, A. PUTTER, and W. TIMS, at that time all staff members of the Central Planning Bureau.

that the number of employed is required to increase because the labour force increases over time. In 1956 there was a very low level of unemployment, while an increase in the size of the wage-earning population was expected of about 2 per cent in 1957 and 1958 and of $1\frac{1}{2}$ per cent in 1959. Now "L" wants to maintain the scarcity of labour at the same level, hence the desired values for n^p of 2, 2, and $1\frac{1}{2}$ per cent per year respectively. "C" is interested in a slowly diminishing overemployment, while "E" wishes to achieve a more "normal" level within a rather short period of time. As regards the alarming deficit on the balance of payments in 1956, "L" and "C" are already satisfied to play even in 1957, but the desires of "E" go farther. In the later years all want to create a certain surplus, but the amounts are different because of different opinions about required foreign exchange reserves for business cycle fluctuations. All want a more or less stable price level, and "L" is even interested in minor price reductions; the desires of "E" do not go that far, partly because a gradual price increase is considered as a suitable social lubricant. Also, "E" is interested in a reduction of consumer subsidies and in a return of house rents to a more "normal" level, both of which necessarily imply a higher price level. Finally, as to the share of wages in national income, "C" is interested in constancy, "L" in a gradual increase, and "E" in a minor decrease. All these desires, together with those of the instruments which will be considered in the next paragraph, are specified numerically in Table 6.12.

Turning to the desired values of the instruments, we notice a general desire for a rather substantial wage increase in 1957. This is partly due to the compensations for premiums to be paid by employees for the newly introduced General Old-Age Pension, but the greater part must be ascribed to wage measures taken in the preceding year 1956. This can be explained as follows. Suppose that the wage rate is w_1 in the first half of year t and that it is then raised to w_2 after which it remains constant until the end of the year. The average wage rate in t is then $\frac{1}{2}(w_1+w_2)$ and that in $t+1$ is w_2 when no further wage measures are taken; but this means that the wage level in $t+1$ exceeds that of t by $\frac{1}{2}(w_2-w_1)$ even if there are no wage increases in $t+1$. In the later years (1958 and 1959) there is no spurious effect of this kind, so that the desires decrease accordingly. It is seen that "C" and "E" desire only minor wage increases in these years; they are already satisfied with the improvement of labour's position due to changes in the job evaluation system. Furthermore, as to the three tax variables, the desires with respect to these show a clear difference

TABLE 6.12

DESIRED VALUES OF INSTRUMENTS AND NONCONTROLLED VARIABLES

Variable	Unit	"L"			"C"			"E"		
		1957	1958	1959	1957	1958	1959	1957	1958	1959
Instruments										
w	*	10.00	4.00	4.00	7.00	2.00	2.00	6.00	2.00	2.00
ΔT^{ia}	**	−0.10	−0.05	0	0	0	0	0	0	0
ΔT^{wa}	**	−0.10	−0.075	−0.025	−0.05	−0.05	0	−0.10	−0.075	−0.025
ΔT^{oa}	**	0.10	0.10	0.05	−0.10	−0.10	0	−0.20	−0.20	−0.15
ΔG	**	0.20	0.20	0.20	0.10	0.10	0.10	0.05	0.05	0.05
Noncontrolled variables										
n^p	*	2.00	2.00	1.50	1.50	1.50	1.50	1.00	1.25	1.50
p^c	*	−1.00	−1.00	−1.00	0	0	0	1.00	1.00	1.00
Δq^w	*	1.00	1.00	1.00	0	0	0	−0.50	−0.50	−0.50
B	**	0	0.50	0.50	0	0.75	0.75	0.25	0.75	1.00

* Percentage change per year.

** 10^9 guilders per year.

between the ideas of "L" and "E" with "C" in a middle position. "L" wishes tax decreases for wage income, tax increases for nonwage income; "E" dislikes taxes generally (going farther in this respect than "C") and therefore agrees with "L" as to the tax decreases for wage income, but it wishes also decreases for nonwage income. Only "L" is interested in reductions of indirect tax rates. Finally, all agree that government spending on commodities should go up, but "E" wants the expansion of the government budget to remain within narrow limits, whereas "L" expects the government to undertake several kinds of spending activities.

6.2.3. Three Sets of Equivalent Deviations

The quadratic part of the preference functions can be explained conveniently if we start by assuming that it has a diagonal form. It is then a weighted sum of squares of the deviations between actual and desired values. The weights will be assumed to be different for different variables, but equal for the different years. This means that the preference function can be written in the form

$$(2.3) \qquad -\sum_{t=1}^{3}\left\{\left(\frac{w_t - w_t^*}{w^0}\right)^2 + \ldots + \left(\frac{B_t - B_t^*}{B^0}\right)^2\right\},$$

i.e., as minus the sum of 27 squares (9 variables times 3 years). In (2.3) $w_t^*, \ldots, B_t^*$ stand for desired values and $w^0, \ldots, B^0$ stand for what will be termed *equivalent deviations*. Thus, if w_t deviates from the desire w_t^* by w^0, this leads to a utility reduction which is precisely the same as the reduction caused by a deviation B^0 between B_t and B_t^*; hence the term "equivalent deviations," and it will be clear that these form a convenient basis for measuring the intensity of the desires. The values chosen are given in Table 6.13. Obviously, only the relative intensities are of importance, which means that we may choose an arbitrary (positive) value for one of the equivalent deviations. This is the unit value for the wage rate in Table 6.13. It is seen that "L" and "C" agree that a $\frac{1}{2}$ per cent deviation for private employment is as serious as a 1 per cent deviation for the wage rate (which means that a 1 per cent deviation for the former variable is considered four times as serious as a 1 per cent deviation for the latter), whereas "E" does not have such strong feelings about employment (relative to the wage rate). All agree that a $1\frac{1}{2}$ per cent deviation for the price level and for the share of wages in national income is equivalent to a 1 per cent deviation for the wage rate, except that "E" does not have such a strong desire with respect to the price level. "C" and "E" agree that a 0.1 billion deviation for indirect taxes and for direct taxes on wage income is to be regarded as serious as a 1 per cent deviation between w_t and w_t^*, but "L" considers the latter deviation more serious. There are substantial differences between "L" and "E" as to the evaluation of the balance of payments surplus and taxes on nonwage income, and "C" occupies an intermediate position (as usual). Evidently,

TABLE 6.13

EQUIVALENT DEVIATIONS OF INSTRUMENTS AND NONCONTROLLED VARIABLES

Variable	Unit	"L"	"C"	"E"
	Instruments			
w	% per year	1.00	1.00	1.00
ΔT^{ia}	10^9 guilders per year	0.15	0.10	0.10
ΔT^{wa}	10^9 guilders per year	0.15	0.10	0.10
ΔT^{oa}	10^9 guilders per year	0.80	0.40	0.10
ΔG	10^9 guilders per year	0.25	0.25	0.15
	Noncontrolled variables			
n^p	% per year	0.50	0.50	1.00
p^c	% per year	1.50	1.50	2.00
Δq^w	% per year	1.50	1.50	1.50
B	10^9 guilders per year	0.60	0.30	0.20

for "L" these variables are relatively unimportant, whereas "E" has more pretensions in this respect. There is a similar difference as to the evaluation of government expenditure on commodities, but it is not as large.

6.2.4. The Carry-Over Amendment

The preference functions as formulated up till now are of the form

$$\frac{1}{2}\sum_{t=1}^{3}[(x_t-\xi_t)'D_x(x_t-\xi_t)+(y_t-\eta_t)'D_y(y_t-\eta_t)], \tag{2.4}$$

where ξ_t and η_t are vectors representing the desired values of x_t and y_t respectively, while D_x and D_y are diagonal matrices. Evidently, D_x has 5 diagonal elements and D_y has 4, and it follows from (2.3) that these 9 values are determined by the equivalent deviations:

$$-2\left(\frac{1}{w^0}\right)^2, \ldots, -2\left(\frac{1}{B^0}\right)^2. \tag{2.5}$$

But the actual preference functions to be used will be slightly more complicated because we wish to apply two amendments. One of these, to be called the *carry-over amendment*, recognizes the fact that if the actual 1957 change in employment, say, is below the desire [e.g., $n^p = \frac{1}{2}$ in 1957, so that $n^p-(n^p)^* = -1\frac{1}{2}$ for "L"], a 1958 change which is equal to the desire of that year is actually too low. Continuing our example, if $n^p = (n^p)^* = 2$ in 1958, then the 1958 level of private employment exceeds the 1956 level by only $2\frac{1}{2}$ per cent, whereas the original desire is 4 per cent. A similar objection applies if $n^p > (n^p)^*$ in 1957, but now in opposite direction. A convenient way to handle this is to add the discrepancy between desire and realization of 1957 to the desire of 1958. More precisely, consider any variable z for which this problem exists, and write z_1^*, z_2^*, z_3^* for the desired values in the three successive years. The "corrected" desire for the second year is then

$$z_2^{**} = z_2^*+z_1^*-z_1. \tag{2.6}$$

For the employment example given above this would mean that we have to add $1\frac{1}{2}$ to the $(n^p)^*$ of 1958, hence $(n^p)^{**} = 3\frac{1}{2}$; on combining this with the realized $n^p = \frac{1}{2}$ of 1957, we see that the aggregate desire for 1957 and 1958 combined is now indeed an increase of 4 per cent.[1] The same procedure will be used for the third year:

$$z_3^{***} = z_3^*+z_2^{**}-z_2 = z_3^*+z_2^*+z_1^*-z_2-z_1. \tag{2.7}$$

It is not considered relevant to apply this carry-over amendment to the instruments, but it will be applied to two noncontrolled variables in each of the three preference functions, viz., n^p (the change in private employment) and Δq^w (the change in the share of wages in national income). This means that the lower half of Table 6.12 specifies only "initially" desired values (z_1^*, z_2^*, z_3^*) for these variables and that the "effectively" desired values are z_1^*, z_2^{**}, z_3^{***}. We could therefore interpret the η_t of (2.4) according to the latter values, rather than according to those of Table 6.12; but we prefer to continue the use of the original figures, which can be done as follows. Before the amendment each noncontrolled variable entered into the preference function in the form

$$k[(z_1-z_1^*)^2+(z_2-z_2^*)^2+(z_3-z_3^*)^2], \tag{2.8}$$

[1] The procedure of adding successive percentage changes is not completely accurate [e.g., a $\frac{1}{2}$ per cent increase in 1957 followed by a $3\frac{1}{2}$ per cent increase in 1958 implies an aggregate percentage increase of $(1.005\times 1.035-1)100 = 4.0175$, not exactly 4 per cent]; but this is neglected here.

where k is the appropriate diagonal element of $\frac{1}{2}D_y$. If we replace z_2^* by z_2^{**} and z_3^* by z_3^{***}, (2.8) takes the following form:

$$(2.9)\qquad k[3(z_1-z_1^*)^2+2(z_2-z_2^*)^2+(z_3-z_3^*)^2+4(z_1-z_1^*)(z_2-z_2^*) \\ +2(z_1-z_1^*)(z_3-z_3^*)+2(z_2-z_2^*)(z_3-z_3^*)],$$

which means that the quadratic part of the preference function has no longer a diagonal form. Since the amendment is applied to two non-controlled variables, we should consider the partitioned matrix

$$(2.10)\qquad \mathbf{B} = \begin{bmatrix} B_{11} & B_{12} & B_{13} \\ B_{21} & B_{22} & B_{23} \\ B_{31} & B_{32} & B_{33} \end{bmatrix},$$

which will take over the role of

$$\begin{bmatrix} D_y & \mathbf{0} & \mathbf{0} \\ \mathbf{0} & D_y & \mathbf{0} \\ \mathbf{0} & \mathbf{0} & D_y \end{bmatrix}$$

from now on. Each of the submatrices $B_{tt'}$ is diagonal. It follows from (2.9) that in B_{11} the relevant diagonal elements (corresponding with n^p and Δq^w) are obtained by multiplying the corresponding elements of D_y by 3 and in B_{22} by 2. Also, the nondiagonal blocks cease to be zero matrices. B_{12} and B_{21} have two diagonal elements which are equal to the corresponding elements of B_{22}, and the other four (B_{13}, B_{31}, B_{23}, B_{32}) have two diagonal elements which are the same as the corresponding elements of B_{33}.[1, 2]

6.2.5. *The Smoothing Amendment*

The second amendment, to be called the *smoothing amendment*, is designed to reduce the possibility of wild fluctuations of instruments.

---

[1] These changes are such that **B** remains symmetric. We could also make B_{12} such that the relevant diagonal elements are twice the corresponding elements of B_{22} and put $B_{21} = \mathbf{0}$, but this would make **B** asymmetric which is less convenient.

[2] It is perhaps useful to state explicitly that there is no question of year-to-year revision of the preference function as regards the variables to which the carry-over amendment is applied. The only thing which we have done is to construct the preference function, right at the beginning of the strategy period, in such a way as to provide for the opportunity of a series of shifting desired values. It will also be clear that we could have solved the problem by defining n^p and Δq^w as levels rather than as percentage increases, which would have necessitated a reformulation of the constraints.

Moderate instrument changes contribute to a feeling of certainty among those groups which are particularly affected by such changes; also, there is the problem of the unavoidable inertia of the execution of a policy, which grows in importance when the measures to be taken are of larger size. To handle this problem we shall employ the same z-notation as that of the first amendment, but z stands now for any of the five instruments. The contribution of z to the preference function is then (2.8), which will be replaced by

$$k[(z_1-z_1^*)^2+(z_2-z_2^*)^2+(z_3-z_3^*)^2 + \tfrac{1}{2}\{(z_1-z_0)^2+(z_2-z_1)^2+(z_3-z_2)^2\}], \tag{2.11}$$

where z_0 is the value which z takes in 1956. In words this means that we add to the sum of squares of the deviations between actual and desired values $\frac{1}{2}$ times another sum of squares, viz., of the successive differences of the instrument values. Hence any given annual change in an instrument is considered half as serious as a discrepancy between an actual and a desired value of the same size. It will prove convenient to re-write (2.11) as the sum of a linear term in $z_t - z_t^*$:

$$k(-z_0+2z_1^*-z_2^*)(z_1-z_1^*)+k(-z_1^*+2z_2^*-z_3^*)(z_2-z_2^*) + k(-z_2^*+z_3^*)(z_3-z_3^*) \tag{2.12}$$

and a quadratic term:

$$k[2(z_1-z_1^*)^2+2(z_2-z_2^*)^2+1\tfrac{1}{2}(z_3-z_3^*)^2 - (z_1-z_1^*)(z_2-z_2^*)-(z_2-z_2^*)(z_3-z_3^*)] \tag{2.13}$$

(apart from an irrelevant constant term). We conclude that the smoothing amendment leads to a nonzero linear part of the preference function. So we introduce

$$\mathbf{a} = \begin{bmatrix} a_1 \\ a_2 \\ a_3 \end{bmatrix}, \quad \mathbf{A} = \begin{bmatrix} A_{11} & A_{12} & A_{13} \\ A_{21} & A_{22} & A_{23} \\ A_{31} & A_{32} & A_{33} \end{bmatrix}, \tag{2.14}$$

where $\mathbf{A}$ takes over the role of

$$\begin{bmatrix} D_x & \mathbf{0} & \mathbf{0} \\ \mathbf{0} & D_x & \mathbf{0} \\ \mathbf{0} & \mathbf{0} & D_x \end{bmatrix}$$

in (2.4). It follows from (2.13) that in A_{11} and A_{22} the diagonal elements are obtained by multiplying the corresponding elements of D_x by 2

TABLE 6.14

THE SUBVECTORS a_1, a_2, a_3 OF THE LINEAR PART OF THE PREFERENCE FUNCTIONS AND THE DIAGONAL ELEMENTS (ARRANGED AS COLUMN VECTORS) OF THE SUBMATRICES OF THE QUADRATIC PART*

Variables	Coefficients of instruments						Coefficients of noncontrolled variables					Variables
	a_1	a_2	a_3	A_{11}, A_{22}	A_{33}	A_{12}, A_{21}, A_{23}, A_{32}	B_{11}	B_{22}	B_{33}	B_{12}, B_{21}	B_{13}, B_{31}, B_{23}, B_{32}	
"L"												
w	−2.98	6.00	0	−4.00	−3.00	1.00	−24.00	−16.00	−8.00	−16.00	−8.00	n^p
ΔT^{ia}	−3.56	0	−2.22	−177.78	−133.33	44.44	−0.89	−0.89	−0.89	0	0	p^c
ΔT^{wa}	2.44	1.11	−2.22	−177.78	−133.33	44.44	−2.67	−1.78	−0.89	−1.78	−0.89	Δq^w
ΔT^{oa}	0	−0.08	0.08	−6.25	−4.69	1.56	−5.56	−5.56	−5.56	0	0	B
ΔG	1.76	0	0	−64.00	−48.00	16.00						
"C"												
w	1.02	5.00	0	−4.00	−3.00	1.00	−24.00	−16.00	−8.00	−16.00	−8.00	n^p
ΔT^{ia}	−23.00	0	0	−400.00	−300.00	100.00	−0.89	−0.89	−0.89	0	0	p^c
ΔT^{wa}	−2.00	5.00	−5.00	−400.00	−300.00	100.00	−2.67	−1.78	−0.89	−1.78	−0.89	Δq^w
ΔT^{oa}	1.25	0.62	−0.62	−25.00	−18.75	6.25	−22.22	−22.22	−22.22	0	0	B
ΔG	3.36	0	0	−64.00	−48.00	16.00						
"E"												
w	3.02	4.00	0	−4.00	−3.00	1.00	−6.00	−4.00	−2.00	−4.00	−2.00	n^p
ΔT^{ia}	−23.00	0	0	−400.00	−300.00	100.00	−0.50	−0.50	−0.50	0	0	p^c
ΔT^{wa}	5.50	2.50	−5.00	−400.00	−300.00	100.00	−2.67	−1.78	−1.78	−1.78	−0.89	Δq^w
ΔT^{oa}	30.00	5.00	−5.00	−400.00	−300.00	100.00	−50.00	−50.00	−50.00	0	0	B
ΔG	11.55	0	0	−177.78	−133.33	44.44						

* The diagonal elements of A_{13} and A_{31} are all zero and not shown in the table.

TABLE 6.15

LIST OF VARIABLES OF THE MODEL USED

Symbol	Description	Exogenous		Endogenous		Occurs in equation*
		Instrument	*Other*	*Noncontrolled*	*Other*	
	(i) *Money values* (in billions of guilders per year)**					
B	Surplus on the balance of payments (current account)			×		7, 24, 25
C	Private consumption				×	1, 14, 19, 20, 26
D	Depreciation of privately owned fixed assets		×			21
E	Total expenditure excluding government wages, minus imports of invisibles				×	19, 21, 37
E'	Total expenditure excluding government wages and inventory changes, minus exports of invisibles				×	3, 20, 38
G	Government expenditure on commodities	×				14, 19, 20, 30
I^f	Non-autonomous gross fixed capital formation				×	2, 14, 19, 20, 27
I^{fa}	Autonomous gross fixed capital formation		×			14, 19, 20, 28
I^i	Change in inventories				×	3, 19, 29
M	Imports of commodities				×	14, 21, 24, 33
O	Non-wage income				×	16, 17, 18, 21, 23
O^d	Disposable non-wage income				×	1, 2, 9, 23
S	Surplus on the balance of invisibles		×			19, 24, 35
T^i	Indirect taxes less subsidies				×	14, 21
ΔT^{ia}	Autonomous change in indirect taxes less subsidies	×				9, 14, 41
T^o	Income taxes on non-wage income				×	16, 23
ΔT^{oa}	Autonomous change in income taxes on non-wage income	×				16
T^w	Income taxes on wage income				×	15, 22
ΔT^{wa}	Autonomous change in income taxes on wage income	×				15

	change)	×			10, 36
Θ^o	Income transfers to non-wage-earners	×			16, 23
Θ^u	Unemployment allowances			×	13, 15, 22
$\Delta\Theta^{ua}$	Autonomous change in unemployment allowances	×			13
Θ^w	Income transfers to wage-earners	×			15, 22
	(ii) *Volumes* (in billions of guilders per year at last year's prices)**				
c	Private consumption			×	4, 5, 26
e	Total expenditure excluding government wages, minus imports of invisibles			×	7, 37
e'	Total expenditure excluding government wages and inventory changes, minus exports of invisibles			×	9, 10, 11, 12, 38
g	Government expenditure on commodities			×	4, 5, 30
i^f	Non-autonomous gross fixed capital formation			×	4, 5, 27
i^{fa}	Autonomous gross fixed capital formation			×	4, 5, 28
i^i	Change in inventories			×	5, 29
l	Deposits and near-money at the end of the year (secondary liquid resources)			×	2, 7
Δl^a	Autonomous change in deposits and near-money	×			7
m	Imports of commodities			×	5, 7, 33
n^d	Wage-earning working population (measured as percentage change)	×			8
n^g	Employment in government service (measured as percentage change)	×			8, 17, 31
n^o	Non-wage-earning working population (measured as percentage change)	×			17
n^p	Employment in private industry (measured as percentage change)		×		4, 8, 9, 10, 11, 12, 17, 18, 32
$\tilde{n}^p$	Ditto, but level (measured in man-years)***			×	4, 18

TABLE 6.15 (continued)

Symbol	Description	*Exogenous*		*Endogenous*		Occurs in equation*
		Instrument	*Other*	*Noncontrolled*	*Other*	
n^u	Registered unemployed as a percentage of the wage-earning working population				×	2, 8, 13
$\tilde{o}$	Non-wage income in prices of 1938***				×	4, 18
q^w	Share of wages in primary national income (measured as percentage)			×		17
s	Surplus on the balance of invisibles				×	7, 35
x	Exports of commodities				×	4, 5, 6, 7, 34
x^r	Exports of competing countries (measured as percentage change)				×	6, 36
	(iii) *Price indices of* (in percentage change per year)**					
k^o	Gross profit margin per unit of output**** (measured as percentage)				×	4, 41
p^c	Private consumption			×		1, 9, 26, 39, 40
p^e	Total expenditure excluding government wages, minus imports of invisibles				×	4, 18, 35, 37, 39
$p^{e'}$	Total expenditure excluding government wages and inventory changes, minus exports of invisibles				×	38, 40, 41
p^g	Government expenditure on commodities				×	12, 30, 39, 40
p^i	Gross fixed capital formation				×	2, 11, 27, 28, 39, 40
p^m	Imports of commodities		×			4, 9, 10, 11, 12, 29, 33, 39, 41
p^x	Exports of commodities				×	6, 10, 34, 39, 40
p^{xr}	Exports of competing countries		×			6, 36
w	Wage rate	×				7, 9, 10, 11, 12, 31, 32, 41

* The equation numbers are those of Section 6.A of the Appendix; hence 1 stands for (A.1), 2 for (A.2), etc.

** Except when other units are mentioned explicitly.

and in A_{33} by $1\frac{1}{2}$; further, that the diagonal elements of A_{12}, A_{21}, A_{23}, A_{32} are equal to those of $\frac{1}{2}D_x$ apart from sign. All submatrices $A_{tt'}$ are diagonal and A_{13} and A_{31} are zero matrices. The elements of the column vector a_1 are obtained by multiplying the appropriate diagonal element of $\frac{1}{2}D_x$ by $-z_0+2z_1^*-z_2^*$, see (2.12); and those of a_2 and a_3 are obtained in the same way except that the multipliers are $-z_1^*+2z_2^*-z_3^*$ and $-z_2^*+z_3^*$, respectively.

This completes the numerical specification of the three alternative preference functions. They are all of the form

$$w(\mathbf{x}, \mathbf{y}) = \mathbf{a}'(\mathbf{x}-\boldsymbol{\xi})+\tfrac{1}{2}[(\mathbf{x}-\boldsymbol{\xi})'\mathbf{A}(\mathbf{x}-\boldsymbol{\xi})+(\mathbf{y}-\boldsymbol{\eta})'\mathbf{B}(\mathbf{y}-\boldsymbol{\eta})], \tag{2.15}$$

where $\boldsymbol{\xi}$ and $\boldsymbol{\eta}$ are the vectors of (initially) desired values as given in Table 6.12. The coefficient matrices **a**, **A**, **B** are given in Table 6.14. They are derived from the equivalent deviations of Table 6.13 in accordance with the transformation (2.5) and the two amendments, the results of which were summarized immediately below (2.10) and (2.14) respectively.

6.2.6. The Constraints

The constraints were derived by Mr. A. P. BARTEN from an econometric model, constructed originally by VERDOORN and VAN EIJK,[1] consisting of 40 equations and 59 variables. These variables are summarized in Table 6.15. They are shown separately for the three categories: values, volumes, and prices; and in each of these groups they are ranked in the alphabetical order of their symbols. Four columns are used to indicate (by a cross) whether a variable is an instrument, a noninstrumental exogenous variable, a noncontrolled variable, or an endogenous variable which is not an argument of the preference functions. It is seen that money values are denoted by capitals and expressed in billions (10^9) of guilders per year; that volumes are denoted by lower-case letters and also expressed in billions of guilders per year but at last year's prices; and that prices are denoted by lower-case letters and expressed as percentage changes measured from the level of the preceding year. In the last column the equations are listed in which each variable occurs. The equation numbers refer to the Appendix of this chapter (Section 6.A) in which the model is considered in more detail.

---

[1] P. J. VERDOORN and C. J. VAN EIJK, "Experimental Short-Term Forecasting Models." Mimeographed report of the Central Planning Bureau, The Hague (1958).

The model has been adapted in such a way that it is linear with constant coefficients, the lags being at most one year. Hence it is of the same type as the model used in Section 6.1. It follows that the constraints take the form $\mathbf{y} = \mathbf{Rx}+\mathbf{s}$, where—given that we have a three-year horizon in the present case—$\mathbf{R}$ can be partitioned as follows:

$$\mathbf{R} = \begin{bmatrix} R_1 & \mathbf{0} & \mathbf{0} \\ R_2 & R_1 & \mathbf{0} \\ R_3 & R_2 & R_1 \end{bmatrix}. \tag{2.16}$$

The three submatrices R_1, R_2, R_3 are shown in Table 6.16. It appears that the three tax variables affect employment negatively in the current year

TABLE 6.16

THE SUBMATRICES R_1, R_2 AND R_3 OF THE MULTIPLICATIVE STRUCTURE OF THE CONSTRAINTS

Noncontrolled variables	*Instruments*				
	w	ΔT^{ia}	ΔT^{wa}	ΔT^{oa}	ΔG
			R_1		
n^p	0.001	−1.075	−0.848	−0.167	1.322
p^c	0.752	3.075	−0.511	−1.350	−0.719
Δq^w	0.043	1.163	0.740	0.499	−0.341
B	0.038	0.371	0.750	−0.037	−0.957
			R_2		
n^p	0.032	−1.201	−0.043	−0.957	−0.175
p^c	0.103	1.984	−0.071	0.533	0.037
Δq^w	−0.044	−0.791	−0.149	−0.167	0.141
B	0.080	0.786	0.350	0.722	−0.426
			R_3		
n^p	0.064	0.155	0.024	0.277	−0.134
p^c	0.023	−0.364	−0.240	−0.080	0.210
Δq^w	−0.020	0.093	0.068	−0.056	−0.082
B	0.050	0.318	0.195	0.264	−0.267

and the next, as could be expected, but that they have minor positive effects in the year thereafter. The effect of government expenditure on commodities with respect to employment is more or less opposite. The three tax variables are positively effective with respect to the surplus on the balance of payments in all three years (apart from a minor negative effect of taxes on nonwage income in the current year), and again the

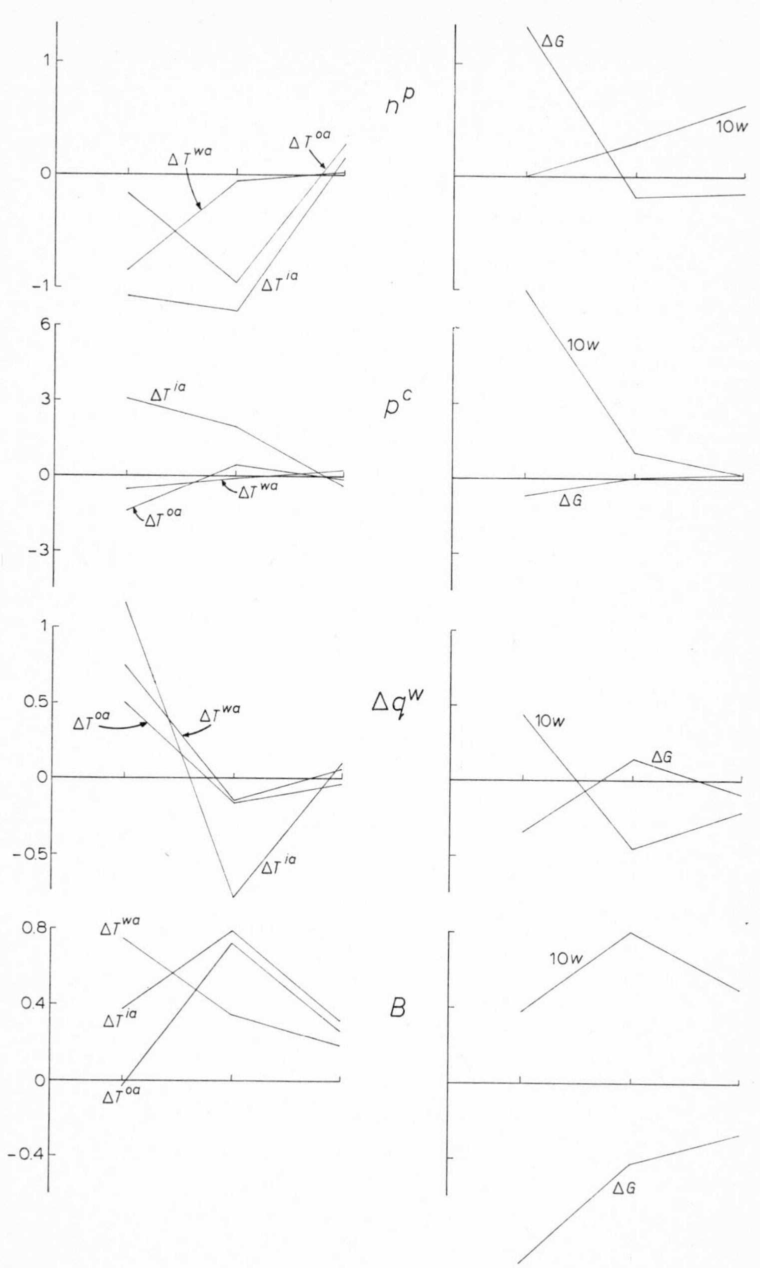

Figure 6.5. The effectiveness of instrument changes with respect to noncontrolled variables. Left: tax instruments, right: wage rate and government expenditure on goods and services. The wage rate changes are expressed in units of 10 per cent to obtain comparable scales.

TABLE 6.17

COEFFICIENT MATRICES DESCRIBING THE DEPENDENCE OF THE ADDITIVE STRUCTURE OF THE CONSTRAINTS ON 1956 VARIABLES, ON NONINSTRUMENTAL EXOGENOUS VARIABLES IN 1957–1959, AND ON STRUCTURAL DISTURBANCES IN 1957–1959

Noncon-trolled variables	*Constant term*	*Values Taken by Variables in 1956*										
		B	$\Delta E'$	ΔO^d	ΔT^{ia}	Δl	100 log*	p^c	p^g	p^i	p^x	p^{xr}
							S_1					
n^p	−0.525	0.000	−0.005	0.802	−0.515	0.485	0.237	−0.025	−0.001	0.002	−0.036	0.036
p^c	−2.835	0.000	−0.042	−0.591	2.052	−0.285	0.152	0.031	0.022	0.047	0.095	−0.095
Δq^w	0.572	0.000	0.139	0.149	−0.791	0.168	−0.008	0.009	−0.022	−0.066	−0.010	0.010
B	−0.253	1.000	0.247	−0.748	0.209	−0.420	0.002	0.029	0.007	0.016	0.015	−0.015
							S_2					
n^p	−0.410	0.485	0.053	−0.353	0.367	−0.254	0.209	0.004	0.010	0.032	−0.005	0.005
p^c	−3.173	−0.285	−0.084	0.027	0.068	0.019	0.162	0.000	0.009	0.015	0.018	−0.018
Δq^w	0.705	0.168	0.040	0.063	0.038	0.021	−0.019	−0.005	−0.008	−0.017	−0.021	0.021
B	−0.501	0.580	0.162	−0.301	0.066	−0.156	0.020	0.014	0.005	0.008	0.000	0.000
							S_3					
n^p	−0.477	0.231	0.027	−0.195	0.176	−0.132	0.200	0.004	0.008	0.022	0.002	−0.002
p^c	−3.166	−0.267	−0.097	0.089	0.089	0.030	0.150	−0.007	0.004	0.011	0.004	−0.004
Δq^w	0.764	0.190	0.049	−0.072	0.012	−0.044	−0.023	0.002	−0.002	−0.003	−0.006	0.006
B	−0.618	0.424	0.108	−0.219	0.086	−0.123	0.028	0.009	0.004	0.008	−0.002	0.002

TABLE 6.17 (continued)

Noncontrolled variables	Values Taken by Noninstrumental Exogenous Variables in 1957–1959											
	ΔD	ΔI^{fa}	ΔS	X^r	$\Delta\Theta^o$	$\Delta\Theta^{ua}$	$\Delta\Theta^w$	Δl^a	n^d	n^g	p^m	p^{xr}
							S_4					
n^p	−0.100	1.289	0.100	0.084	0.100	0.747	0.747		−0.065	0.031	−0.026	0.015
p^c	−0.810	−0.980	0.810	−0.137	0.810	0.450	0.450		0.087	0.002	0.240	−0.041
Δq^w	2.660	0.516	−2.660	−0.037	−0.310	−0.651	−0.651		−0.072	−0.011	0.074	0.004
B	−0.022	−1.274	1.022	−0.012	0.022	−0.660	−0.660		0.056	−0.027	−0.042	−0.007
							S_5					
n^p	−1.379	−0.748	1.791	0.020	0.574	0.038	0.038	0.485	0.057	−0.009	−0.102	0.038
p^c	−0.196	0.049	−0.047	−0.013	−0.320	0.062	0.062	−0.285	−0.001	0.003	0.079	−0.103
Δq^w	−0.073	0.073	0.216	0.037	0.100	0.131	0.131	0.168	0.002	0.003	−0.062	0.019
B	0.425	−0.488	0.218	0.018	−0.433	−0.308	−0.308	−0.420	0.018	−0.010	−0.013	−0.015
							S_6					
n^p	−0.545	−0.393	0.814	0.011	−0.166	−0.021	−0.021	−0.254	0.028	−0.003	−0.058	0.004
p^c	−0.599	0.101	0.330	−0.001	0.048	0.211	0.211	0.019	0.005	0.006	−0.006	−0.019
Δq^w	0.032	−0.130	0.155	0.009	0.034	−0.060	−0.060	0.021	0.006	−0.003	−0.035	0.023
B	0.089	−0.377	0.358	0.015	−0.158	−0.172	−0.172	−0.156	0.017	−0.007	−0.021	0.001

TABLE 6.17 (continued)

Noncontrolled variables	*Structural Disturbances in* 1957–1959**											
	u^C	u^{If}	u^{Ii}	u^{np}	u^m	u^x	u^l	u^{nu}	u^{pc}	u^{px}	u^{pi}	u^{pg}
							S_7					
n^p	0.841	1.469	0.019	1.200	−0.105	0.512		−0.109	0.095	0.046	0.009	−0.003
p^c	−1.035	−0.865	0.136	0.769	−0.842	−1.364		0.144	1.487	0.421	0.166	0.067
Δq^w	−0.297	0.510	−0.447	−0.040	2.766	0.138		−0.120	−0.487	−0.360	−0.235	−0.068
B	−0.972	−1.273	−0.796	0.011	−1.023	−0.218		0.093	0.128	0.132	0.058	0.022
							S_8					
n^p	−0.138	−0.769	−0.171	−0.140	−1.846	0.065	0.485	0.096	0.173	0.066	0.113	0.030
p^c	0.016	0.057	0.270	0.053	0.039	−0.256	−0.285	−0.001	0.058	0.160	0.054	0.026
Δq^w	0.162	0.064	−0.127	−0.057	−0.219	0.299	0.168	0.004	0.004	−0.049	−0.061	−0.023
B	−0.465	−0.474	−0.523	0.092	−0.201	0.005	−0.420	0.029	0.071	0.105	0.029	0.015
							S_9					
n^p	−0.124	−0.400	−0.086	−0.046	−0.836	−0.032	−0.254	0.046	0.090	0.101	0.079	0.024
p^c	0.231	0.092	0.313	−0.061	−0.354	−0.051	0.019	0.008	0.033	0.042	0.038	0.013
Δq^w	−0.076	−0.133	−0.158	−0.019	−0.153	0.079	0.021	0.011	0.001	−0.020	−0.012	−0.007
B	−0.287	−0.371	−0.349	0.040	−0.355	0.033	−0.156	0.029	0.065	0.062	0.030	0.013

* 100 times the 10-log of $\tilde{o}/\tilde{n}^p$.

** For the meaning of the symbols u^C, u^{If}, . . ., see equations (A.1)-(A.12) of the Appendix (Section 6.A).

picture is opposite for government expenditure on commodities. The wage rate appears to be primarily effective with respect to the price level of consumption goods in the current year.

We proceed to consider the additive structure of the constraints, in time-partitioned form:

$$\mathbf{s} = \begin{bmatrix} \mathbf{s}_1 \\ \mathbf{s}_2 \\ \mathbf{s}_3 \end{bmatrix}. \tag{2.17}$$

In principle, the additive structure is of the same general form as that of 6.1.1: it contains values taken by various variables in the year preceding the strategy period, values taken by noninstrumental exogenous variables during the strategy period, and structural disturbances. Now in 6.1.1 we were able to handle this in a very simple manner, for the only non-instrumental exogenous variable was time which is perfectly predictable during the strategy period, while moreover we assumed that all values relating to the year before the strategy period are known. In that case the vector (2.17) is a vector of known numbers plus a linear combination of structural disturbances, see (1.9). Here, however, it is not true that the noninstrumental exogenous variables are perfectly predictable; furthermore, we shall not assume that all past events are known completely but rather that they are re-estimated every year. This forces us to consider the way in which the additive structure depends on these unknown factors. It is then easily seen that the vector (2.17) can be written as the sum of the following three terms (apart from a vector of constant terms). First, there is the dependence on 1956 values:

$$\begin{bmatrix} \mathbf{S}_1 \\ \mathbf{S}_2 \\ \mathbf{S}_3 \end{bmatrix} \times \text{ vector of values taken by relevant variables in 1956.} \tag{2.18}$$

Second, there is the dependence on noninstrumental exogenous variables during the strategy period:

$$\begin{bmatrix} \mathbf{S}_4 & \mathbf{0} & \mathbf{0} \\ \mathbf{S}_5 & \mathbf{S}_4 & \mathbf{0} \\ \mathbf{S}_6 & \mathbf{S}_5 & \mathbf{S}_4 \end{bmatrix} \begin{bmatrix} \mathbf{z}_1 \\ \mathbf{z}_2 \\ \mathbf{z}_3 \end{bmatrix}, \tag{2.19}$$

where $\mathbf{z}_t$ stands for the vector of values taken by these variables in the tth year of the strategy period. Third, there is the dependence on the structural disturbances:

$$\begin{bmatrix} \mathbf{S}_7 & \mathbf{0} & \mathbf{0} \\ \mathbf{S}_8 & \mathbf{S}_7 & \mathbf{0} \\ \mathbf{S}_9 & \mathbf{S}_8 & \mathbf{S}_7 \end{bmatrix} \begin{bmatrix} u_1 \\ u_2 \\ u_3 \end{bmatrix}, \tag{2.20}$$

TABLE 6.18

ESTIMATES OF 1956 VALUES OF RELEVANT VARIABLES, FORECASTS AND ESTIMATES OF 1957–1961 VALUES OF NONINSTRUMENTAL EXOGENOUS VARIABLES, ESTIMATES OF 1957–1959 DISTURBANCES, AND THE CORRESPONDING REALIZED VALUES

	Endogenous variables in 1956									*Instruments in 1956*	*Noninstr. ex. var. 1956*
	B	$\Delta E'$	ΔO^d	Δl	100 log*	p^c	p^g	p^i	p^x	ΔT^{ia}	p^{xr}
$\mathscr{E}_0$	−0.59	3.76	−0.08	−0.55	9.94	1.50	4.00	6.00	2.00	−0.23	4.00
$\mathscr{E}_1$	−0.65	3.54	−0.11	−1.04	2.50	1.47	2.00	5.46	2.00	−0.23	3.00
$\mathscr{E}_2$	−0.69	3.74	−0.33	−0.86	10.61	1.65	2.92	7.60	2.76	−0.30	3.81
1962	−0.70	3.99	−0.42	−0.71	11.02	1.46	6.15	6.35	2.01	−0.30	4.17

	Noninstrumental exogenous variables in 1957–1961												
	ΔD	ΔI^{fa}	ΔS	X^r	$\Delta\Theta^o$	$\Delta\Theta^{ua}$	$\Delta\Theta^w$	Δl^a	n^d	n^g	n^o	p^m	p^{xr}
	Values of 1957												
$\mathscr{E}_0$	0.16	0.31	0.29	7.00	−0.43	0.00	−0.13	−0.27	1.32	1.96	0.20	4.00	3.30
$\mathscr{E}_1$	0.21	0.53	0.25	6.40	−0.42	0.01	−0.12	−0.08	1.33	0.86	−0.51	5.20	3.00
$\mathscr{E}_2$	0.30	0.37	0.43	9.04	−0.36	0.01	0.15	0.19	1.45	0.65	−0.51	4.42	2.53
1962	0.28	0.53	0.35	8.75	−0.46	−0.04	0.31	0.27	1.90	1.05	−0.75	5.10	1.55
	Values of 1958												
$\mathscr{E}_0$	0.13	−0.10	0.12	6.00	−0.03	0.00	0.10	−0.88	1.10	1.05	0.20	0.00	0.00
$\mathscr{E}_1$	0.06	−0.16	0.01	2.20	−0.11	0.00	0.10	−0.50	1.43	0.20	0.20	−2.00	−1.00

$\mathscr{E}_1$	0.09	0.05	0.03	0.94	0.00	0.00	−0.29	−0.50	1.37	2.00	0.20	1.00	1.00
$\mathscr{E}_2$	0.12	0.05	0.15	3.50	−0.03	0.01	−0.25	−0.49	1.33	1.01	0.10	−1.00	0.00
1962	0.11	0.05	0.17	7.01	−0.24	0.01	−0.08	**	0.70	0.83	−1.21	−3.08	−2.45
	Values of 1960												
$\mathscr{E}_1$	0.10	0.05	0.04	5.00	−0.13	0.00	0.25	**	1.41	2.00	0.20	1.00	1.00
$\mathscr{E}_2$	0.18	0.22	0.18	4.00	0.02	0.00	0.22	−0.48	1.20	1.20	0.20	−2.00	−2.00
	Values of 1961												
$\mathscr{E}_2$	0.24	0.22	0.15	7.00	−0.04	0.00	−0.05	**	1.65	1.20	0.20	2.00	2.00

Structural disturbances of 1957–1959

	u^C	u^{If}	u^{Ii}	u^{np}	u^m	u^x	u^l	u^{nu}	u^{pc}	u^{px}	u^{pi}	u^{pg}
	Values of 1957											
$\mathscr{E}_1$	0.18	0.46	0.03	−1.23	0.02	−0.57	0.85	−0.09	4.83	−0.28	−3.69	−1.79
$\mathscr{E}_2$	−0.14	0.60	0.76	−1.50	−0.21	−0.66	0.24	−0.01	2.88	−3.18	−4.34	−1.25
1962	−0.10	0.36	0.45	−1.02	0.26	−1.38	0.23	−0.01	2.58	−3.93	−5.19	−1.31
	Values of 1958											
$\mathscr{E}_2$	0.29	−0.64	−0.47	−1.96	0.04	0.46	−0.23	0.33	1.21	−0.58	−1.78	−3.89
1962	−0.12	−0.48	0.81	−1.64	−0.46	1.70	−1.80	0.37	0.49	−0.19	−1.72	−3.57
	Values of 1959											
1962	0.41	0.20	−0.61	−2.48	−0.31	0.11	0.07	−0.37	−0.61	2.48	1.06	1.86

* 100 times the 10-log of $\tilde{o}/\tilde{n}^p$.

** These are not required for the computations.

u_t being the structural disturbance vector in the tth year. It will be clear that the special form of the partitioned matrices in (2.19) and (2.20) is due to the fact that the system is linear with constant coefficients. The matrices $S_1, S_2, \ldots, S_9$ are given in Table 6.17 except for the columns which are exactly zero. Their derivation from reduced-form coefficients is straightforward and is explained in more detail in the Appendix (see Section 6.B); the same applies to the coefficient matrices R_1, R_2, R_3 of the multiplicative structure.

To apply the theorem on first-period certainty equivalence we should have at our disposal the various conditional forecasts and estimates of the vectors occurring in (2.18)–(2.20). They have been reconstructed from internal data of the Central Planning Bureau and are presented in Table 6.18. $\mathscr{E}_0$ stands for the conditional expectation at the beginning of 1957, $\mathscr{E}_1$ for that at the beginning of 1958, and so on. The table contains also some data which are needed only if a three-year moving horizon is used, as well as the final estimates which are available at the moment when these lines are written (spring 1962). The latter estimates are indicated by "1962".

6.2.7. *Summary*

(1) This section and its successor deal with the Dutch economy in 1957–1959. The 1956 advice of the Social and Economic Council has been taken as the basis for the choice of five instruments and four noncontrolled variables. The instruments are: the general wage rate, indirect taxes less subsidies, direct taxes on wage income, direct taxes on nonwage income, and government expenditure on commodities. The noncontrolled variables are: private employment, the price level of consumer goods, the share of wages in national income, and the surplus on the balance of payments.

(2) Three different preference functions are constructed, one for each of the three groups in the Social and Economic Council, viz., the employees ("L"), the members appointed by the Crown ("C"), and the employers ("E"). Three sets of desired values are formulated for the five instruments and four noncontrolled variables in each of the three years 1957–1959. "L" desires larger increases in the wage rate, in employment, and in government expenditure on commodities than "C" does, and "C" desires larger increases in these variables than "E". The desires of "E" go particularly in the direction of lower taxes and a larger surplus on the balance of payments. "L" desires an increasing share of wages in

national income and a decreasing price level, the desires of "E" are opposite in this respect, and "C" wishes constancy of these two variables.

(3) The quadratic part of the preference functions is described in terms of equivalent deviations, which measure the relative intensity of the desires with respect to the various variables. Thus, if we take the disutility of a 1 per cent discrepancy between corresponding actual and desired wage rates as a standard, then "E" considers a 1 per cent discrepancy for employment just as serious as the wage rate discrepancy, but "L" and "C" consider the employment discrepancy four times as serious. The greatest differences exist with respect to taxes on nonwage income and the surplus on the balance of payments: given the standard mentioned, the intensity of the desires of "L" for these variables is much less than that of "E".

(4, 5) Two amendments are made, both of which affect the quadratic part of the preference function and one also the linear part. The smoothing amendment introduces the sum of squares of the successive differences of each of the instrument variables; it is designed to reduce the possibility of wild fluctuations of these variables. The carry-over amendment is applied in order to take account, for two of the noncontrolled variables, of unfulfilled desires in the past. It amounts to the addition of the discrepancy between last year's realization and desire to this year's desire. This is done because these variables are defined as annual percentage changes.

(6) The constraints are derived from the linearized version of a complete 40-equation model in 59 variables. They have the same mathematical structure as the constraints used in Section 6.1; but it is no longer assumed that past events are known without error. This implies that it is necessary to express the additive structure of the constraints explicitly in terms of relevant 1956 values, noninstrumental exogenous values in 1957–1959, and disturbances of that period.

6.3. THREE-YEAR STRATEGIES FOR THE NETHERLANDS IN 1957–1959

6.3.1. Derivation of the Maximizing Strategies, 1957-1959

To find the first-year decision vector $\tilde{x}_1$ of the maximizing strategy we need the inverse of **K**. There are three such inverses, one corresponding with each of the three preference functions, and they are all of the form $(\mathbf{A}+\mathbf{R}'\mathbf{B}\mathbf{R})^{-1}$ since $\mathbf{C} = \mathbf{0}$, see (2.15). Now both **A** and **B** consist of nine diagonal submatrices, the diagonal elements of which are specified in Table 6.14, and $\mathbf{R}$ is determined by the three matrices R_1, R_2, R_3 which are given in Table 6.16. The derivation of the three inverses $(\mathbf{A}+\mathbf{R}'\mathbf{B}\mathbf{R})^{-1}$ is hence a matter of straightforward computation. Each has then to be postmultiplied by the appropriate conditional expectation of $\mathbf{k}$, given the information available at the beginning of 1957. Since $\mathbf{b} = \mathbf{0}$ and $\mathbf{C} = \mathbf{0}$ [see (2.15)], $\mathbf{k}$ is of the form $\mathbf{a}+\mathbf{R}'\mathbf{B}\mathbf{s}$, hence the relevant expectation is $\mathscr{E}_0\mathbf{k} = \mathbf{a}+\mathbf{R}'\mathbf{B}\mathscr{E}_0\mathbf{s}$. The three subvectors of $\mathbf{a}$ are given in Table 6.14 for each of the three preference functions, and $\mathbf{R}$ and $\mathbf{B}$ have been discussed above. The remaining problem is therefore to find $\mathscr{E}_0\mathbf{s}$. Now we found at the end of 6.2.6 that $\mathbf{s}$ is equal to a vector of known elements plus the sum of the vectors (2.18)–(2.20). Hence $\mathscr{E}_0\mathbf{s}$ is the vector of known elements plus the conditional expectation ($\mathscr{E}_0$) of (2.18)–(2.20). Regarding (2.18), this is a linear combination of values taken by certain variables in 1956. The $\mathscr{E}_0$ of (2.18) is then the same linear combination of the estimates of these values which were available at the beginning of 1957, and these estimates are given in Table 6.18. Similarly, (2.19) is a linear combination of values taken by noninstrumental exogenous variables in 1957–1959, and the $\mathscr{E}_0$ of (2.19) is the same linear combination of predictions of these values (made at the beginning of 1957); these too are given in Table 6.18. Finally, the $\mathscr{E}_0$ of (2.20) is simply zero, because it is a linear combination of future disturbances with zero mean which are assumed to be uncorrelated over time. The first-year decisions $\tilde{x}_1$, for each of the three preference functions, are then found by computing $-(\mathbf{A}+\mathbf{R}'\mathbf{B}\mathbf{R})^{-1}(\mathbf{a}+\mathbf{R}'\mathbf{B}\mathscr{E}_0\mathbf{s})$ and taking the first 5 elements; except, however, for the subtlety that an adjustment is necessary because the variables of the preference function are measured as deviations from desired values whereas this is not the case for the constraints.[1]

The second-year decisions $\tilde{x}_2$ are then derived as if they are first-year decisions of a strategy with a two-year horizon. This strategy starts at the beginning of 1958, hence the relevant conditional expectation ($\mathscr{E}_1$) refers to the information which is available at that point of time. Both

[1] The easiest way to handle this is to write the constraints in the form

$$\mathbf{y}-\boldsymbol{\eta} = \mathbf{R}(\mathbf{x}-\boldsymbol{\xi})+\mathbf{s}-(\boldsymbol{\eta}-\mathbf{R}\boldsymbol{\xi}),$$

so that the variables of the constraints are then measured as deviations from desired values. This requires that $\boldsymbol{\eta}-\mathbf{R}\boldsymbol{\xi}$ be subtracted from the additive structure, which is a vector of known elements (but, of course, different for the three preference functions). The same subtraction procedure also applies to the derivation of $\tilde{x}_2$ and $\tilde{x}_3$.

the preference functions and the constraints are now changed compared with those of the preceding paragraph, partly because 1957 is deleted from the three-year period, partly because the stream of information which became available in that year can now be used. The constraints take the form

$$\begin{bmatrix} y_2 \\ y_3 \end{bmatrix} = \begin{bmatrix} R_1 & \mathbf{0} \\ R_2 & R_1 \end{bmatrix} \begin{bmatrix} x_2 \\ x_3 \end{bmatrix} + \begin{bmatrix} s_2 + R_2 \tilde{x}_1 \\ s_3 + R_3 \tilde{x}_1 \end{bmatrix},$$

see (4.1.22) and (1.17). Hence the "new" **R** and **s** are

$$\begin{bmatrix} R_1 & \mathbf{0} \\ R_2 & R_1 \end{bmatrix} \quad \text{and} \quad \begin{bmatrix} s_2 + R_2 \tilde{x}_1 \\ s_3 + R_3 \tilde{x}_1 \end{bmatrix},$$

respectively. To find the conditional expectation of this new **s**, we have to compute $\mathscr{E}_1 s_2 + R_2 \tilde{x}_1$ and $\mathscr{E}_1 s_3 + R_3 \tilde{x}_1$. The crucial point is evidently the calculation of $\mathscr{E}_1 s_2$ and $\mathscr{E}_1 s_3$. Again, we go back to the end of 6.2.6, where we found that the original **s** is a vector of known elements plus the sum of (2.18)–(2.20). We now need only the last 8 elements of **s** (corresponding with s_2 and s_3) and hence also the last 8 components of the vector of known elements. To this we must add the last 8 elements of the $\mathscr{E}_1$ of (2.18); i.e., we add

$$\begin{bmatrix} S_2 \\ S_3 \end{bmatrix}$$

multiplied by the estimated 1956 values of certain variables, these estimates being derived on the basis of the information which was available at the beginning of 1958. The estimates are given in Table 6.18. We must also add the last 8 elements of the $\mathscr{E}_1$ of (2.19), which is

$$\begin{bmatrix} S_5 & S_4 & \mathbf{0} \\ S_6 & S_5 & S_4 \end{bmatrix}$$

times the estimated values of the noninstrumental exogenous variables in 1957–1959; again, the estimates are those of the beginning of 1958, hence they are partly estimates of past realizations, partly forecasts of future values. Finally, we have to add the last 8 elements of the $\mathscr{E}_1$ of (2.20). This is

$$\begin{bmatrix} S_8 \\ S_9 \end{bmatrix}$$

times the end-of-1957 estimates of the 1957 disturbances. The estimates of the disturbances of 1958 and 1959 are zero as before.

We now turn to the preference function in the form which is relevant for the two-year decision problem. Going back to (4.1.20) and (4.1.21), we notice that the matrix of the quadratic part is simply reduced in size. The "new" **A** and **B** are

$$\begin{bmatrix} A_{22} & A_{23} \\ A_{32} & A_{33} \end{bmatrix} \quad \text{and} \quad \begin{bmatrix} B_{22} & B_{23} \\ B_{32} & B_{33} \end{bmatrix},$$

respectively, and **C** is now the 10×8 zero matrix. Furthermore, an inspection of (4.1.20) shows that the linear part of the preference function is affected more drastically; in particular, there is now also a linear term in the noncontrolled variables. The "new" **a**-vector is

$$\begin{bmatrix} a_2 + A_{21}(\tilde{x}_1 - \xi_1) \\ a_3 + A_{31}(\tilde{x}_1 - \xi_1) \end{bmatrix},$$

where use is made of the fact that the arguments of the preference function are measured as deviations from desired values. In addition, there is now a nonzero **b**-vector for the noncontrolled variables, viz.,

$$\begin{bmatrix} B_{21}(\tilde{y}_1 - \eta_1) \\ B_{31}(\tilde{y}_1 - \eta_1) \end{bmatrix},$$

where $\tilde{y}_1 = R_1 \tilde{x}_1 + s_1$ is the vector of first-year noncontrolled values associated with the behaviour according to the maximizing strategy.

By computing $-(\mathbf{A}+\mathbf{R}'\mathbf{B}\mathbf{R})^{-1}(\mathbf{a}+\mathbf{R}'\mathscr{E}_1\mathbf{b}+\mathbf{R}'\mathbf{B}\mathscr{E}_1\mathbf{s})$ and taking the first 5 elements we obtain $\tilde{x}_2$. The matrices **A**, **B**, **R**, ... should of course be interpreted in the appropriate two-year manner (as outlined in the two preceding paragraphs) and the expectation operator $\mathscr{E}_1$ should not only be applied to **s** but also to **b**. This is so because **b** is random; it is a linear function of $\tilde{y}_1 = R_1 \tilde{x}_1 + s_1$ and hence of s_1. Thus $\mathscr{E}_1 s_1$ enters not only in the term $\mathbf{R}'\mathbf{B}\mathscr{E}_1\mathbf{s}$ but also in $\mathbf{R}'\mathscr{E}_1\mathbf{b}$.

The derivation of $\tilde{x}_3$ is now relatively straightforward. The multiplicative structure of the constraints is reduced to R_1 and the additive structure to $s_3 + R_3 \tilde{x}_1 + R_2 \tilde{x}_2$. The relevant conditional expectation of the additive structure is the same except that s_3 is replaced by $\mathscr{E}_2 s_3$, which is a four-element column vector that can be written as the sum of (i) a vector of known elements; (ii) S_3 times the end-of-1958 estimated values of 1956 variables, see (2.18); (iii) $[S_6 \quad S_5 \quad S_4]$ times the end-of-1958 estimated values of noninstrumental exogenous variables in 1957-1959, see (2.19); and (iv) $[S_9 \quad S_8]$ times the end-of-1958 estimated values of 1957 and 1958 disturbances. Furthermore, the preference function is now reduced such that **A** and **B** become A_{33} and B_{33}, respectively, **C** becomes the 5×4 zero matrix, **a** becomes $a_3+A_{31}(\tilde{x}_1-\xi_1)+A_{32}(\tilde{x}_2-\xi_2)$, and **b** becomes $B_{31}(\tilde{y}_1-\eta_1)+B_{32}(\tilde{y}_2-\eta_2)$ where $\tilde{y}_2 = R_2\tilde{x}_1+R_1\tilde{x}_2+s_2$. The result for all three preference functions in all three years is summarized in Table 6.19. The table contains also the observed and the desired values (for comparison purposes) as well as the realized values of the noncontrolled variables of the maximizing strategies; for $\tilde{y}_1$ and $\tilde{y}_2$ the relevant formulas have been given above, for $\tilde{y}_3$ it is $R_3\tilde{x}_1+R_2\tilde{x}_2+R_1\tilde{x}_3+s_3$.

6.3.2. *Discussion of the Maximizing Strategies*

We proceed to consider the figures of Table 6.19 in more detail and start with the employment variable n^p. "C" wishes a 1.50 per cent increase in 1957 and gets only slightly more than half of it (0.88 per cent). The gap between desire and realization is therefore 0.62 per cent, which is added to the 1958 desire according to the carry-over amendment.[1] This adjustment implies that the 1958 desire becomes an increase of more than 2 per cent. But what "C" achieves in 1958 is a decrease, so that the carry-over amendment implies a further raise of the 1959 desire to almost 4 per cent. The realization is now positive but not nearly that big. For the three-year period as a whole "C" achieves an increase of less than 2 per cent, whereas the desired increase is $4\frac{1}{2}$ per cent. For "L" and "E" too the realizations are below the desired level. The observed development is rather close to the results of the "E"-strategy.

The outcomes of the balance-of-payments variable B are closer to the desired development. All desire a zero or minor positive surplus in the first year; all achieve a negative surplus, which is however to some extent compensated by the fact that in the second year the realized surplus is larger than desired. In the third year the realizations are again somewhat above the desires, so that in the three-year period as a whole there are only minor discrepancies between facts and ideals. As in the case of

---

[1] In Table 6.19 the carry-over amendment has been applied in the sense that such gaps have been added to the original desires specified in Table 6.12. Note, however, that the right-hand part of Table 6.19 is entirely based on data available in 1962, which means that the carry-over amendment as actually applied by "L", "C" and "E" is based on different values. For example, the 0.88 value for the n^p-realization of "C" in 1957 is the 1962 figure; at the beginning of 1958 this realization was estimated as 0.24 (see Table 6.20 below), hence the gap between realization and desire which was added by "C" to his 1958 desire was not $1.50-0.88 = 0.62$ but $1.50-0.24 = 1.26$.

TABLE 6.19

THE RESULTS OF THE MAXIMIZING STRATEGIES, 1957–1959*

	"L"	"C"	"E"	*Observed*	"L"	"C"	"E"	*Observed*
		Instruments				*Noncontrolled variables*		
		w				n^p		
1957	8.30 (10.00)	5.91 (7.00)	6.16 (6.00)	10.55	1.14 (2.00)	0.88 (1.50)	1.19 (1.00)	1.64
58	5.05 (4.00)	3.87 (2.00)	3.92 (2.00)	4.34	0.18 (2.86)	−0.23 (2.12)	−0.70 (1.06)	−0.81
59	4.36 (4.00)	2.92 (2.00)	2.96 (2.00)	2.86	2.88 (4.18)	0.79 (3.85)	1.16 (3.26)	1.45
		ΔT^{ia}				p^c		
1957	−0.11 (−0.10)	0.03 (0)	−0.02 (0)	−0.33	3.50 (−1.00)	3.14 (0)	3.71 (1.00)	5.64
58	−0.34 (−0.05)	−0.12 (0)	0.01 (0)	−0.00	2.26 (−1.00)	1.40 (0)	1.52 (1.00)	1.84
59	−0.05 (0)	−0.02 (0)	0.01 (0)	0.20	−0.35 (−1.00)	−0.34 (0)	0.16 (1.00)	1.04
		ΔT^{wa}				Δq^w		
1957	−0.04 (−0.10)	−0.03 (−0.05)	−0.08 (−0.10)	−0.01	1.93 (1.00)	1.72 (0)	1.38 (−0.50)	1.31
58	−0.18 (−0.075)	−0.08 (−0.05)	−0.03 (−0.075)	−0.03	−0.39 (0.07)	0.27 (−1.72)	0.91 (−2.38)	1.09
59	−0.01 (−0.025)	−0.00 (0)	0.00 (−0.025)	0.02	−1.83 (1.46)	−2.09 (−1.99)	−2.20 (−3.80)	−2.32
		ΔT^{oa}				B		
1957	0.99 (0.10)	0.33 (−0.10)	−0.11 (−0.20)	0.09	−0.51 (0)	−0.37 (0)	−0.51 (0.25)	−0.55
58	−0.82 (0.10)	−0.45 (−0.10)	−0.16 (−0.20)	−0.07	0.94 (0.50)	0.87 (0.75)	1.07 (0.75)	1.57
59	0.06 (0.05)	−0.29 (0)	−0.17 (−0.15)	−0.34	0.59 (0.50)	1.05 (0.75)	1.54 (1.00)	1.83
		ΔG						
1957	0.14 (0.20)	−0.02 (0.10)	0.09 (0.05)	0.24				
58	0.82 (0.20)	0.49 (0.10)	−0.05 (0.05)	−0.35				
59	0.15 (0.20)	−0.02 (0.10)	−0.10 (0.05)	0.07				

* Desired values are indicated between brackets. For the variables to which the carry-over amendment is applied (n^p and Δq^w), see foot-

employment, the observed development is close to the results of the "E"-strategy.

We next consider the two price variables w and p^c. We note that the large desired wage rate increases for 1957 are not realized except in the case of "E". This is partly due to the smoothing amendment, which puts a penalty on a large difference between 1956 and 1957 values, partly to the desires with respect to the price level of consumer goods. "L" desires a small decrease of prices, "C" desires constancy, and "E" desires a small increase. It is therefore understandable that the desires of "L" and "C" with respect to the wage rate in 1957 are not completely realized. In later years the desired price changes are the same as in 1957 but the desired wage rate increases are all smaller than the 1957 desire. As regards prices, "L" and "C" and "E" achieve an increase of 4 to 6 per cent for the three-year period as a whole, which is less than the observed price increase and more favourable from the standpoint of the three preference functions which are considered here. The wage rate increases in 1958 and 1959 are all above the desired levels, which may be ascribed to the smoothing amendment, given the large increases in 1957. For the three-year period as a whole, "L" desires a wage rate increase of 18 per cent and gets almost what he wants; "C" desires an increase of 11 per cent and gets slightly more; and "E" wishes an increase of 10 per cent and achieves 13 per cent. The observed wage rate increase is about 18 per cent, most of which was realized in 1957.

The three tax variables and, of course, the share of wages in national income have directly to do with the relative position of labour and nonlabour. The observed development of the share of wages amounts to increases in the first two years, followed by a decrease in the third year which almost completely compensates the earlier increases. The strategy approaches are similar in this respect: there are increases in the first year and decreases in the last, the second year being characterized by figures which are rather small in absolute value. The picture of the three-year period as a whole is essentially that of constancy of the share of wages. It is rather unexpected that in the case of "L" this share becomes smaller than in that of "E", but this effect is numerically of minor importance. At the level of direct taxes on wage income all wish and achieve negative autonomous changes, especially "L" who unlike "E" is not hampered by the more or less inconsistent desire of a decrease of the share of wages. For direct taxes on nonwage income the picture is less regular, the 1957 realizations of "L" and "C" being large increases

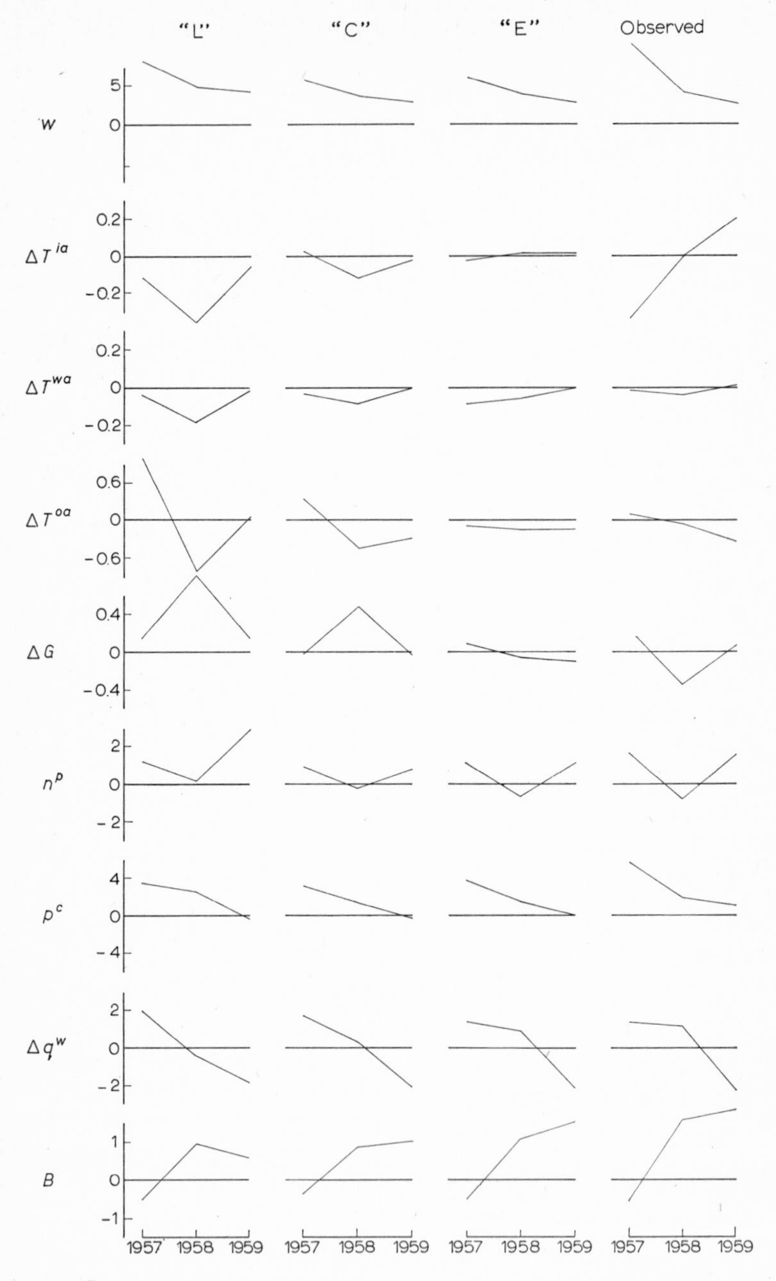

Figure 6.6. The results of the maximizing strategies corresponding with the three alternative preference functions and the observed development

which are followed by 1958 values of the same order of magnitude but of opposite sign. This implies that the smoothing amendment was not very effective with respect to this variable; a feature which is due to the rather small weight attached to ΔT^{oa} by "L" and "C". The equivalent deviation of ΔT^{oa} is very large for these two preference functions, particularly for "L", and this implies that the weight of this variable in the smoothing amendment is small. As to indirect taxes, finally, "E" desires and gets constancy, "C" desires constancy but achieves a moderate decline, and "L" desires a moderate decline and achieves a larger decline. The observed development of ΔT^{ia} amounts to a decrease in the first year, no change in the second, and an increase in the third. The observed values of ΔT^{wa} are all close to zero, which implies that there were only minor changes in the tax rates for wage income. For ΔT^{oa} we have an observed small increase in 1957, followed by a small decrease in 1958 and a larger decrease in 1959.

Government expenditure on commodities is raised moderately by "L" in 1957 and 1959, but drastically in 1958. The desired aggregate increase is 600 millions of guilders, the realization is almost twice as large. The picture for "C" is similar but less pronounced; his aggregate desire is an increase of 300 millions of guilders, the realization is about 50 per cent larger. "E" desires small increases; what he gets on the average are small decreases.

An interesting question is to what extent the policy followed under these three approaches should be regarded as being "inflationary" or "deflationary" in character. Let us agree to count positive values of ΔG on the inflationary side and positive values of the ΔT's on the deflationary side. Then the inflationary excess of the instrumental desires of "C" in 1957 is 0 (for ΔT^{ia})+0.05 (for ΔT^{wa})+0.10 (for ΔT^{oa})+0.10 (for ΔG); i.e., it is 0.25 billions of guilders. The same value applies to 1958, and the 1959 inflationary excess of the instrumental desires of "C" amounts to 0.1 billions. The actual policy followed by "C" in 1957 is deflationary, the inflationary excess being -0.35 billions. This is understandable in view of the balance-of-payments difficulties and the overemployment prevailing at the end of 1956. In 1958 both aspects changed and the inflationary excess for "C" became more than 1 billion, which was followed by a smaller positive excess in 1959. The instrumental desires of the two other preference functions are more inflationary in character, which is largely due to a desire for tax reduction in the case of "E" and for a larger amount of government expenditure on commodities in that of "L".

TABLE 6.20

FORECASTS, ESTIMATES, AND REALIZATIONS OF INSTRUMENTS AND NONCONTROLLED VARIABLES

Computations made at the beginning of	"L"			"C"			"E"		
	1957	1958	1959	1957	1958	1959	1957	1958	1959
					Instruments				
					w				
1957	*8.30*	4.41	3.81	*5.91*	2.24	1.93	*6.16*	2.71	2.20
58		*5.05*	4.34		*3.87*	2.98		*3.92*	2.93
59			*4.36*			*2.92*			*2.96*
					ΔT^{ia}				
1957	*−0.11*	−0.05	−0.01	*0.03*	0.06	0.05	*−0.02*	0.02	0.02
58		*−0.34*	−0.17		*−0.12*	−0.08		*0.01*	−0.00
59			*−0.05*			*−0.02*			*0.01*
					ΔT^{wa}				
1957	*−0.04*	−0.06	−0.04	*−0.03*	−0.04	−0.03	*−0.08*	−0.08	−0.06
58		*−0.18*	−0.09		*−0.08*	−0.03		*−0.03*	−0.01
59			*−0.01*			*−0.00*			*0.00*
					ΔT^{oa}				
1957	*0.99*	0.95	0.97	*0.33*	0.19	0.15	*−0.11*	−0.17	−0.16
58		*−0.82*	−0.30		*−0.45*	−0.41		*−0.16*	−0.17
59			*0.06*			*−0.29*			*−0.17*
					ΔG				
1957	*0.14*	0.22	0.24	*−0.02*	0.01	0.09	*0.09*	0.07	0.07

1957	2.61	1.61	2.05	2.36	1.73	2.18	2.66	2.41	2.52
58	0.50	1.29	2.69	0.24	0.88	1.36	0.55	0.41	0.25
59	1.03	0.07	4.64	0.77	−0.33	3.54	1.08	−0.80	2.91
62	*1.14*	*0.18*	*2.88*	*0.88*	*−0.23*	*0.79*	*1.19*	*−0.70*	*1.16*
					p^c				
1957	2.34	0.73	−0.07	1.96	0.30	−0.61	2.56	0.69	−0.18
58	6.31	1.16	−0.44	5.94	0.32	−0.48	6.52	0.42	0.13
59	4.30	0.62	−0.77	3.94	−0.22	−0.76	4.51	−0.13	−0.26
62	*3.50*	*2.26*	*−0.35*	*3.14*	*1.40*	*−0.34*	*3.71*	*1.52*	*0.16*
					Δq^w				
1957	1.27	0.19	0.70	1.06	0.02	0.55	0.73	−0.11	0.45
58	0.20	−0.78	0.76	−0.01	−0.11	0.74	−0.35	0.51	0.87
59	0.47	0.06	1.35	0.27	0.73	1.08	−0.08	1.36	0.99
62	*1.93*	*−0.39*	*−1.83*	*1.72*	*0.27*	*−2.09*	*1.38*	*0.91*	*−2.20*
					B				
1957	0.30	1.72	2.28	0.44	1.44	1.67	0.31	0.97	1.24
58	−0.48	0.22	−0.71	−0.33	0.14	−0.15	−0.47	0.34	0.65
59	−0.68	−0.59	−0.28	−0.53	0.52	0.17	−0.67	0.71	0.66
62	*−0.52*	*0.94*	*0.59*	*−0.37*	*0.87*	*1.05*	*−0.51*	*1.07*	*1.54*

Thus, the inflationary excess of the instrumental desires in the three years 1957–1959 decreases from 0.3 to 0.175 billions in the case of "L" and from 0.35 to 0.225 billions in that of "E". The actual policy followed by "E" is more moderate than his desires, the realized inflationary excess decreasing gradually from 0.3 to less than 0.1 billions. This means that the policy followed by "E" is consistently inflationary throughout the three-year period, contrary to that of "C". "L" is on the other extreme. He creates an inflationary excess of -0.7 billions in the first year, then a positive excess in the second which is about three times larger, and finally a mild inflationary excess of 0.15 billions in the third year. In the first two years the "L"-policy implies government spending and receiving measures which are on balance about twice as large as those of the "C"-policy. The "E"-policy is comparable in this respect with that of "C" as far as taxes are concerned, but the changes in government spending are confined to much narrower limits. Hence, at the level of realized policy on the inflationary excess we may say that "C" occupies an intermediate position between "L" and "E", even though this is not true with respect to the inflationary character of the instrumental desires. The observed policy shows excesses which decrease from 0.5 to 0.2 billions in absolute value; they are positive in the first and the last year, negative in the second.

6.3.3. Predicting the Future and Estimating the Past

Table 6.20 summarizes the various forecasts of future instrument and noncontrolled values and estimates of past noncontrolled values together with the realizations which are printed in italics. It is similar to Tables 6.4 and 6.5 of Section 6.1 except that, in the case of the noncontrolled variables, past values are re-estimated every year. The last lines in the lower half of the table are estimates based on the data which are available on the moment when these lines are written (spring 1962); these will be regarded as the realized values from now on.

We shall consider in particular to what extent the directions of change have been predicted correctly. Since all of our variables are either in first differences or in link-relative form, this amounts to comparing signs. An exception is the surplus on the balance of payments (B), which is measured as a level, not as a change. But we prefer to compare signs for this variable too, because the surplus itself is more important than its change. For all other variables the converse is true.

The aspect which is probably most interesting is the question to what

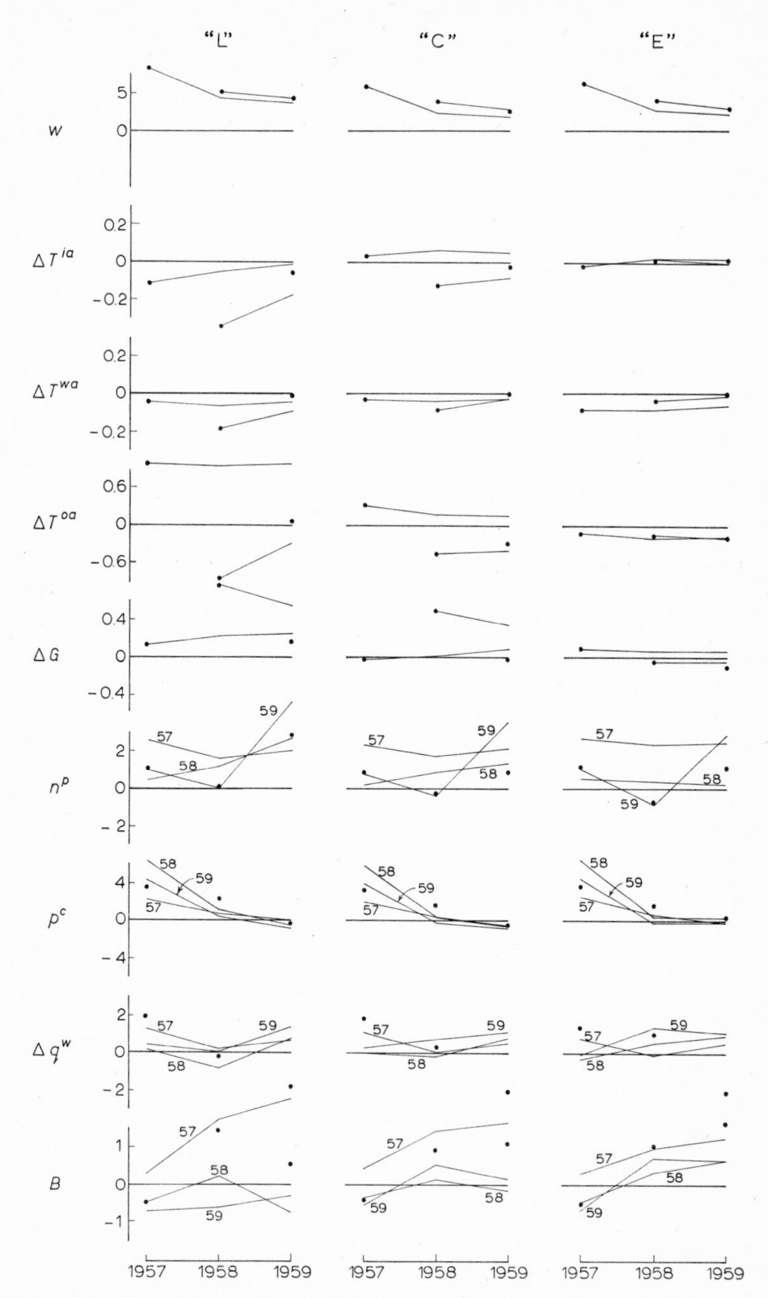

Figure 6.7. Forecasts, revisions of forecasts, estimates, revisions of estimates, and realizations (indicated by heavy dots) of the three strategies

extent the progress of time contributes to the precision of our knowledge. As an example we take employment (n^p) of 1957 as it was predicted and (later) estimated by "C". At the beginning of that year he predicts an increase of 2.36 per cent. This overstates the actual change, which is only 0.88 per cent; but the forecast is at least correct as far as signs are concerned. One year later he revises his forecast in downward direction; the new value (which is now an estimate, no longer a forecast) is a small increase of 0.24 per cent. It is even below the actual change, but the error has become much smaller in absolute value. At the beginning of 1959 another revision is made, this time in upward direction, and the error has now become very small. In this way we see the progress of our knowledge when a prediction for next year is replaced by an estimate for last year and then by an estimate for two years back. But there are two more "layers" besides these three, since there are also forecasts for two years and for three years ahead. For example, "C" predicts at the beginning of 1957 that the 1959 change in n^p (a forecast three years ahead) will be an increase of 2.18 per cent. One year later he revises this to a smaller increase (1.36 per cent), which is closer to the realized value (0.79 per cent). One more year later he makes another forecast, but the error is now larger. So we see that apart from the exception just mentioned, the forecasts and estimates of "C" for n^p in 1957 and 1959 become more accurate as time proceeds.

TABLE 6.21

SIGN SCORES OF FORECASTS AND ESTIMATES AND SUCCESS SCORES OF REVISIONS

	"L"	"C"	"E"	Total
Forecasts three years ahead	3–1	3–1	2–2	8–4
Forecasts two years ahead	10–3	7–6	8–5	25–14
Forecasts for next year	17–5	15–7	15–7	47–19
Estimates for last year	7–1	6–2	6–2	19–5
Estimates two years back	4–0	4–0	3–1	11–1
All forecasts	30–9	25–14	25–14	80–37
All estimates	11–1	10–2	9–3	30–6
All forecasts (relative sign score)	0.77	0.64	0.64	0.68
All estimates (relative sign score)	0.92	0.83	0.75	0.83
1958-revisions	11–6	9½–7½	10½–6½	31–20
1959-revisions	6–6	6–6	6–6	18–18

Table 6.21 supplies an answer to the question to what extent forecasts and estimates as a whole are successful as far as signs are concerned and to what extent revisions proved to be successful in the sense that they reduced the error in absolute value. Thus we find that there are, for each of the three preference functions, four forecasts three years ahead, all made at the beginning of 1957 and referring to the realizations in 1959 of the four noncontrolled variables. In the same way we have 13 forecasts two years ahead for each preference function, 5 of which are 1957 forecasts of the instrument values to be applied at the beginning of 1959,

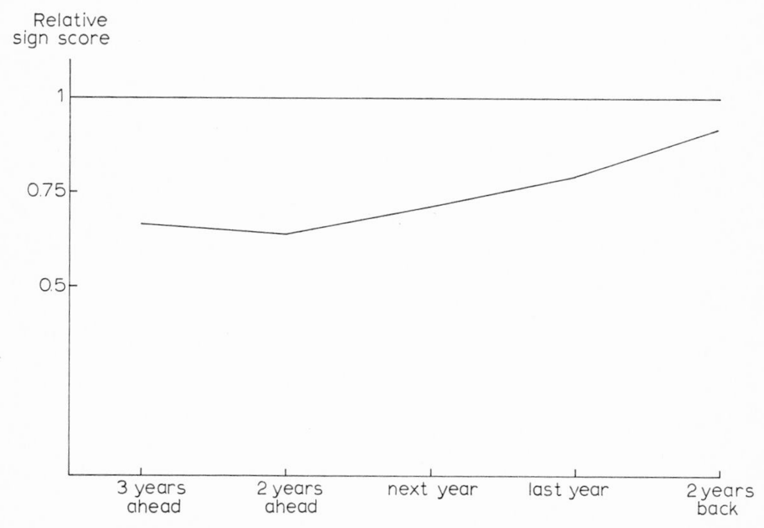

Figure 6.8. Relative sign score of forecasts and estimates (for all three strategies combined)

4 are 1957 forecasts of noncontrolled values that are realized during 1958, and 4 are 1958 forecasts of 1959 noncontrolled values. Finally, there are 22 forecasts one year ahead (for next year), 10 of which refer to instruments and 12 to noncontrolled variables. The relative sign scores for these forecasts vary from about two thirds to about three quarters for the three preference functions. As could be expected, the sign scores for estimates of past events are higher; they vary from almost 80 to about 90 per cent. There are 8 estimates one year back (for last year) and 4 estimates two years back, all of which refer to noncontrolled variables.

The last two rows of Table 6.21 deal with the success of revisions. There are 17 such revisions made at the beginning of 1958, 5 of which deal with 1957 forecasts of 1959 instrument values and 12 with 1957 forecasts of various noncontrolled values. It is seen that a majority of these revisions reduced the forecast error. This does not hold for the revisions made at the beginning of 1959, which are "good" and "bad" in an equal number of cases. Needless to say, all these results have to be taken with a grain of salt. In particular, one should not be impressed too much by the rather large numbers of Table 6.21, since the phenomena which they serve to describe are highly interdependent: the results for "L" and "C" and "E" are all subject to the same random shocks and for each of these preference functions the separate outcomes in each year are interdependent too.

6.3.4. Three-Year Moving Horizons

We shall now consider what happens in case the decision maker's interests in events after 1959 are not to be neglected. Specifically, we shall assume that he wishes to maximize utility at the beginning of every year while keeping a constant horizon of three years in mind; and we shall derive the decisions to be made for 1957, 1958, and 1959, which can then be compared with the corresponding decisions that were derived earlier in this section. Obviously, this is trivial for 1957, since the decision for that year as it was found in 6.3.1 was already based on a three-year horizon. But for the other two years we shall have to adjust the constraints and the three preference functions.

The adjustment of the constraints is straightforward. For each of the years 1958 and 1959 they take the form $\mathbf{y} = \mathbf{Rx}+\mathbf{s}$, where $\mathbf{y}$ consists of three subvectors (y_1, y_2, y_3 for 1958, 1959 and 1960, respectively, when we derive the 1958 decision; and for 1959, 1960, 1961 when we consider the 1959 decision). It is then easily seen that $\mathbf{R}$ is given by (2.16), i.e., we have precisely the same multiplicative structure of the constraints as in 1957. A similar result holds with minor modifications for the additive structure. This is given by (2.17), where $\mathbf{s}_1$ now refers, of course, to 1958 when the 1958 decision is computed, to 1959 when the 1959 decision is computed, and so on. The decomposition of $\mathbf{s}$ in terms of the vector of known elements and the three vectors (2.18)–(2.20) is also as in 1957; except that the 1956 values of (2.18) are to be replaced by 1957 values when the 1958 decision is calculated and by 1958 values when we consider the 1959 decision, and that $\mathbf{z}_1$, $\mathbf{z}_2$, $\mathbf{z}_3$ of (2.19) and u_1, u_2, u_3 of (2.20) are likewise shifted over time.

The reformulation of the preference functions for 1958 and 1959 requires somewhat more effort, particularly in view of the two amendments which were introduced in Section 6.2. Let us first consider the instrument part of the preference functions. Obviously, we now need also desired values for 1960 and 1961, and these are given in Table 6.22 (together with those of the noncontrolled variables). On comparing this table with Table 6.12 we see that the instrumental desires amount to a continuation of the wishes for 1959, except that "C" desires the wage rate to increase by 2½ per cent instead of 2 per cent and that "E" wishes an autonomous change in direct taxes on nonwage income amounting to −100 instead of −150 millions of guilders. It will be noted that the desires for 1960 have to be formulated at the beginning of 1958 if we use a three-year moving horizon, and those for 1961 at the beginning of 1959.

TABLE 6.22

DESIRED VALUES OF INSTRUMENTS AND NONCONTROLLED VARIABLES IN 1960 AND 1961

Variables	"L"		"C"		"E"	
	1960	1961	1960	1961	1960	1961
			Instruments			
w	4.00	4.00	2.50	2.50	2.00	2.00
ΔT^{ia}	0	0	0	0	0	0
ΔT^{wa}	−0.025	−0.025	0	0	−0.025	−0.025
ΔT^{oa}	0.05	0.05	0	0	−0.10	−0.10
ΔG	0.20	0.20	0.10	0.10	0.05	0.05
			Noncontrolled variables			
n^p	2.50	2.50	2.00	2.25	2.00	2.00
p^c	−0.50	−0.50	0	0	1.00	1.00
Δq^w	1.00	0.50	0	0	−0.25	0
B	0.55	0.60	0.80	0.80	1.00	1.00

The initial formulation of the part of the preference function which refers to the instruments is:

$$\frac{1}{2}\sum_{t=1}^{3}(x_t-\xi_t)'D_x(x_t-\xi_t) \tag{3.1}$$

[see (2.4)], and this applies to all three years in case we adopt a three-year moving horizon. But the smoothing amendment implies that (3.1) has to be replaced by the sum of a linear and a quadratic part. The latter part is

$$(3.2)\qquad \tfrac{1}{2}\begin{bmatrix} x_1-\xi_1 \\ x_2-\xi_2 \\ x_3-\xi_3 \end{bmatrix}' \begin{bmatrix} A_{11} & A_{12} & A_{13} \\ A_{21} & A_{22} & A_{23} \\ A_{31} & A_{32} & A_{33} \end{bmatrix} \begin{bmatrix} x_1-\xi_1 \\ x_2-\xi_2 \\ x_3-\xi_3 \end{bmatrix}$$

$$= \tfrac{1}{2}\begin{bmatrix} x_1-\xi_1 \\ x_2-\xi_2 \\ x_3-\xi_3 \end{bmatrix}' \begin{bmatrix} 2D_x & -\tfrac{1}{2}D_x & \mathbf{0} \\ -\tfrac{1}{2}D_x & 2D_x & -\tfrac{1}{2}D_x \\ \mathbf{0} & -\tfrac{1}{2}D_x & 1\tfrac{1}{2}D_x \end{bmatrix} \begin{bmatrix} x_1-\xi_1 \\ x_2-\xi_2 \\ x_3-\xi_3 \end{bmatrix},$$

which is completely analogous to the procedure of 6.2.5, see (2.13); the only exception is, of course, that x_1 and ξ_1 now refer to 1958 when the decision for that year is considered, to 1959 when the 1959 decision is calculated, and so on for x_2, ξ_2, x_3, ξ_3. The linear part is derived from (2.12). It is of the form

$$(3.3)\qquad \mathbf{a}'(\mathbf{x}-\boldsymbol{\xi}) = [a_1' \quad a_2' \quad a_3'] \begin{bmatrix} x_1-\xi_1 \\ x_2-\xi_2 \\ x_3-\xi_3 \end{bmatrix},$$

where, once again, the interpretation of x_1, ξ_1, x_2, ... shifts in the successive years. But contrary to the coefficients of the quadratic part (3.2), the coefficient vectors a_1, a_2, a_3 are not constant over time. They are of the form

$$(3.4)\qquad \begin{bmatrix} a_1 \\ a_2 \\ a_3 \end{bmatrix} = \tfrac{1}{2}\begin{bmatrix} D_x(-x_0+2\xi_1-\xi_2) \\ D_x(-\xi_1+2\xi_2-\xi_3) \\ D_x(-\xi_2+\xi_3) \end{bmatrix},$$

where it must be understood again that the vectors between brackets shift in meaning in the successive years. For example, x_0 is the 1956 decision vector when the computations for 1957 are made, it is the 1957 vector for 1958, and the 1958 vector for 1959. It will be clear that information on these realized instrument values should be available on time.

In precisely the same way, the initial formulation of the noncontrolled part of the preference function was (and is now for each of the three successive years):

$$(3.5)\qquad \tfrac{1}{2}\sum_{t=1}^{3}(y_t-\eta_t)'D_y(y_t-\eta_t),$$

the desired values η_t being given in Tables 6.12 and 6.22. The latter table shows that both "L" and "C" and "E" desire larger employment increases in 1960 and 1961 than they did in the years before; that "L" wishes a smaller price decrease than before but that "C" and "E" prefer to go on as before; that both "L" and "E" have become more moderate as to their desires with respect to the share of wages in national income; and, finally, that all three continue their desires of 1959 regarding the surplus on the balance of payments, at least approximately. Of course, (3.5) has to be adjusted in view of the carry-over amendment, which applies to two of the noncontrolled variables (n^p and Δq^w). The easiest way to do this is to introduce a "corrected" first-period vector of desires:

$$\eta_C = \begin{bmatrix} (n^p)^* + (n^p)^*_{-1} - (n^p)_{-1} \\ (p^c)^* \\ (\Delta q^w)^* + (\Delta q^w)^*_{-1} - (\Delta q^w)_{-1} \\ B^* \end{bmatrix}, \tag{3.6}$$

i.e., the vector η_1 to which the unfulfilled desire of the preceding year is added for the two relevant variables. The noncontrolled part of the preference function is then

$$\frac{1}{2}\begin{bmatrix} y_1 - \eta_C \\ y_2 - \eta_2 \\ y_3 - \eta_3 \end{bmatrix}' \begin{bmatrix} B_{11} & B_{12} & B_{13} \\ B_{21} & B_{22} & B_{23} \\ B_{31} & B_{32} & B_{33} \end{bmatrix} \begin{bmatrix} y_1 - \eta_C \\ y_2 - \eta_2 \\ y_3 - \eta_3 \end{bmatrix}, \tag{3.7}$$

the B's of which are given in Table 6.14. It will be clear that the η_C of 1957 coincides with the uncorrected desired values of Table 6.12 (since any feelings of unhappiness regarding years before the strategy period are expressed in the desired values immediately), and that the η_C of 1958 and 1959 require knowledge of noncontrolled values realized one year earlier. These values are in general not known perfectly, so that we have to replace them by unbiased estimates. It is not difficult to see that this implies the application of the first-period certainty equivalence theorem in the generalized form dealing with random coefficients of the linear part of the preference function.

By adding (3.2), (3.3) and (3.7) with $\mathbf{a}$ and η_C as defined in (3.4) and (3.6), respectively, we obtain the quadratic preference functions which are relevant for the successive years. Maximizing expected utility subject to the constraints as formulated above is then straightforward, and the results are shown in Table 6.23. This table is comparable with Table 6.20 except that we now have forecasts for 1960 and 1961 in addition to those for the earlier years. A comparison shows that there are also differences for the earlier years, as could be expected. For example, the 1957 predictions of the wage rate change to be applied in 1958 are all understatements when the approach of Table 6.20 is adopted, but the same forecasts when considered as predictors of the 1958 change under three-year moving horizon conditions are all overstatements. We shall not discuss

TABLE 6.23

FORECASTS, ESTIMATES, AND REALIZATIONS OF INSTRUMENTS AND NONCONTROLLED VARIABLES UNDER CONDITIONS OF A THREE-YEAR MOVING HORIZON

Computations made at the beginning of	"L"					"C"					"E"				
	1957	1958	1959	1960	1961	1957	1958	1959	1960	1961	1957	1958	1959	1960	1961
								Instruments							
								w							
1957	*8.30*	4.41	3.81			*5.91*	2.24	1.93			*6.16*	2.71	2.20		
58		*3.32*	4.12	4.20			*0.75*	1.46	2.45			*0.30*	1.15	1.49	
59			*4.55*	4.36	4.32			*2.16*	2.74	2.63			*1.68*	1.60	1.73
								ΔT^{ia}							
1957	*−0.11*	−0.05	−0.01			*0.03*	0.06	0.05			*−0.02*	0.02	0.02		
58		*0.12*	0.10	0.04			*0.04*	0.02	0.01			*−0.04*	−0.05	−0.03	
59			*0.02*	−0.02	−0.01			*−0.06*	−0.05	−0.03			*−0.12*	−0.10	−0.05
								ΔT^{wa}							
1957	*−0.04*	−0.06	−0.04			*−0.03*	−0.04	−0.03			*−0.08*	−0.08	−0.06		
58		*−0.04*	−0.01	−0.03			*−0.05*	0.01	−0.01			*−0.14*	−0.06	−0.07	
59			*0.02*	−0.02	−0.03			*0.01*	−0.00	−0.00			*−0.09*	−0.09	−0.07
								ΔT^{oa}							
1957	*0.99*	0.95	0.97			*0.33*	0.19	0.15			*−0.11*	−0.17	−0.16		
58		*0.05*	−0.35	−0.47			*−0.14*	−0.07	0.03			*−0.26*	−0.19	−0.11	
59			*−0.05*	−0.45	−0.53			*−0.05*	−0.12	−0.02			*−0.17*	−0.13	−0.10
								ΔG							
1957	*0.14*	0.22	0.24			*−0.02*	0.01	0.09			*0.09*	0.07	0.07		

[illegible]	[illegible]	[illegible]	[illegible]			[illegible]	[illegible]	[illegible]			[illegible]	[illegible]	[illegible]		
58	0.50	1.10	1.90	3.23		0.24	1.82	1.86	2.52		0.55	2.72	2.20	2.71	
59	1.03	−1.42	3.67	3.98	4.44	0.77	−0.85	3.89	3.63	3.57	1.08	0.05	4.24	3.79	3.55
62	*1.14*	*−1.66*	*1.35*			*0.88*	*−1.09*	*1.59*			*1.19*	*−0.19*	*1.94*		
								p^c							
1957	2.34	0.73	−0.07			1.96	0.30	−0.61			2.56	0.69	−0.18		
58	6.31	1.70	2.98	2.12		5.94	−0.64	−0.31	−0.33		6.52	−1.45	−0.80	−0.99	
59	4.30	2.94	1.19	1.57	1.61	3.94	0.68	−1.59	−0.68	−0.42	4.51	−0.13	−2.15	−1.66	−0.93
62	*3.50*	*1.71*	*1.38*			*3.14*	*−0.55*	*−1.41*			*3.71*	*−1.36*	*−1.97*		
								Δq^w							
1957	1.27	0.19	0.70			1.06	0.02	0.55			0.73	−0.11	0.45		
58	0.20	0.61	0.61	0.09		−0.01	0.33	0.88	0.39		−0.35	0.15	0.78	0.22	
59	0.47	−0.17	0.74	0.22	0.93	0.27	−0.40	0.81	0.46	1.12	−0.08	−0.58	0.70	0.35	0.98
62	*1.93*	*0.88*	*−0.23*			*1.72*	*0.65*	*−2.24*			*1.38*	*0.47*	*−2.35*		
								B							
1957	0.30	1.72	2.28			0.44	1.44	1.67			0.31	0.97	1.24		
58	−0.48	1.22	1.34	0.71		−0.33	0.47	0.49	0.08		−0.47	−0.22	−0.16	−0.54	
59	−0.68	1.84	1.26	1.14	0.71	−0.53	1.20	0.28	0.22	0.14	−0.67	0.51	−0.39	−0.43	−0.39
62	*−0.52*	*1.90*	*2.01*			*−0.37*	*1.26*	*1.08*			*−0.51*	*0.58*	*0.41*		

the figures of Table 6.23 in any detail, since their interpretation is a straightforward extension of that of our earlier results. We notice that the annual changes of the tax and government spending variables have a tendency to be somewhat less extreme than in the case when 1959 is and remains the last year. There are 24 such annual changes as a whole in 1958 and 1959, four of which are above 0.4 billions and two between 0.2 and 0.4 billions in Table 6.20; the three-year moving horizon reduces this to zero above 0.4 billions and four between 0.2 and 0.4 billions. We note further that the development of the share of wages in national income is now more in accordance with what could be expected a priori: in the three-year period 1957–1959 "L" realizes an increase of the share of wages of $2\frac{1}{2}$ per cent, for "C" this share remains practically constant, and for "E" there is a small decrease. There are, finally, some interesting features with respect to the development of the inflationary excess. It was observed at the end of 6.3.2 that this excess is characterized by rather sizable ups and downs, at least for "L" and "C". In the three-year moving horizon case there is more regularity. For "L" the excess is negative in the first year, viz., -0.70 (in billions of guilders), after which it is less negative in the second year and positive in the third: -0.25 and 0.05 respectively. "C" too starts with a negative value, which is then replaced by increasing positive values: -0.35, 0.18 and 0.33. "E" starts with a positive excess and has then still larger values: 0.30, 0.66, 0.71. Thus there are two interesting features for all three preference functions: the policy followed becomes less deflationary or more inflationary in the successsive years, but the difference between the second and the third year is less than that between the first and the second.

6.3.5. Summary

(1) The derivation of the numerical results corresponding to each of the three maximizing strategies is analogous to that of the four-year strategy for the United States which was considered in Section 6.1. The main difference is that the additive structure of the constraints is more complicated because past events are not supposed to be known with certainty. Also, the preference functions which are relevant at the beginning of the second and the third year contain a part which is linear in the noncontrolled variables (contrary to the preference functions of the first year for which this linear part vanishes).

(2) The numerical results show that the development of employment corresponding to each of the three preference functions is below the de-

sires, whereas the surplus on the balance of payments behaves closer to the desired pattern, on the average at least. For the three-year period as a whole the realized wage rate increases are of the same order of magnitude as the desires or slightly larger; the increase of the price level is moderate and below the rise which was actually observed. In some cases certain tax variables are subject to rather large autonomous changes, partly because of the large equivalent deviations used for these variables. Further, a simple analysis is carried out on the inflationary or deflationary character of the policies followed, where tax increases and decreases of government expenditure are regarded as deflationary. The policy which was actually followed was inflationary in the three-year period as a whole. The same holds for the policy followed by "C"; those of "E" and "L" are less and more inflationary, respectively, than that of "C". This applies to the aggregate three-year period; there are several changes of sign of the inflationary excess in the separate years.

(3) There are 39 forecasts of future instrument and noncontrolled values and 12 estimates of past noncontrolled values for each of the three preference functions. This gives 117 forecasts and 36 estimates as a whole, the signs of which are correct in almost 70 and 90 per cent, respectively, of all cases. The total number of forecast revisions made at the beginning of 1958 is 51; and 60 per cent of these are successful in the sense that they reduce the prediction error. The revisions made at the beginning of 1959 are smaller in number and have only a 50 per cent success score.

(4) The use of a three-year moving horizon requires that at the beginning of each new year desired values for the new third year are formulated. The values chosen here (for 1960 and 1961) amount largely to a continuation of the desires for 1959. The computation of the numerical results for a three-year moving horizon necessitates some adjustments compared with the case when 1959 is and remains the last year; these adjustments deal in particular with the additive structure of the constraints and the linear part of the preference function. The results (which now include forecasts for 1960 and 1961) show more regularity with respect to the development of the inflationary excess: both "L" and "C" and "E" become gradually more inflationary, the difference between the excesses of the first two years being larger than the difference between those of the last two years; and "C" occupies an intermediate position between "L" and "E", who tend to be deflationary and inflationary, respectively.

Appendix to Chapter 6

6.A. THE MODEL IN STRUCTURAL FORM

6.A.1. Introductory

The econometric model which underlies the constraints of 6.2.6 consists of 12 behavioural equations, 4 institutional equations, and 24 definitional equations. Its statistical estimation was carried out for data of the period 1923–38, 1949–54 in the form of link relatives, i.e., first differences divided by the level of the preceding year, $(z_t - z_{t-1})/z_{t-1}$. This form was chosen, partly to make interwar and postwar data more comparable (since the latter data show much bigger figures, particularly for the value variables), partly also to handle the problem of autocorrelation of the disturbances. The statistical method employed was mainly least-squares applied to the various structural equations separately, but some two-stage least-squares estimates were also obtained by VERDOORN and VAN EIJK, which however turned out to be close to the corresponding ordinary least-squares estimates.

A model which is linear in link relatives yields constant elasticities. But the constraints of 6.2.6 are linear in the original variables, which implies the necessity of linearization. This can be explained as follows. Suppose that one of the structural equations contains a term

$$\alpha \frac{\Delta z_t}{z_{t-1}},$$

where α is a structural coefficient and $\Delta z_t = z_t - z_{t-1}$. Then the formulation used here is

$$\left(\frac{\alpha}{z_{t-1}}\right) \Delta z_t,$$

and the factor between brackets is interpreted as the coefficient of Δz_t after z_{t-1} is replaced by the z-value of 1957. This is not completely correct, of course, since the term in brackets actually changes from year to year. Also, it is not correct to assume that the 1957 value is really known at the beginning of the strategy period. Both simplifying procedures could have been avoided if we would have accepted the computational burden of the following iterative procedure. We start by guessing the values to be taken by relevant variables in the strategy period, which leads to estimated values of coefficients of the type α/z_{t-1}. We then compute the first-year decisions of the maximizing strategy on the basis of these estimated values, together with the corresponding forecasts of future decisions and noncontrolled values. Then we re-compute the coefficients α/z_{t-1} for each of the years on the basis of these predictions, after which new first-year decisions and forecasts are derived, and so on. We feel that the final results of this iterative procedure will be close to the corresponding results of the text, but we are unable to formulate more precise statements since no such computations have been carried out.

As to the economic contents of the model, we can say (in broad terms) that its behavioural side consists of two main parts, one of which is a set of demand relations describing quantities bought and sold as determined by the buyers on the relevant market, while the other is a set of price relations describing the prices paid as determined by the sellers. Two qualifications must be made. First, the expression "quantities bought and sold" suggests that the variables explained by the demand equations are volumes, but in fact they are money values in several cases. Some reasons for choosing money-value relations have been given by VERDOORN and VAN EIJK.[1] The demand relations are considered in some detail in 6.A.2. The second qualification is that some of the price relations are not structural relations in the full sense of the word, since they contain certain demand factors as well. This is explained in 6.A.3, where other behavioural equations will also be considered. The institutional and definitional equations will be summarized in 6.A.4, after which the model in reduced form follows in Section 6.B.

6.A.2. Demand Equations

The equation for total *private consumption* (C) describes this (money) variable linearly in terms of disposable wage income (W^d), of disposable non-wage income (O^d), of the same variable lagged one year $[(O^d)_{-1}]$, of the percentage change in the consumption price level (p^c),[2] and of time. When formulated in first differences, so that the time variable is

---

[1] See "Experimental Short-Term Forecasting Models," page 4.

[2] Note that p^c and most of the other price variables are already measured as an annual percentage change; see Table 6.11 of the text.

represented by a constant term, this consumption function runs as follows:

$$\text{(A.1)} \quad \Delta C = 0.90\Delta W^d + 0.09\Delta O^d + 0.22(\Delta O^d)_{-1} + 0.03\Delta p^c - 0.13 + u^C,$$

where u^C is the disturbance of this equation. Hence this equation implies a marginal propensity to consume out of disposable wage income equal to 0.9, and a marginal propensity for nonwage income of 0.31, about 70 per cent of which refers to the preceding year. The fourth term represents a thin monetary veil: if the price increase of this year exceeds that of last year by 5 per cent, say, the value change in total consumption is 0.15 billions of guilders larger than it would have been if the price level would have risen by last year's percentage. The fifth term represents an autonomous annual decline. An idea of the relative importance of the last two terms in the postwar period can be gained from a comparison with the amount of 1.55 billions of guilders per year, which is the median value (disregarding signs) of ΔC in the period 1950–57.

Investment is divided into fixed capital formation and inventory changes. The former component, in turn, is divided into autonomous and *non-autonomous fixed capital formation*, the autonomous category consisting largely of investment in housing, in public utilities, and in large companies which are close to being public utilities (such as the Netherlands Railways, the State Mines, etc.). Both variables are "gross." Autonomous fixed capital formation is taken as exogenous, but for the non-autonomous category (I^f) there is an equation which describes this (money) variable linearly in terms of disposable nonwage income lagged one year $[(O^d)_{-1}]$, of the available liquid assets at the beginning of the year (deposits and near-money, l_{-1}), of the number of unemployed measured as a percentage of the total wage-earning working population (n^u), of the price level of investment goods (p^i), and of time. In first differences the equation is as follows:

$$\text{(A.2)} \quad \Delta I^f = 0.42(\Delta O^d)_{-1} + 0.33(\Delta l)_{-1} - 0.12\Delta n^u + 0.02p^i + 0.12 + u^{If}.$$

The meaning of the first two terms on the right is rather obvious; the lag of disposable nonwage income is primarily based on the gestation period between the time of the initial investment decision and that of its execution. The third term implies that a higher investment level is promoted by a movement in the direction of full capacity utilization, and this movement is in turn considered as being accompanied by a decreasing percentage of unemployed. The positive price term (the fourth) should not, of course, be interpreted as a positive influence of a price change of investment goods on the volume of investment. The left-hand variable refers to investment value, hence this term implies only that a price increase leads to a value increase. In fact, the latter increase must be regarded to be less than proportionate due to a reduction in volume, the underlying volume-price elasticity being -0.49.

A very simple equation is used for *changes in inventories* (I^i). They are related directly and (except for a trend) solely to the change in aggregate expenditure ($\Delta E'$). This explanatory variable is measured such that it does not include the inventory changes themselves. In first differences the inventory equation is:

$$\text{(A.3)} \qquad \Delta I^i = 0.31\{\Delta E' - (\Delta E')_{-1}\} + 0.06 + u^{Ii}.$$

In one of VERDOORN's and VAN EIJK's alternative inventory equations there is a speculative explanatory variable in the form of a term which represents the effect of an acceleration of the percentage change in the import price level. But this term is omitted here for reasons of simplicity, so that the inventory explanation of (A.3) is largely technical in nature. It will further be observed that the trend coefficients of the two investment equations (A.2) and (A.3) are both positive, whereas the corresponding constant in the consumption function (A.1) is negative. The constant term in the present equation, (A.3), implies that (apart from the other explanatory variable) the level of inventories is subject to a parabolic trend, for I^i is the first and hence ΔI^i the second difference of inventories. Obviously, such a parabolic trend must be considered unrealistic for longer time periods.

The demand equations considered up till now have all money values as variables "to be explained," but for the other three which will be considered now this is not the case. First, we consider the *demand for labour by private enterprise*, its percentage change being denoted by n^p. The equation describes n^p in terms of volume changes of various expenditure groups, but in addition to this it contains such refinements as the gross profit margin per unit of output, profits per worker (in logarithmic form), and the divergent development of domestic and foreign prices. It runs as follows:

$$\text{(A.4)} \qquad n^p = (0.77\Delta c + 1.17\Delta g + 1.32\Delta i^f + 1.17\Delta i^{fa} + 0.51\Delta x)$$
$$+0.51\Delta k^o + 19.72\,{}^{10}\!\log\left(\frac{\tilde{o}}{\tilde{n}^p}\right)_{-1} - 0.12(p^e - p^m) - 0.46 + u^{np}.$$

The term in brackets on the first line specifies the effect of volume changes.

It deals with the volume of private consumption (c), of government expenditure on commodities (g), of autonomous and non-autonomous fixed capital formation (i^{fa} and i^{f}), and of exports (x). These volumes are all values measured at last year's prices. The coefficients attached to these variables are derived from the underlying constant-elasticity relations; it will be clear that this linearization is only applicable to a limited range of the variables concerned. As to the other terms, the first deals with the change in k^{o}, which is the gross profit margin per unit of output. Its coefficient (0.51) implies that a 5 per cent increase, say, of this margin leads to an additional increase in private employment by about $2\frac{1}{2}$ per cent; this is to be regarded as an approximation to expectations about future production and sales possibilities. The second term contains $\tilde{o}_{-1}$, which is the level of nonwage income in the preceding year measured in prices of 1938, and $(\tilde{n}^{p})_{-1}$ which is the level of private employment in the preceding year. Their ratio measures last year's profitability per worker at constant prices. The logarithmic form is chosen because it is believed that the linear form would give an excessive effect for large values of $\tilde{o}_{-1}$. The third term deals with substitution between domestic and foreign employment. Its variables are p^{e}, which is the percentage change in the price level of total national expenditure, and p^{m} which is the percentage change in the price level of imported commodities. Thus, if $p^{e}-p^{m} = 5$, say, this means that the domestic price level increases by 5 per cent relative to the import price level; and according to the term discussed here this increase leads to a reduction in private employment by 0.6 per cent. The constant term, finally, is negative. It implies an annual reduction in the demand for labour by almost $\frac{1}{2}$ per cent as the consequence of a combination of several factors, such as an increase of capital intensity of the economy and labour-saving technical innovation [as far as this innovation is not induced by output increases and hence represented by the term in brackets of (A.4)].

There are two demand equations dealing with international trade. One of them describes the change in the *imports of commodities* (Δm), measured at last year's prices, linearly in terms of different kinds of output:

$$\text{(A.5)}\quad \Delta m = 0.40\Delta c+0.39\Delta g+0.70(\Delta i^{f}+\Delta i^{fa})+0.80\Delta i^{i} +0.64\Delta x-0.17+u^{m}.$$

The variables on the right are the same as those in brackets of the employment equation (A.4), except that the volume of inventory changes

(i^i) plays a role in the present equation. The various multiplicative coefficients should be interpreted as the marginal import contents of the corresponding output categories. The negative constant term can be regarded as measuring a structural substitution of domestic production for imports, but we should add that in most of the postwar years the positive contribution of the other terms on the right was such as to make the negative constant term relatively unimportant. Viewed as a whole, the present import equation has largely a technical character. It was taken from one of the earlier models of the Dutch economy that were constructed before those of VERDOORN and VAN EIJK. Some of the alternatives constructed by these authors contain price terms as well, which seems quite reasonable given that the employment equation contains such a term; but nothing of this kind was attempted in the present import equation, the main argument being a preference for simplicity.

The last demand equation describes the change in the volume of *exports of commodities* (Δx) in terms of two determining factors. One of these is the percentage volume change in the exports of competing countries, to be written x^r. The corresponding volume level is obtained by applying fixed weights (market shares of 1952) to the export volumes of seven countries (Belgium-Luxemburg, Denmark, France, Italy, United Kingdom, U.S.A., and Western Germany). The theory underlying this variable is that *ceteris paribus* Dutch and foreign exports will move proportionally. The second factor, then, accounts for deviations from this proportionality; it deals with the possibility of a divergent development pattern of the Dutch and the competing price level. The equation as a whole is

$$\text{(A.6)} \qquad \Delta x = 0.15x^r - 0.18(p^x - p^{xr}) - 0.07(p^x - p^{xr})_{-1} + 0.27 + u^x,$$

where p^x and p^{xr} are the percentage changes in the Dutch and the competing export price levels, respectively; the latter price index has been derived in the same way as the volume index whose link relative is x^r. The equation implies that, if the increase in the Dutch export price level exceeds that of the competitors by 5 per cent, say, this leads to a reduction of the volume of Dutch exports by 0.9 billions of guilders in the same year and of 0.35 billions in the next. Hence the total reduction of the export volume is $1\frac{1}{4}$ billions of guilders, which is of the order of 10 per cent of the total volume of exports of commodities in the relevant period. Therefore, the price elasticity of the demand for exports according to (A.6) is about -2, and roughly 70 per cent of this figure refers to the effect in the current year and about 30 per cent to that in the next.

All variables of the six equations discussed so far are endogenous in the model as a whole, except p^m [the price level of imported goods, occurring in (A.4)] and p^{xr} [the competitive price level in the international market, occurring in (A.6)] which are taken as exogenous. However, in addition to these two there are several variables which are close to being exogenous although they are endogenous in the strict sense. Examples are the volumes of government expenditure on commodities (g), of autonomous fixed capital formation (i^{fa}), and of the exports of competing countries (x^r). These volumes are endogenous, but the corresponding values will all be taken as exogenous.

6.A.3. Other Behavioural Equations

There are six behavioural equations which have still to be considered, four of them dealing with prices. We shall begin with the other two, one of which deals with the supply of *deposits and near-money* (l, taken at the end of the year but measured at prices of the preceding year). As long as the decision maker's horizon does not exceed one year, no equation for this variable is needed because it occurs in the other equations only in lagged form. However, if we wish to consider this variable as endogenous and if a strategy for a two-year period or longer is under investigation, we do need an explicit "explanation" of such a variable. The equation used is partly of the definitional type, witness its numerous unit cofficients:

$$\text{(A.7)} \quad \Delta l = (\Delta x - \Delta m + \Delta s) + B_{-1} - 0.15(\Delta e - \Delta m + \Delta W^g - 0.03w) + \Delta l^a + u^l.$$

The change in the level of deposits and near-money is thus described as the sum of four terms (apart from u^l, the usual additive error term). The first two terms represent the surplus on the balance of payments at last year's prices, which can be regarded as the sum of the current year's change in the balance of payments at last year's prices ($\Delta x - \Delta m + \Delta s$, where x and m refer to exports and imports, respectively, of commodities and s to the surplus on the balance of invisibles) and last year's surplus on the balance of payments at that year's prices, B_{-1}. The change in deposits and near-money is therefore in first instance described in terms of balance-of-payments effects. But some qualifications have to be made. For example, part of the liquidities created by such effects are drained away into cash balances in the form of notes and coins, which is the result of the increase in total output. This is represented by the third term, which consists of a negative coefficient multiplied by the change in total output minus imports valued at last year's prices, $\Delta e - \Delta m$, including a correction term for government wages. This correction is applied because e does not include the government wage bill whereas the nature of the present equation does require its inclusion.[1] Finally, there is a group of exogenous factors affecting the level of deposits and near-money; capital exports are prominent among them. They are combined in one autonomous change term, Δl^a.

We proceed to consider the complement of n^p, viz., unemployment, which will be specified here as *registered unemployment* and written n^u; it is defined as the number of registered unemployed measured as a percentage of the total wage-earning working population. The unemployment equation describes the rate of change of this percentage, Δn^u. This rate of change is positively affected by n^d, which is the percentage change in the wage-earning working population, and negatively by n^p and n^g which are the percentage changes in private and government employment respectively. The equation is

$$\text{(A.8)} \qquad \Delta n^u = 0.60 n^d - 0.52 n^p - 0.08 n^g + 0.14 + u^{nu},$$

the positive constant term of which indicates an increasing tendency of the unemployed to register at the labour exchange offices as unemployment allowances increase (as they did in the postwar period). It will be noticed that the first three terms on the right can be written as the sum of $0.52(n^d - n^p)$ and $0.08(n^d - n^g)$; the former effect can be said to deal with unemployment in the sphere of private industry, the latter with that of the government. The ratio of the two coefficients is an indicator of the relative importance of the two sources of employment. Their sum, which is 0.6 and not 1, indicates that many of the unemployed (particularly women) do not register.

Finally, we have the four price equations. We shall start with the *price*

---

[1] We have to subtract from Δe the change in the government wage bill at last year's prices. Now W^g is the government wage bill at current prices, hence we have to use w (the percentage change in the wage rate) to find the change which we need. This change is

$$\Delta W^g - \frac{(W^g)_{-1}}{100} w$$

according to the procedure that will be explained in the third paragraph of 6.A.4. In (A.7) the lagged value $(W^g)_{-1}$ is replaced by the 1957 value of W^g.

level of private consumption, the percentage change of which is denoted by p^c. The equation runs as follows:

$$\text{(A.9)} \quad p^c = 0.40(w+n^p-2.33\Delta e')+0.06p^m+1.67\{1.89\Delta T^{ia}+(\Delta T^{ia})_{-1}\} +0.97(\Delta W^d+\Delta O^d)-1.24+u^{pc};$$

hence, disregarding disturbance and constant term, the right-hand side consists of four parts. The first stands for the effect of the change in labour costs per unit of output. The percentage change in total labour costs is $w+n^p$, where w stands for the price component and n^p for the volume component of this change. To find the percentage change in labour cost per unit of output, we should subtract from $w+n^p$ the percentage change in total output; the latter change is $100\Delta e'/(e')_{-1}$, and in (A.9), $(e')_{-1}$ has been replaced by the 1957 value of e'. The second term stands for the effect of the percentage change in the import price level (p^m); its small coefficient indicates that the greater part of consumption is of domestic origin. The third term deals with the effect of changes in indirect taxes less subsidies. The level of these taxes is of the order of 3 billions of guilders per year; when their rates are increased such that there is an autonomous increase of 0.2 billions, say, then according to the relevant coefficients of (A.9) we have a price increase of almost 1 per cent, one third of which is located in the second year. The fourth term, finally, represents a demand factor (see the end of 6.A.1), since it specifies a positive effect of disposable wage and nonwage income (W^d and O^d) on the price level. [Equation (A.9) was constructed especially for this study and not derived from the models of VERDOORN and VAN EIJK.]

The equation for the *price level of exported commodities* has a very similar structure. Its left-hand variable is again a percentage change (p^x), and the equation runs as follows:

$$\text{(A.10)} \quad p^x = 0.38(w+n^p-2.33\Delta e')+0.51p^m+0.16X^r-1.51+u^{pr}.$$

As in (A.9), the first two variables deal with the labour costs per unit of output and the import price level, respectively, but in the present case the influence of the latter variable is much larger. This reflects the fact that the import contents of exported commodities is considerable. The third term represents competitive market conditions abroad. The variable X^r stands for the percentage change in the value of competing exports (similar to the volume and price variables x^r and p^{xr}), and its theory is that an expanding foreign market as measured by an increasing value of these exports enables Dutch exporters to obtain higher prices.

The last two price equations are even more similar. They deal with the percentage changes in the *price levels of gross private fixed capital formation* and of *commodities purchased by the government*, to be denoted by p^i and p^g respectively. The equations are:

$$\text{(A.11)} \quad p^i = 0.62(w+n^p-2.33\Delta e')+0.36p^m+0.28(p^i)_{-1}+0.78+u^{pi}$$

$$\text{(A.12)} \quad p^g = 0.49(w+n^p-2.33\Delta e')+0.34p^m+0.33(p^g)_{-1}+0.51+u^{pg}.$$

The labour costs per unit of output play now a larger role, particularly for the investment price equation, whereas the influence of the import price level is about half-way between that of (A.9) and (A.10). In addition, the present equations contain lagged values of their left-hand variables as explanatory factors. Their interpretation may either be "direct," i.e., as a persistency effect, or indirect in terms of KOYCK's method of handling distributed lags.[1] The latter possibility implies that labour cost changes and import price changes of previous years are supposed to have a positive influence on p^i and p^g. It is of some interest to add that the price equations which contain demand factors [viz., (A.9) with W^d and O^d and (A.10) with X^r] have both negative constant terms, whereas the present equations which do not contain such factors have both positive constant terms. A difference of this kind is not entirely unexpected, since these demand factors with their positive coefficients imply upward trends in the long run.

The four price equations considered here describe all relevant prices of the model. The remaining price levels are either taken as exogenous (this applies to p^m and p^{xr} as was explained at the end of 6.A.2), or they are defined as weighted averages of other prices, or identified with such prices. This will be explained at the end of 6.A.4. As to the distinction between endogenous and exogenous variables, six new exogenous variables have been introduced in addition to the two just mentioned. They are:

w, the percentage change in the wage rate [occurring in (A.7) and in each of the four price equations];

Δl^a, the autonomous change in deposits and near-money [occurring in (A.7)];

n^d and n^g, the percentage changes in the wage-earning population and in government employment, respectively [occurring in (A.8)]:

[1] See L. M. KOYCK, *Distributed Lags and Investment Analysis* (Amsterdam 1954), Chap. II.

ΔT^{ia}, the autonomous change in indirect taxes less subsidies [occurring in (A.9)];

X^r, the percentage change in the export value of competing countries [occurring in (A.10)].

6.A.4. *Institutional and Definitional Equations*

There are four institutional equations, one of which deals with the total value of *unemployment allowances* (Θ^u). Its first difference is described in terms of the change in the percentage of registered unemployed (Δn^u) and an autonomous change which handles changes in the allowance rates in the same way as the autonomous tax terms handle changes in tax rates. The equation is

$$\text{(A.13)} \qquad \Delta\Theta^u = 0.09\Delta n^u + \Delta\Theta^{ua}$$

and implies that a unit increase in the percentage of unemployed leads to an additional 90 million guilders of allowances. The three other institutional equations all deal with taxes. For the change in *indirect taxes less subsidies*, ΔT^i, we have

$$\text{(A.14)} \qquad \Delta T^i = 0.09(\Delta C + \Delta I^f + \Delta I^{fa} + \Delta G) + 0.04\Delta M + \Delta T^{ia}.$$

The first term on the right represents mainly sales taxes levied on consumption (C), gross investment in fixed assets (I^f and I^{fa}) and government expenditure on commodities (G). The second term stands for import duties, M being the value of imported commodities. The two coefficients approximate the marginal tax rates in the relevant area and ΔT^{ia} stands for the autonomous change in indirect taxes. The equations for *income taxes on wage income* (T^w) and *income taxes on nonwage income* (T^o) have a similar form:

$$\text{(A.15)} \qquad \Delta T^w = 0.12(\Delta W^p + \Delta W^g + \Delta\Theta^u + \Delta\Theta^w) + \Delta T^{wa}$$

$$\text{(A.16)} \qquad \Delta T^o = 0.40(\Delta O + \Delta\Theta^o) + \Delta T^{oa}.$$

Here W^p is the wage bill of private industry, W^g that of the government, Θ^u unemployment allowances, Θ^w income transfers to wage-earners, O the value of nonwage income, and Θ^o income transfers to nonwage-earners.

The remaining equations are all of the definitional type. They can be divided into three large groups except for two of them which will therefore be considered first. One of them deals with the *share of wages in national income*, expressed as a percentage and written q^w. We follow the definition accepted by the Social and Economic Council, viz., private wage bill (W^p) per head of the active wage-earning labour force divided by total national income (W^p+W^g+O) per head of the active working population. According to this definition we should divide the numerator (W^p) by private employment, the percentage change of which is n^p; and we should divide the denominator (W^p+W^g+O) by the sum of private employment, government employment, and the nonwage-earning population, the percentage changes of the last two variables being written n^g and n^o respectively. After applying the usual linearizations we obtain for the first difference of q^w:

$$\Delta q^w = 2.90\Delta W^p - 0.23n^p - 2.36\Delta O - 2.36\Delta W^g + 0.07n^g + 0.15n^o. \tag{A.17}$$

The second definitional equation is based on the logarithmic expression

$$^{10}\log\frac{\tilde{o}}{\tilde{n}^p} = \Delta(^{10}\log\tilde{o} - {}^{10}\log\tilde{n}^p) + {}^{10}\log\left(\frac{\tilde{o}}{\tilde{n}^p}\right)_{-1},$$

which occurs in lagged form in the employment equation (A.4). Now

$$\Delta(^{10}\log\tilde{o}) \approx 0.4343\,\frac{\tilde{o}-\tilde{o}_{-1}}{\tilde{o}_{-1}}$$

and since $\tilde{o}$ is identical with O (the value of nonwage income) except that it is measured in 1938 prices, we can linearize in the usual way to obtain an expression in ΔO and p^e (for $\tilde{o}$) and in n^p (for $\tilde{n}^p$). The result is

$$^{10}\log\frac{\tilde{o}}{\tilde{n}^p} = 0.034\Delta O - 0.004p^e - 0.004n^p + {}^{10}\log\left(\frac{\tilde{o}}{\tilde{n}^p}\right)_{-1}, \tag{A.18}$$

after wich the lagged logarithm on the right can be eliminated by successive application of the same procedure. This equation is analogous to (A.7) to the extent that both are needed only if the decision maker's horizon exceeds one year.

The other definitional equations are summarized in Table 6.24. The first group consists of *accounting identities* which need no further comment.[1] The second group, consisting of *value-volume-price identities*, are mainly linearizations of the following kind. Consider the value of

[1] One exception should be made. Equation (A.25) does not belong to the model but has been added because the surplus on the balance of payments (one of the non-controlled variables) occurs in the model only in first-difference form. (This explains why the total number of equations given here is 41, not 40.)

TABLE 6.24

SURVEY OF DEFINITIONAL EQUATIONS

Number	Description of left-hand variable	Equation
	(i) *Accounting identities*	
(A.19)	Total expenditure excluding government wages, minus imports of invisibles	$\Delta E = \Delta(C+I^f+I^{fa}+I^i+G+X+S)$
(A.20)	Total expenditure excluding government wages and inventory changes, minus exports of invisibles	$\Delta E' = \Delta(C+I^f+I^{fa}+G+X)$
(A.21)	Nonwage income	$\Delta O = \Delta(E-W^p-T^i-D-M)$
(A.22)	Disposable wage income	$\Delta W^d = \Delta(W^p+W^g+\Theta^w+\Theta^u-T^w)$
(A.23)	Disposable nonwage income	$\Delta O^d = \Delta(O+\Theta^o-T^o)$
(A.24)	Surplus on balance of payments (current account)	$\Delta B = \Delta(X-M+S)$
(A.25)	Ditto (level instead of change)	$B = B_{-1}+\Delta B$
	(ii) *Value-volume-price identities*	
(A.26)	Private consumption	$\Delta C = \Delta c+0.21p^c$
(A.27)	Non-autonomous gross fixed capital formation	$\Delta I^f = \Delta i^f+0.05p^i$
(A.28)	Autonomous gross fixed capital formation	$\Delta I^{fa} = \Delta i^{fa}+0.03p^i$
(A.29)	Changes in inventories	$\Delta I^i = \Delta i^i+0.01p^m$
(A.30)	Government expenditure on commodities	$\Delta G = \Delta g+0.03p^g$
(A.31)	Government wage bill	$\Delta W^g = 0.03n^g+0.03w$
(A.32)	Wage bill of private industry	$\Delta W^p = 0.13n^p+0.13w$
(A.33)	Imports of commodities	$\Delta M = \Delta m+0.15p^m$
(A.34)	Exports of commodities	$\Delta X = \Delta x+0.21p^x$
(A.35)	Balance of invisibles	$\Delta S = \Delta s+0.03p^e$
(A.36)	Exports of competing countries	$X^r = x^r+p^{xr}$
(A.37)	Total expenditure excluding government wages, minus imports of invisibles	$\Delta E = \Delta e+0.47p^e$
(A.38)	Total expenditure excluding government wages and inventory changes, minus exports of invisibles	$\Delta E' = \Delta e'+0.43p^{e'}$
	(iii) *Definition of price aggregates*	
(A.39)	Price index of total expenditure excluding government wages, minus imports of invisibles	$p^e = 0.47p^c+0.18p^i+0.06p^g+0.02p^m+0.27p^x$
(A.40)	Price index of total expenditure excluding government wages and inventory changes, minus exports of invisibles	$p^{e'} = 0.48p^c+0.18p^i+0.07p^g+0.27p^x$
(A.41)	[illegible]	

consumption in any given year, C, the volume c in the same year (i.e., the value measured in prices of the preceding year), and the percentage change in the price index, p^c. The familiar linearization technique implies that the value change, ΔC, is the sum of two terms, one of which is last year's price times the volume change while the other is last year's volume times the price change. Now the first term is simply Δc, given that all last year's values of the price indices are put equal to 1. At the same time this implies that the price change is equal to the percentage price change (apart from a factor 100), hence the second term is $c_{-1}p^c$. Therefore,

$$\Delta C = \Delta c + c_{-1} p^c/100,$$

and this is the general form of most of the identities (A.26)–(A.38); lagged volumes such as c_{-1} are throughout replaced by 1957 values. Three identities have a slightly different structure. One case is (A.36), where value, volume, and price variables are all in link-relative form. The two other cases are (A.31) and (A.32) in which the volume component is in link-relative form and expressed in man-years rather than in billions of last year's guilders. It will also be observed that in several cases a price index has been taken from or joined with the index of another output category. For example, the inventory equation (A.29) contains the price index of imported goods, the equation for the balance of invisibles (A.35) uses the price index of total expenditure, the two equations (A.27) and (A.28) on fixed capital formation have the same price index, and the same applies to the two equations (A.31) and (A.32) dealing with wage bills.

The third group of definitional equations deals with *price aggregates* which are described in terms of price indices of separate output categories. In (A.39) and (A.40) the relevant weights of 1958 have been used. A special case is the definition of the gross profit margin (k^o), which contains autonomous change terms of indirect taxes, both in current and in lagged form.

The following are the seven exogenous variables introduced in the four institutional equations (apart from the eight exogenous variables introduced in 6.A.2 and 6.A.3):

$\Delta\Theta^{ua}$, ΔT^{wa}, ΔT^{oa}, which are the autonomous change terms in the equations for unemployment allowances and for income taxes;

I^{fa} and G, the values of autonomous gross fixed capital formation and of government expenditure on commodities [both occurring in (A.14)];

TABLE 6.25

THE REDUCED-FORM EQUATIONS OF ELEVEN ENDOGENOUS VARIABLES

	Endogenous variables lagged one year									*Current instruments*				
	B	$\Delta E'$	ΔO^d	Δl	100 log*	p^c	p^g	p^i	p^x	w	ΔT^{ia}	ΔT^{wa}	ΔT^{oa}	ΔG
					P_1							P_2		
n^p		−0.005	0.802	0.485	0.237	−0.025	−0.001	0.002	−0.036	0.001	−1.075	−0.848	−0.167	1.322
p^c		−0.042	−0.591	−0.285	0.152	0.031	0.022	0.046	0.095	0.752	3.074	−0.511	−1.350	−0.719
Δq^w		0.139	0.149	0.168	−0.008	0.009	−0.022	−0.066	−0.010	0.043	1.163	0.740	0.499	−0.341
B	1.000	0.247	−0.748	−0.420	0.002	0.029	0.007	0.016	0.015	0.038	0.371	0.750	−0.037	−0.957
$\Delta E'$		−0.005	0.741	0.389	0.033	−0.034	0.001	0.008	−0.074	0.141	−0.084	−1.063	−0.158	1.185
ΔO^d		−0.035	−0.008	−0.025	0.011	−0.003	0.006	0.017	0.001	0.067	−0.336	−0.220	−1.133	0.136
Δl	1.000	0.257	−0.731	−0.410	−0.014	0.028	0.006	0.012	0.009	−0.019	0.360	0.766	−0.003	−0.968
100 log*		−0.189	−0.099	−0.208	0.908	−0.023	0.016	0.058	−0.021	0.105	−2.128	−0.989	−0.376	0.608
p^g		−0.009	−0.785	−0.363	0.152	0.044	0.350	0.037	0.119	0.674	0.388	0.898	−0.292	−1.159
p^i		−0.012	−0.991	−0.458	0.193	0.056	0.026	0.327	0.150	0.852	0.490	1.133	−0.369	−1.462
p^x		−0.007	−0.605	−0.279	0.118	0.034	0.016	0.028	0.092	0.522	0.298	0.692	−0.226	−0.892

	Instr.s lagged one year	*Current noninstrumental exogenous variables*												
	ΔT^{ia}	ΔD	ΔI^{fa}	ΔS	X^r	$\Delta\Theta^{ɔ}$	$\Delta\Theta^{ua}$	$\Delta\Theta^{w}$	Δl^a	n^d	n^g	n^o	p^m	p^{xr}
	P_3							P_4						
n^p	−0.515	−0.100	1.289	0.100	0.084	0.100	0.747	0.747		−0.065	0.031		−0.026	0.015
p^c	2.052	−0.810	−0.980	0.810	−0.137	0.810	0.450	0.450		0.087	0.002		0.240	−0.041

100 log	[illegible]	[illegible]	[illegible]	[illegible]	[illegible]	[illegible]	[illegible]	[illegible]		[illegible]	[illegible]		[illegible]	[illegible]
p^g	0.298	−0.175	−1.215	0.175	−0.191	0.175	−0.790	−0.790		0.036	−0.029		0.586	−0.051
p^i	0.375	−0.222	−1.534	0.222	−0.241	0.222	−0.997	−0.997		0.046	−0.036		0.670	−0.064
p^x	0.229	−0.136	−0.936	0.136	0.013	0.136	−0.609	−0.609		0.028	−0.022		0.700	−0.039
	Noninstr. ex. var.[s] *lagged one year*	*Const. term*	*Structural disturbances*											
	p^{xr}	1	u^C	u^{If}	u^{Ii}	u^{np}	u^m	u^x	u^l	u^{nu}	u^{pc}	u^{px}	u^{pi}	u^{pg}
	P_5	p_6						P_7						
n^p	0.036	−0.525	0.841	1.469	0.017	1.200	−0.105	0.512		−0.109	0.095	0.046	0.009	−0.003
p^c	−0.095	−2.835	−1.035	−0.865	0.136	0.769	−0.842	−1.364		0.144	1.487	0.421	0.166	0.067
Δq^w	0.010	0.572	−0.297	0.510	−0.447	−0.040	2.766	0.138		−0.120	−0.487	−0.360	−0.235	−0.068
B	−0.015	−0.253	−0.972	−1.273	−0.796	0.011	−1.023	−0.218		0.093	0.128	0.132	0.058	0.022
$\Delta E'$	0.074	0.229	1.117	1.179	0.016	0.166	−0.098	1.059		−0.057	0.059	−0.041	0.029	0.002
ΔO^d	−0.001	−0.165	0.107	−0.075	0.114	0.055	−0.707	−0.016		0.026	0.127	0.093	0.060	0.017
Δl	−0.009	0.040	−0.949	−1.243	−0.830	−0.070	−0.852	−0.135	1.000	0.088	0.091	−0.021	0.044	0.017
100 log*	0.021	0.246	0.756	−0.631	0.609	−0.466	−3.771	0.299		0.154	0.318	0.244	0.208	0.049
p^g	−0.119	−1.217	−1.469	−1.099	0.029	0.772	−0.182	−1.698		0.061	0.438	0.401	0.132	1.062
p^i	−0.150	−1.402	−1.855	−1.387	0.037	0.977	−0.230	−2.145		0.077	0.553	0.506	1.166	0.078
p^x	−0.092	−2.844	−1.133	−0.846	0.023	0.598	−0.141	−1.310		0.047	0.338	1.309	0.102	0.048

* 100 times the 10-log of $\tilde{o}/\tilde{n}^p$.

Θ^w and Θ^o, income transfers to wage-earners and to others [occurring in (A.15) and (A.16) respectively].

Finally, there are three new exogenous variables introduced in the definitions, viz.:

n^o, the percentage change in the nonwage-earning working population [occurring in (A.17)];

S, the surplus on the balance of invisibles [occurring in (A.19), (A.24) and (A.35)];

D, depreciation of privately owned fixed assets [occurring in (A.21)].

6.B. THE MODEL IN REDUCED AND FINAL FORM

Since the model as a whole contains a substantial number of variables, its reduced form is rather unwieldy. Fortunately, we do not need all reduced-form equations. A little reflection shows that we need them only for two groups of endogenous variables, viz., the four noncontrolled variables of the decision problem and the endogenous variables which occur in the model in lagged form. The latter feature applies to nine endogenous variables (listed in the first nine columns of Table 6.25) and two of these (B and p^c) are also noncontrolled variables. Thus, we have 11 endogenous variables for which the reduced-form equations have to be derived. A survey of their coefficients is presented in Table 6.25. The influence of endogenous variables lagged one year is measured by P_1, which is an 11×11 matrix. Only nine columns are shown, however, the two zero columns being deleted; also, in each nonzero column only those elements are shown which are not exactly zero. P_2 is the 11×5 coefficient matrix describing the effect of current instruments and P_3 refers to the instruments lagged one year. The latter matrix is also of order 11×5 but it contains only one nonzero column. P_4 is the 11×13 matrix describing the effect of current noninstrumental exogenous variables, which is followed by P_5 for the effect lagged one year; again, the latter matrix has only one nonzero column. Finally, p_6 is the vector of constant terms and P_7 the 11×12 matrix referring to the 12 structural disturbances.

We can write the reduced form as follows:

$$\text{(B.1)} \qquad h = P_1 h_{-1} + P_2 x + P_3 x_{-1} + P_4 g + P_5 g_{-1} + p_6 + P_7 u,$$

which is identical with (1.5) except that (i) h is not the complete vector of all current endogenous variables but only of the 11 variables mentioned above, (ii) x is the vector of the 5 current instruments, (iii) g is not the vector of all current exogenous variables but only of the 13 current noninstrumental exogenous variables, and (iv) p_6 is the vector of constant terms. By eliminating h_{-1} successively we obtain

$$\begin{aligned} h &= P_2 x + (P_1 P_2 + P_3) x_{-1} + P_1 (P_1 h_{-2} + P_3 x_{-2} + P_5 g_{-2}) \\ &+ P_4 g + (P_1 P_4 + P_5) g_{-1} + (\mathbf{I} + P_1) p_6 + P_7 u + P_1 P_7 u_{-1}, \end{aligned} \tag{B.2}$$

$$\begin{aligned} h &= P_2 x + (P_1 P_2 + P_3) x_{-1} + P_1 (P_1 P_2 + P_3) x_{-2} \\ &+ P_1^2 (P_1 h_{-3} + P_3 x_{-3} + P_5 g_{-3}) \\ &+ P_4 g + (P_1 P_4 + P_5) g_{-1} + P_1 (P_1 P_4 + P_5) g_{-2} \\ &+ (\mathbf{I} + P_1 + P_1^2) p_6 + P_7 u + P_1 P_7 u_{-1} + P_1^2 P_7 u_{-2}, \end{aligned} \tag{B.3}$$

which can be used to describe the constraints for 1958 and 1959, respectively. We recall that our noncontrolled variables are the first four components of h and introduce the convention of writing Π_i for the submatrix consisting of the first four rows of P_i (for relevant values of the index i). It follows then from (B.1)–(B.3) that the multiplicative structure of the constraints is determined by

$$\begin{bmatrix} R_1 \\ R_2 \\ R_3 \end{bmatrix} = \begin{bmatrix} \Pi_2 \\ \Pi_1 P_2 + \Pi_3 \\ \Pi_1 (P_1 P_2 + P_3) \end{bmatrix}. \tag{B.4}$$

Furthermore, for the coefficient matrices S_1, S_2, S_3 of (2.18) we obtain

$$\begin{bmatrix} S_1 \\ S_2 \\ S_3 \end{bmatrix} = \begin{bmatrix} (\Pi_1 \quad \Pi_3 \quad \Pi_5) \\ \Pi_1 (P_1 \quad P_3 \quad P_5) \\ \Pi_1 P_1 (P_1 \quad P_3 \quad P_5) \end{bmatrix} \tag{B.5}$$

with the understanding that the 1956 values are to be arranged in the order: endogenous, instruments, noninstrumental exogenous (i.e., in the order h, x, g). For the coefficient matrices $S_4, \ldots, S_9$ of (2.19)–(2.20) we have

$$\begin{bmatrix} S_4 \\ S_5 \\ S_6 \end{bmatrix} = \begin{bmatrix} \Pi_4 \\ \Pi_1 P_4 + \Pi_5 \\ \Pi_1 (P_1 P_4 + P_5) \end{bmatrix}, \quad \begin{bmatrix} S_7 \\ S_8 \\ S_9 \end{bmatrix} = \begin{bmatrix} \Pi_7 \\ \Pi_1 P_7 \\ \Pi_1 P_1 P_7 \end{bmatrix}, \tag{B.6}$$

and, finally, for the constant terms of the additive structure of the constraints:

$$\begin{bmatrix} \pi_6 \\ \pi_6 + \Pi_1 p_6 \\ \pi_6 + \Pi_1 p_6 + \Pi_1 P_1 p_6 \end{bmatrix}, \tag{B.7}$$

where π_6 stands for the first four elements of p_6.

CHAPTER 7

On Multi-Person Problems

7.1. A BRIEF REVIEW OF SOME MULTI-PERSON SITUATIONS

7.1.1. Introductory

The analysis of the preceding chapters was exclusively concerned with one-person decision problems. One might perhaps argue that several places can be indicated where more than one person entered into the picture, but it appears on closer scrutiny that nevertheless the analysis was essentially of the one-person variety. For example, we considered three government decision makers in Chapter 6, not just one. However, they were only considered as three alternatives and in each case we disregarded the preferences of the two rival decision makers; we confined ourselves to comparing the three sets of numerical outcomes. A second example, which is slightly more profound, deals with the decisions made by other individuals which are represented by our constraints. For example, buyers of paint determine the quantity sold by the paint factory of Chapter 5; and these sales have an important impact on the decision rules for production and work force. Similarly, family households determine the amount spent on consumer goods, and consumption is one of the crucial variables of the anti-depression strategy of Section 6.1. But these examples are irrelevant. What matters is that in all these cases there is one decision maker who maximizes a preference function (or its expectation) subject to certain constraints. These constraints may represent the behaviour patterns of other individuals; but these patterns are taken as given, hence the latter individuals play a completely passive role in the analysis.

However, we observe numerous interactions of numerous individuals in the real world. It is therefore appropriate that we try to extend the analysis to multi-person situations. The first thing to be done is to formulate a catalogue of possible situations. The following will be considered here:

(i) We may have a case in which one person's preferences are decisive while the others have to adjust their actions accordingly; e.g., the former is an entrepreneur and the latter are his division chiefs. The position of a research manager falls under this case and will be considered briefly in 7.1.2.

(ii) A second case deals with the position of several persons (a team) who work for a common goal; e.g., a directorate of a company whose objective is to maximize the company's net profit over a certain horizon, each member of the directorate being in charge of a certain subset of instrument variables. We shall consider this situation in 7.1.3.

(iii) The directorate may also act as a committee of members who are jointly responsible for the manipulation of all instruments. No special problems arise when all committee members agree about the objective to be pursued; the case becomes interesting when preferences are in conflict with each other. We shall go deeper into this case than into the other ones; it will be considered in Section 7.2.

(iv) Finally, there is the situation of individuals whose preferences are in conflict and who control different variables; e.g., the case of two duopolists. Some remarks on this topic will be made in 7.1.4.

7.1.2. The Position of the Research Manager

We shall consider the situation of a research manager who works for some decision maker. The latter has a quadratic preference function which he maximizes subject to linear constraints. Both the coefficients of the preference function and those of the constraints depend on certain parameters which are not known completely. It is the research manager's task to set up investigations which make this knowledge less imperfect and to do so in such a manner, given a limited budget per unit of time, that the decision maker's objective (as specified by his preference function) is approached as well as possible. Also, it is his task to formulate a budget proposal which is optimal with respect to this objective.

Let us go back to Section 4.1. The quadratic preference function and the linear constraints are given in (4.1.3) and (4.1.4) respectively and the optimal first-period decision (disregarding uncertainty) can be written as follows:

$$x_1^0 = h(\boldsymbol{\pi}), \tag{1.1}$$

where h stands for an m-element column vector of functions and $\boldsymbol{\pi}$

for a column vector of basic parameters. In principle the elements of $\boldsymbol{\pi}$ may form a complete enumeration of all elements of **a, b, A, B, C, R, s**; but this is not always necessary. For example, let the decision maker be the factory manager of 4.2.5; then (4.2.37) specifies that the optimal first-period production decision is

$$P_1^0 = (1-\gamma)\sum_{t=1}^{\infty}\gamma^{t-1}S_t+(1-\gamma)(I^*-I_0), \tag{1.2}$$

from which it follows that the determining parameters are: γ and I^* (which are in turn determined by the cost coefficients) and the sales variables in the successive months. (The easiest way to handle the initial inventory level I_0 is by subtraction from S_1.) For the factory manager example, therefore, we can define $\boldsymbol{\pi}$ as follows:

$$\boldsymbol{\pi} = \begin{bmatrix}\gamma \\ I^* \\ \mathbf{v}\end{bmatrix}, \quad \mathbf{v} = \begin{bmatrix}S_1-I_0 \\ S_2 \\ S_3 \\ \vdots\end{bmatrix}. \tag{1.3}$$

Suppose now that the decision maker is imperfectly informed and acts as if $\boldsymbol{\pi}+\Delta\boldsymbol{\pi}$ is the vector of basic parameters, where $\Delta\boldsymbol{\pi}$ is the vector of specification errors. This leads to a first-period decision error,

$$\Delta x_1 = h(\boldsymbol{\pi}+\Delta\boldsymbol{\pi})-h(\boldsymbol{\pi}) \approx H\Delta\boldsymbol{\pi}, \tag{1.4}$$

H being the matrix of first-order derivatives of the vector function h with respect to $\boldsymbol{\pi}$ evaluated at the point of the "true" $\boldsymbol{\pi}$. (The $\approx$ sign implies that we linearize as usual.) The first-period loss associated with this error is $(\Delta\boldsymbol{\pi})'Q\Delta\boldsymbol{\pi}$, where

$$Q = -\tfrac{1}{2}H'(xx)_{11}^{-1}H \tag{1.5}$$

and the expected first-period loss is:

$$\mathscr{E}[(\Delta\boldsymbol{\pi})'Q(\Delta\boldsymbol{\pi})] = \operatorname{tr} Q\mathbf{S} \text{ where } \mathbf{S} = \mathscr{E}[(\Delta\boldsymbol{\pi})(\Delta\boldsymbol{\pi})'], \tag{1.6}$$

tr $Q\mathbf{S}$ being the trace of the square matrix $Q\mathbf{S}$ (the sum of its diagonal elements) and $\mathbf{S}$ the moment matrix of the specification error $\Delta\boldsymbol{\pi}$.

The loss expression (1.6) is of crucial importance to the research manager. Assuming that adequate probabilistic ideas exist with respect to the order of magnitude of the components of the specification error $\Delta\boldsymbol{\pi}$, we can determine or at least approximate its matrix of second-order moments, $\mathbf{S}$. Also, we can approximate Q from preference function and constraints; and (1.6) tells us then that tr $\mathbf{QS} = \sum\sum q_{ij} s_{ji}$ is the expected loss which is suffered by the decision maker, period after period, due to the fact that his knowledge of the basic parameters is limited. Evidently, (1.6) is the expression which the research manager should minimize. The variables of this expression are the **S**-elements since the Q-elements are fixed. In fact, it is of considerable interest to observe that we started with a decision maker whose preferences are described by a quadratic function and that this leads to a linear objective function for the research manager [because (1.6) is linear in the **S**-elements]. The minimization of the latter objective function does not take place unconditionally, of course. There are at least two different approaches. One is the combinatorial approach, which is useful when the number of research projects is limited; it consists of considering all possible combinations of such projects, estimating the reduction of tr $\mathbf{QS}$ caused by each such combination, and selecting the combination which leads to the largest reduction (taking account of the costs of the projects involved). But this approach is awkward when the number of possible research projects is large. When there are so many ways of doing research that one can sacrifice research resources practically continuously in favour of expected squares and products of the elements of $\boldsymbol{\Delta\pi}$, it may be useful to introduce a research production function which formalizes this transformation. The research manager's task is then to minimize the linear objective function (1.6) subject to this research production function, which will generally be nonlinear.

The situation can be made concrete when we consider (1.6) for the special case of the factory manager whose optimal first-period decision is given in (1.2). The matrix H of (1.4) is then a row vector; its first element is the derivative of P_1^0 with respect to γ, which is

$$-\sum_{t=1}^{\infty} \gamma^{t-2}\{1-(1-\gamma)t\}S_t-(I^*-I_0).$$

This is rather complicated, so that it is not unreasonable to assume that the research manager decides to proceed under the assumption that sales are constant at some normal level, $\bar{S}$ say. The derivative is then simplified to $-(I^*-I_0)$ and therefore independent of the level of sales. The evaluation of the other derivatives is straightforward and the result is:

$$H = [-(I^*-I_0) \quad 1-\gamma \quad 1-\gamma \quad (1-\gamma)\gamma \quad (1-\gamma)\gamma^2 \ldots].$$

The substitution matrix of the first-period instruments, $(xx)_{11}$, is a scalar in this case; we found in 4.2.5 that it is equal to $-\gamma/2c$. Hence $-\frac{1}{2}(xx)_{11}^{-1} = [c/\gamma]$, which we should premultiply by H' and postmultiply by H in order to obtain the matrix Q of (1.5). The quadratic form $(\mathbf{\Delta\pi})'Q\mathbf{\Delta\pi}$ can then be written as the sum of three expressions in the specification errors $\Delta\gamma$, ΔI^* and $\mathbf{\Delta v}$. The first is a quadratic form in the cost coefficient errors $\Delta\gamma$ and ΔI^*:

$$L_1(\Delta\gamma, \Delta I^*) = \frac{c}{\gamma}\{(I^*-I_0)^2(\Delta\gamma)^2+(1-\gamma)^2(\Delta I^*)^2 - 2(1-\gamma)(I^*-I_0)\Delta\gamma\Delta I^*\}. \tag{1.7}$$

The second is a quadratic form in sales prediction errors:

$$L_2(\mathbf{\Delta v}) = \frac{(1-\gamma)^2 c}{\gamma}\sum_{t=1}^{\infty}\sum_{t'=1}^{\infty}\gamma^{t+t'-2}\Delta S_t\Delta S_{t'}. \tag{1.8}$$

The third, finally, is a bilinear form in the two sets of errors:

$$L_3(\Delta\gamma, \Delta I^*, \mathbf{\Delta v}) = -\frac{2(1-\gamma)c(I^*-I_0)}{\gamma}\Delta\gamma\sum_{t=1}^{\infty}\gamma^{t-1}\Delta S_t + \frac{2(1-\gamma)^2 c}{\gamma}\Delta I^*\sum_{t=1}^{\infty}\gamma^{t-1}\Delta S_t. \tag{1.9}$$

To obtain the expected first-period loss we should add the expectations of L_1, L_2, and L_3. This involves the expected squares and product of the cost coefficient errors $\Delta\gamma$ and ΔI^*; it involves also the expected squares and products of the sales prediction errors ΔS_t; and it involves, finally, the expected products of cost coefficient errors on the one hand and sales prediction errors on the other.

The numerical specification of the expected first-period loss is then a matter of substituting figures for $\mathscr{E}(\Delta\gamma)^2$, $\mathscr{E}(\Delta I^*)^2, \ldots$ and also for c and γ which act as multipliers of these separate expectations. Regarding the moments of the sales prediction errors, the simplest approach is to impose a certain statistical pattern like (3.2.35)–(3.2.36). Additional simplifications can be obtained when it is possible to assume that the cost coefficient errors $\Delta\gamma$, ΔI^* have zero cross-moments with the sales prediction errors, because the expectation of L_3 vanishes in that case. The research manager's objective function is then a linear function of $\mathscr{E}(\Delta\gamma)^2$, $\mathscr{E}(\Delta I^*)^2$ and $\mathscr{E}(\Delta\gamma\Delta I^*)$ plus an expected first-period loss expression in sales forecast errors of the same general type as we analyzed in Table 5.6 of Chapter 5. In other words, his objective is split up into two separate objectives, one dealing with cost analysis and the other with market analysis. (We shall have more to say about this kind of "partitioning" in 7.1.3 below.) If the research manager is able to formulate a satisfactory approximation to his research production function, we can define his task as that of finding the extremum of his linear objective function subject to the constraints implied by the production function. This is in principle a straightforward application of the theory of the firm which operates under conditions of perfect competition.[1]

7.1.3. On Team Decision Problems

The older literature on economic policy is usually formulated in terms of separate "policies," e.g., monetary policy, price policy, foreign exchange policy, etc., at the macroeconomic level; and similarly wage policy, sales policy, investment policy, etc., at the microeconomic level of the individual firm. We may say that it is TINBERGEN's important contribution in *On the Theory of Economic Policy* that he stressed the interrelationships between such different policies and introduced one single "policy" as a coherent system. There is a similar development in consumer's utility theory. Originally the utility function was considered to be additive in the sense that the utility of a certain batch of commodities can be written as the sum of the utilities of the quantities (q_i) of the separate commodities:

$$u(q_1, \ldots, q_n) = u_1(q_1) + \ldots + u_n(q_n).$$

This assumption implies that there is no interrelationship between the various commodities at the level of utility evaluation; they are only related in the sense that all have to compete for the consumer's dollar (as expressed by the budget constraint). Later on it was realized that the additive utility assumption is restrictive and it was generally abandoned. We can therefore say that by this change utility theory describes the consumer's expenditure pattern as an interdependent system.

However, it was realized more recently (by FRISCH, STROTZ, HOUT-

[1] For further details, see H. THEIL, "On the Optimal Management of Research: A Mathematical Approach," Report 6212 of the Econometric Institute of the Netherlands School of Economics.

HAKKER and others [1]) that such a system is not very practical from the standpoint of statistical estimation of demand equations, because it involves so many unknown parameters. If it is true that utility can be written in the additive manner—and there are rather good intuitive reasons for this when the commodities are suitably grouped—, the structure of the demand equations is simplified substantially. The question arises whether it has some merits to do the same with the more general theory of decision-making; i.e., whether it is useful to go back (possibly half-way) to the separate policies. Of course, the point is not the convenience of statistical estimation; it is rather that a decision maker becomes over-burdened when he is supposed to be in charge of a great many heterogeneous components of an instrument vector. Specifically, we shall consider the question whether it is possible to replace one single decision maker by a team of decision makers without suffering a loss due to this replacement.

To keep the formulas simple we shall consider a team of two persons; the extension to a larger number is straightforward. Also, we shall confine ourselves to the static case, mainly for typographical reasons: we have to partition by variables, which would lead to a cumbersome large-scale asterisk notation in the dynamic case. (But otherwise the dynamic extension is straightforward, too.) Suppose then that we consider delegating the vectors x_1 and y_1 to decision maker No. 1 and x_2 and y_2 to No. 2; the instrument vector x consists of all elements of x_1 and x_2 and similarly with respect to y, y_1, y_2. The linear constraints are written in partitioned form as follows:

$$\begin{bmatrix} y_1 \\ y_2 \end{bmatrix} = \begin{bmatrix} R_{11} & R_{12} \\ R_{21} & R_{22} \end{bmatrix} \begin{bmatrix} x_1 \\ x_2 \end{bmatrix} + \begin{bmatrix} s_1 \\ s_2 \end{bmatrix},$$

where R_{11} specifies the effectiveness of the instruments controlled by No. 1 with respect to his "own" noncontrolled variables, R_{21} the effectiveness of the same instruments with respect to the noncontrolled variables of No. 2, and so on. The coefficient matrices of the quadratic preference function are partitioned in the same way.

---

[1] See R. FRISCH, "A Complete Scheme for Computing All Direct and Cross Elasticities in a Model with Many Sectors," *Econometrica*, Vol. 27 (1959), pp. 177–196; R. H. STROTZ, "The Empirical Implications of a Utility Tree," *ibidem*, Vol. 25 (1957), pp. 269–280; H. S. HOUTHAKKER, "Additive Preferences," *ibidem*, Vol. 28 (1960), pp. 244–257. See also W. M. GORMAN, "Separable Utility and Aggregation," *ibidem*, Vol. 27 (1959), pp. 469–488; further, the notes added to this article by Strotz and Gorman.

The optimal decision is $x^0 = -K^{-1}k$, where K is the sum of the four matrices A, $R'BR$, CR and $R'C'$. In partitioned form these matrices are:

$$A = \begin{bmatrix} A_{11} & A_{12} \\ A_{21} & A_{22} \end{bmatrix}$$

$$R'BR = \begin{bmatrix} R'_{11}B_{11}R_{11}+R'_{21}B_{21}R_{11}+R'_{11}B_{12}R_{21}+R'_{21}B_{22}R_{21} \\ R'_{12}B_{11}R_{11}+R'_{22}B_{21}R_{11}+R'_{12}B_{12}R_{21}+R'_{22}B_{22}R_{21} \end{bmatrix.$$

$$\begin{matrix} R'_{11}B_{11}R_{12}+R'_{21}B_{21}R_{12}+R'_{11}B_{12}R_{22}+R'_{21}B_{22}R_{22} \\ R'_{12}B_{11}R_{12}+R'_{22}B_{21}R_{12}+R'_{12}B_{12}R_{22}+R'_{22}B_{22}R_{22} \end{bmatrix}$$

$$CR = \begin{bmatrix} C_{11}R_{11}+C_{12}R_{21} & C_{11}R_{12}+C_{12}R_{22} \\ C_{21}R_{11}+C_{22}R_{21} & C_{21}R_{12}+C_{22}R_{22} \end{bmatrix}$$

$$R'C' = (CR)'.$$

We have to invert the sum of these four matrices and to postmultiply the inverse by k, which can be written as the sum of

$$\begin{bmatrix} a_1+R'_{11}b_1+(C_{11}+R'_{11}B_{11})s_1 \\ a_2+R'_{22}b_2+(C_{22}+R'_{22}B_{22})s_2 \end{bmatrix} \tag{1.10}$$

and

$$\begin{bmatrix} R'_{21}(b_2+B_{21}s_1+B_{22}s_2)+(C_{12}+R'_{11}B_{12})s_2 \\ R'_{12}(b_1+B_{11}s_1+B_{12}s_2)+(C_{21}+R'_{22}B_{21})s_1 \end{bmatrix}.$$

Now if we carry out the partitioned inversion of K, the resulting inverse is a complete mixture of all elements of $A_{11}, A_{12}, \ldots, B_{11}, B_{12}, \ldots$; and if we then postmultiply by k, it turns out that the optimal decisions x_1^0 and x_2^0 cannot at all be separated in terms of determining parameters which belong to the decision makers separately. This is the general case. The special case is the one in which the matrices

$$A_{12}, B_{12}, C_{12}, C_{21}, R_{12}, R_{21} \tag{1.11}$$

are all zero matrices. Then K is block-diagonal with leading block

$$A_{11}+R'_{11}B_{11}R_{11}+C_{11}R_{11}+R'_{11}C'_{11}$$

(the lower right-hand block is the same except that the index 1 is replaced by 2) and k becomes simply the vector (1.10). It follows immediately that the special case is characterized by

$$x_1^0 = -(A_{11}+R'_{11}B_{11}R_{11}+C_{11}R_{11}+R'_{11}C'_{11})^{-1} \times [a_1+R'_{11}b_1+(C_{11}+R'_{11}B_{11})s_1]$$

and similarly for the optimal decision x_2^0 of decision maker No. 2. In the special case, therefore, there is a complete separation of the two decision processes.

The crucial point is of course to what extent the zero values of the matrices (1.11) can be considered realistic. Regarding the coefficient matrices of the preference function (A_{12}, B_{12}, C_{12}, C_{21}), the condition implies that the marginal utilities of the variables of decision maker No. i should be independent of the variables of No. j, $i \neq j$. This condition is satisfied by the preference function of the American anti-depression case of Sections 3.1 and 6.1, since the marginal utility of every variable depends on that variable only. It is also satisfied by the three Dutch preference functions of Section 6.2, provided that we partition the variables such that the same variable in different years is in the hands of one decision maker; this proviso must be made because the marginal utilities of certain variables depend on earlier and later values of the same variable. The condition is *not* satisfied by the cost function of the paint factory, since the production and work force instruments are interrelated at the cost level due to the desirability of operating close to capacity, see (3.2.3) and (3.2.11).

Regarding the zero values of the matrices R_{12} and R_{21}, this condition implies that the instruments controlled by decision maker No. i should not affect the noncontrolled variables of No. j, $i \neq j$. It is easily seen that this condition is met by the paint factory case when we imagine that the factory manager is replaced by a production-inventory manager and a personnel manager. It is not satisfied by the macroeconomic applications, since all instruments affect all noncontrolled variables. Therefore, the conclusion is that in the cases considered here it is impossible to partition the variables of the problem in the way indicated above, either because these variables are interrelated at the level of utility evaluation ($A_{12} \neq \mathbf{0}$, $B_{12} \neq \mathbf{0}, \ldots$) or because they are interrelated at the purely instrumental level ($R_{12} \neq \mathbf{0}$, $R_{21} \neq \mathbf{0}$).[1] Of course, it is conceivable that this interrelation is of limited quantitative significance. There is an indication of that kind in Section 6.2, where it was found that the wage rate is primarily effective with respect to the price level of consumption goods (see Table 6.16), the importance of this instrument for other noncontrolled variables being rather moderate. If it is also true that the effectiveness of other

[1] Note that the additive-utility case discussed above is also characterized by interrelation in the latter sense (because of the budget constraint).

instruments with respect to the price level is of secondary importance, a separate wage-price policy can be expected to lead to a rather small loss; in fact, it is not at all difficult to compute such a loss. When the zero condition on the matrices (1.11) is violated more seriously it becomes important to co-ordinate the members of the team more closely, but this is a topic which is beyond the scope of this book.[1]

7.1.4. The Case of Independent Decision Makers

Consider two duopolists, No. 1 and No. 2. They supply one product each; the cost functions are linear and the demand for each product is a linear function of both prices. Hence:

$$K_i(q_i) = \alpha_i + \beta_i q_i; \quad q_i = \gamma_i + \delta_{ii} p_i + \delta_{ij} p_j,$$

where q_i is the quantity produced and sold by No. i, p_i his price, p_j the price of the competitor, $K_i(q_i)$ the cost of producing and selling q_i units; the α's, β's, γ's and δ's are constant coefficients. Net profit of No. i is then

$$\text{(1.12)} \qquad \begin{aligned} p_i q_i - K_i(q_i) = & -(\alpha_i + \beta_i \gamma_i) + (\gamma_i - \beta_i \delta_{ii}) p_i - \beta_i \delta_{ij} p_j \\ & + \delta_{ii} p_i^2 + \delta_{ij} p_i p_j, \end{aligned}$$

i.e., it is a quadratic function of the two prices. We shall assume that each duopolist is interested in maximizing his own profit and that his price is his instrument.

The difficulty is, of course, that both preference functions depend on an instrument which is controlled by the competitor. The two could come to an agreement and fix the prices at a level which maximizes combined total profit; but we shall suppose that they prefer to retain their independence and to make their individual price policies dependent on the expected reaction of the rival. This is the "conjectural" approach. Specifically, No. i tries to maximize his quadratic profit function by adjusting his price p_i, but when doing so he must take account of the fact that such a change in p_i will in general induce a change in his rival's price p_j. Now suppose that No. i proceeds under the assumption that p_j varies linearly with p_i. Then his problem is to maximize a quadratic preference

---

[1] For further reading we mention J. Marschak, "Elements for a Theory of Teams," *Management Science*, Vol. 1 (1955), pp. 127–137; R. Radner, "Team Decision Problems," *The Annals of Mathematical Statistics*, Vol. 33 (1962), pp. 857–881. The latter article considers in particular the case of quadratic preference functions.

function subject to a linear constraint; and we know from Chapter 4 that, if this maximization problem is formulated in dynamic terms, this leads to a linear decision rule for p_i. But suppose that No. j does precisely the same thing (with indices i and j interchanged); then there is a linear decision rule for p_j too, which is precisely the assumption under which No. i proceeds.

A result of this kind holds more generally when we imagine a society of N decision-making units, all of which have quadratic preference functions which are maximized subject to linear constraints. Some of these constraints will have nothing to do with behaviour patterns of other decision makers, such as technical constraints (e.g., production functions); but some do. More precisely, part of the constraints subject to which decision maker No. i maximizes his preference function is of the non-behavioural type, but another part deals with the ideas which No. i has about the decision rules followed by decision makers No. j, k, ... Suppose then that the non-behavioural constraints are all linear; suppose also that No. i proceeds under the assumption that No. j, k, . . . follow linear decision rules. Then No. i's task is to maximize a quadratic preference function subject to linear constraints and the result is that he follows a linear decision rule himself. If this procedure is followed by all decision makers, so that everyone assumes that all others behave linearly, then it is indeed true that everybody behaves linearly. We may therefore say that quadratic preference functions combined with the assumption of linear decision rules followed by others lead to some kind of "social harmony." But this harmony is not necessarily perfect. It would be perfect if No. i's ideas about the decision rule followed by No. j are identical with the decision rule which is actually followed by the latter, for all combinations (i, j). This, however, is more than one can reasonably expect.

7.1.5. Summary

(1) Some alternative multi-person situations are mentioned. One is the case in which a person adjusts his preferences to those of another person (his employer); the second deals with a team of persons working for a common goal; the third with committee decisions; the fourth with independent decision makers. The third case will be considered in Section 7.2, the three others are discussed briefly in Section 7.1.

(2) A research manager is taken as a typical example of a person who adjusts his preferences to those of his employer. The starting point is the

assumption that the latter has quadratic preferences and linear constraints and is imperfectly informed about the coefficients of these functions. This leads to an objective function of the research manager which is linear in the second moments of the errors of these coefficients. The procedure is illustrated by means of a simple production-inventory example.

(3) Team decision problems, too, are analyzed under conditions of quadratic preferences and linear constraints; in particular it is asked to what extent it is possible to partition the decision process without the necessity of co-ordinating the members of the team.

(4) Two duopolists are taken as an example of independent decision makers. The results suggest that a further analysis of a set of decision-making units, all characterized by quadratic preference functions and an assumed linearity of decision rules followed by others, is very promising.

7.2. ON THE DESIGN OF COMMITTEE DECISIONS [1]

7.2.1. Introduction; Arrow's Postulates

We shall now consider in somewhat more detail the problems which arise when a committee is the decision-making unit. It has to maximize a committee preference function subject to certain constraints, but before this is possible the members of this committee have to agree on the specification of the preference function. It will be assumed that not all members have the same preferences, because otherwise the problem is trivial.

A convenient starting point is ARROW'S wellknown monograph *Social Choice and Individual Values.* He considers a number of individual preference orderings which should form the basis of the committee preference ordering. Thus, going back to 1.1.1 and 1.1.2, let there be three alternatives, A, B and C, then the objective is to formulate a committee preference ordering among these three; e.g., the committee prefers A to B and B to C. The committee may consist of three members, say, to be denoted by P, Q and R. If all agree there is no problem, since it is then natural to make the committee preference ordering identical with the three individual orderings. So suppose that P and Q prefer A to B and B to C, while R prefers B to A and A to C. The problem is then no

---

[1] This section is largely based on H. THEIL, "On the Symmetry Approach to the Committee Decision Problem," *Management Science*, Vol. 9 (1963), pp. 380–393; and P. J. M. VAN DEN BOGAARD and J. VERSLUIS, "The Design of Optimal Committee Decisions," *Statistica Neerlandica*, Vol. 16 (1962), pp. 271–289.

longer trivial. A way out is the method of majority decision: there is a majority (P and Q versus R) preferring A to B and all prefer B to C, so this particular method implies a committee preference of A over B and of B over C. But this method does not always work. Suppose that P prefers A to B and B to C; Q prefers B to C and C to A; R prefers C to A and A to B. Then there is a majority (P and R) preferring A to B; there is another majority (P and Q) preferring B to C; and a third majority (Q and R) preferring C to A. Hence the committee preference system based on the majority rule is now no longer transitive and ceases to represent a true ordering.

Arrow's approach amounts to the introduction of a number of postulates which the committee preference system ought to satisfy. One is that this system should be transitive. Another is that the individual preferences and the committee preferences ought to be positively related, or at least not negatively. Specifically, suppose that one member of the committee changes his preferences in the sense that he now prefers B to A, whereas originally he had preferred A to B. This may or may not change the committee preference ordering; but if there is a change, we should require that this alteration does not lead to an improvement of A relative to B in the committee preference scale. A third postulate is known as "the independence of irrelevant alternatives" and can be described as follows. Let $A, B, C, \ldots$ be the available alternatives and let the individual preference orderings be such that alternative X is the first on the committee's scale, given a particular way of deriving a committee preference ordering from the individual orderings. Let X be different from A and suppose that for some reason A ceases to be an available alternative. Then nothing changes except that A is canceled; and the postulate requires that X is first on the committee's scale as before. As an example we take the square-root scoring method: each committee member ranks the n alternatives in decreasing order, the best alternative gets the score $n^{\frac{1}{2}}$, the next-best $(n-1)^{\frac{1}{2}}$, and so on, and the alternative with the highest total score is chosen by the committee. Let the scores be as follows:

	A	B	C
P	$\sqrt{2}$	1	$\sqrt{3}$
Q	1	$\sqrt{3}$	$\sqrt{2}$
R	1	$\sqrt{3}$	$\sqrt{2}$

The score totals are A, 3.41; B, 4.46; C, 4.56. Hence C is chosen by the committee. But if A is deleted (which all three consider inferior to C!) the score total of B becomes 3.83 and that of C, 3.41; hence the committee prefers B to C. Therefore, the square-root scoring method does not satisfy the requirement of independence of irrelevant alternatives.

Finally, there are two postulates which serve to exclude committee preference orderings which are constructed in a very one-sided manner. The condition of nondictatorship is one of them; it implies that the committee ordering should not be determined, partly or wholly, by the preferences of only one of the members. The second requires that the committee ordering should not be imposed (partly or wholly) in the sense that it is determined by considerations beyond the preferences of the members, such as taboos, etc.

The main result of Arrow's analysis is that if the number of alternatives is two, the method of majority decision leads to a committee preference ordering which satisfies all postulates; and if the number is three or more, the members of the committee being free to order these alternatives in any way, there exists no committee preference ordering which obeys all these postulates simultaneously. In other words, a method which meets all requirements except that of nondictatorship is necessarily dictatorial; a method which meets all requirements except the condition of independence of irrelevant alternatives must violate that condition; and so on.

7.2.2. Linear Combination of Individual Preference Functions

The negative result just mentioned is certainly of great interest, but since committee decisions have to be made on a large scale in the real world it is worthwhile to continue the analysis in the hope that some more positive results can be obtained.

From now on we shall write $\mathbf{x}$ for the vector of instruments to be manipulated by the committee; its components may or may not be real-valued. We shall consider the general situation of uncertain prospects, so that the consequences of any given committee decision are partly determined by a probability mechanism. It will be assumed that the preferences of all committee members satisfy the Von Neumann-Morgenstern axioms, so that each can be said to be interested in maximizing expected utility, where "utility" refers to an individual preference function (unique up to a linear transformation, see 1.3.6). Let us write w_g for such a preference function, $g = 1, \ldots, G$; G being the number of members of the committee; then $\mathscr{E}w_g(\mathbf{x})$ is No. g's evaluation of $\mathbf{x}$ as committee decision. For example, we may have the situation in which all committee members have quadratic preference functions:

$$w_g(\mathbf{x}) = \mathbf{k}_g'\mathbf{x} + \tfrac{1}{2}\mathbf{x}'\mathbf{K}_g\mathbf{x} \qquad (g = 1, \ldots, G) \tag{2.1}$$

(apart from an irrelevant constant term). Of course, we may also have quadratic preference functions in committee instruments and noncontrolled variables, the latter being linearly related to the former in terms of linear constraints. But the exposition will be simplified if we agree to eliminate the noncontrolled variables as arguments of the preference function by using these constraints.

The problem of uncertainty has to be faced by the members but also by the committee as a whole. The easiest way to handle this is to require, as HARSANYI did,[1] that the committee preference system which we are going to derive satisfies the Von Neumann-Morgenstern axioms as well. That is, the committee is supposed to maximize expected "social" utility and the underlying committee preference function is then unique up to a linear transformation, too. Harsanyi imposed another, very plausible, condition on the committee preference system: Whenever each of the G members is indifferent between any two prospects, then the committee should also be indifferent between them. These conditions are sufficient, as Harsanyi showed, for the conclusion that the committee preference function is a *linear combination* of the individual preference functions. He showed also that the weights of this combination are necessarily positive when the following condition is imposed: Whenever one of the committee members prefers A to B while none of the members prefers B to A, the committee should prefer A to B. This condition is of course closely related to Arrow's postulate of a positive relation between individual and committee preferences.

We shall accept these conditions in what follows, which means that our committee preference function will be a linear combination of the individual preference functions with positive weights. Thus, if the latter functions are all quadratic as in (2.1), so will our committee preference function be. Our task is to find an appropriate rule for the determination of the weights of the combination; or better, for their ratios, since these are the things that matter. Now since the individual preference functions

---

[1] J. C. HARSANYI, "Cardinal Welfare, Individualistic Ethics, and Interpersonal Comparisons of Utility," *Journal of Political Economy*, Vol. 63 (1955), pp. 309–321. For a criticism of this condition, see J. F. ROTHENBERG, *The Measurement of Social Welfare* (Englewood Cliffs, N. J., 1961), Chapter 10.

are unique up to a linear transformation, they have all two arbitrary features (a zero and a unit); and we shall be able to simplify the exposition if we agree to replace utility by disutility. More precisely, let us write $w_g(\mathbf{x}_g^0)$ for the highest utility level which is available to committee member No. g, where $\mathbf{x}_g^0$ is the best decision from his point of view. For example, we have $\mathbf{x}_g^0 = -\mathbf{K}_g^{-1}\mathbf{k}_g$ when (2.1) is his preference function and $\mathbf{K}_g$ is negative definite. Then

$$l_g(\mathbf{x}) = w_g(\mathbf{x}_g^0) - w_g(\mathbf{x}) \tag{2.2}$$

is the loss suffered by No. g when $\mathbf{x}$ is the decision made by the committee, and

$$l_C(\mathbf{x}) = \sum_{g=1}^{G} d_g l_g(\mathbf{x}) \tag{2.3}$$

is the committee loss function, the d_g being the (positive) weights which we shall have to derive. Note that these loss functions have all natural zeros, their only arbitrariness being their units of measurement; they are all unique up to a homogeneous linear transformation. Note also that we have made the implicit assumption that all individual preference functions have a unique maximum, $\mathbf{x}_g^0$. This is not necessary for the existence of the loss functions (it is sufficient that the preference functions have finite upper bounds), but it will be necessary for the definition of the loss matrix which will be introduced in 7.2.3. Note finally that we have defined (as in previous chapters) losses in terms of the preference functions themselves, not in terms of their expectations. When applying our ideas to uncertain prospects we shall have to make an adjustment, which however will turn out to be of minor importance; see 7.2.6 below.

7.2.3. Loads, Raw Loss Functions, and the Loss Matrix

We can describe (2.3) by saying that the committee loss function is a weighted sum of the individual loss functions. There is no formal objection to doing so, but it has the disadvantage that a weighting procedure of the committee members is suggested in the same way as a weighted price index number is obtained by treating prices of important commodities differently from those of less important commodities. Evidently, this is not what we mean by "weighted sum of individual loss functions." What we wish to do is to treat all individuals "equally" (in accordance with fairly generally accepted ethical standards), but it must be admitted that at the present stage it is not very clear what "equally" really means.

However, there is an easy way to avoid the expression "weighted sum." We recall that $l_g(\mathbf{x})$ is unique up to a homogeneous linear transformation, so that No. g's preferences are perfectly well described by any positive multiple of $l_g(\mathbf{x})$. Now let us choose d_g for that multiple, then $d_g l_g(\mathbf{x})$ is "the" loss function of No. g and the committee loss function is simply the sum (unweighted) of all these, see (2.3). The original functions l_g are then merely auxiliary concepts. They will be called the "raw" loss functions and have to be multiplied by the appropriate d_g—to be called the "load" of the raw loss function—in order to yield the corresponding individual loss function.

Our problem is to formulate an adequate rule for the numerical specification of the loads. There are in principle two possibilities. The loads are either determined by the ingredients which have been introduced until now (which amounts effectively to a determination by raw loss functions), or they are partly or wholly determined by "outside" ingredients such as side payments from one committee member to another. Here we shall exclude the latter possibility and confine ourselves to the former. This means that each load d_g becomes a function of G functions, viz., of the G individual raw loss functions:

$$d_g = f_g\{l_1, \ldots, l_g, \ldots, l_G\}. \tag{2.4}$$

Such a function of functions is usually called a functional, which is the term that will be used in what follows.

The committee loss function takes now the form:

$$l_C(\mathbf{x}) = \sum_{g=1}^{G} f_g\{l_1, \ldots, l_g, \ldots, l_G\} l_g(\mathbf{x}), \tag{2.5}$$

from which it is evident that we should impose certain restrictions on the functionals f_g. For suppose that we multiply the individual raw loss function l_g by some positive number c. This should leave the committee loss function unchanged because nobody's preferences are changed, hence the corresponding f_g should be multiplied by $1/c$ and the other f's should remain as they are. It follows that the dependence of f_g on l_g is different from that on the "alien" raw loss functions l_h, $h \neq g$. In fact, considerations of symmetry should convince us to choose for the f_g a functional f (the same for all g) which is symmetric in the alien l_h. It is convenient to introduce a $(G-1)$-element row vector $\mathbf{m}_g$ containing all l_h except the gth:

$$\mathbf{m}_g = [l_1 \ldots l_{g-1} \quad l_{g+1} \ldots l_G]; \tag{2.6}$$

then our functional f_g can be written as follows:

$$f_g\{l_1, \ldots, l_g, \ldots, l_G\} \equiv f\{l_g; \mathbf{m}_g\} \text{ for } g = 1, \ldots, G. \tag{2.7}$$

If f is to be symmetric in the alien raw loss functions, we should have

$$f\{l_g; \mathbf{m}_g \mathbf{\Pi}\} \equiv f\{l_g; \mathbf{m}_g\}, \tag{2.8}$$

where $\mathbf{\Pi}$ is any permutation matrix of order $G-1$. Furthermore, if multiplication of l_g by c should lead to multiplication of f_g by $1/c$ and to unchanged values of f_h, $h \neq g$, then the functional f should be homogeneous of degree -1 in l_g and homogeneous of degree 0 in $\mathbf{m}_g$:

$$f\{cl_g; \mathbf{m}_g \mathbf{C}\} \equiv \frac{1}{c} f\{l_g; \mathbf{m}_g\}, \tag{2.9}$$

where c is a positive real number and $\mathbf{C}$ a $(G-1)\times(G-1)$ diagonal matrix whose diagonal elements are also positive and real.

We can make the situation more concrete by considering a simple example. Let the committee consist of G persons whose task is to determine the typical height of the group. Person No. 1 announces: "My height is 172 centimeters and that's typical." No. 2 replies: "No, my height is 180 centimeters and I think that's typical. If No. 1 insists on 172 centimeters he is 8 centimeters in error." This continues with everyone arguing that he is of typical height. The result (for $G = 3$) may be summarized by the following error matrix:

	Height of		
Viewpoint of	No. 1 (172)	No. 2 (180)	No. 3 (179)
No. 1	0	8	7
No. 2	−8	0	−1
No. 3	−7	1	0

How is this problem solved? We shall consider two solutions, the median and the arithmetic mean, and show that they can both be justified in terms of the ideas set forth in the preceding pages. We notice, first of all, that none of the persons is satisfied with any other height than his own as the typical height. Suppose then that No. g's loss in case some value is accepted at the typical height can be measured by d_g times the absolute difference between his own height and the proposed typical height, where d_g (for $g = 1, 2, \ldots$) is a positive load. Then, if somebody succeeds in imposing his height as the typical height, he causes a loss to the others as shown by the following matrix, to be called the "loss matrix":

	Imposed height of		
Loss suffered by	No. 1 (172)	No. 2 (180)	No. 3 (179)
No. 1	0	$8d_1$	$7d_1$
No. 2	$8d_2$	0	d_2
No. 3	$7d_3$	d_3	0

Going back to the general terminology, the typical $(g, h)^{th}$ element of the loss matrix is $d_g l_g(\mathbf{x}_h^0)$. Given the loads and the individual preference functions, its elements are well-defined when the latter have unique maxima. The elements of the loss matrix are always nonnegative and the diagonal elements are all zero.

The optimal committee decision is that height which minimizes the sum of the individual losses for some suitable choice of the loads. The approach of the median is to take equal d's (e.g., $d_g = 1$ for all g), so that the loss matrix becomes:

$$\begin{bmatrix} 0 & 8 & 7 \\ 8 & 0 & 1 \\ 7 & 1 & 0 \end{bmatrix}. \tag{2.10}$$

We may also say that we have adjusted the d's such that the loss matrix is symmetric. It is wellknown that in this case the median (the height of No. 3, 179 centimeters) minimizes total disutility. By adding the elements of each column we obtain the committee loss which each member of the committee causes in case he succeeds in imposing his own optimal decision. These three committee losses are 15, 9, and 8 centimeters and the last value is also the minimum attainable. It is worthwhile to note that this procedure falls under our general approach and is in fact a special case. Firstly, the loads are determined by the raw loss functions as (2.4) prescribes, since they can be said to be determined by the requirement of a symmetric loss matrix (which in turn is completely determined by the individual raw loss functions for any given set of d's). Secondly, it is obvious that the loads are obtained in a perfectly symmetrical way and that they are not affected by the order in which the committee members are arranged; hence (2.7) and (2.8) are satisfied. Finally, suppose that No. g decides to multiply his raw losses by 10, so that these are now expressed in millimeters rather than in centimeters. The only change is from $d_g = 1$ to $d_g = 0.1$, all other d's and the loss matrix (2.10) and the committee loss function remaining unchanged.[1] Hence condition (2.9) is satisfied as well.

The approach of the arithmetic mean is completely similar except that it is based on the idea that No. g's loss can be measured by d_g times the square of the difference between his height and the proposed typical height. The loss matrix is then:

	Imposed height of		
Loss suffered by	No. 1 (172)	No. 2 (180)	No. 3 (179)
No. 1	0	$64d_1$	$49d_1$
No. 2	$64d_2$	0	d_2
No. 3	$49d_3$	d_3	0

Again, we take equal d's. Putting $d_g = 1$ we obtain a symmetric loss matrix as before:

$$\begin{bmatrix} 0 & 64 & 49 \\ 64 & 0 & 1 \\ 49 & 1 & 0 \end{bmatrix}. \tag{2.11}$$

Then, by minimizing the committee loss function (the sum of squares of the discrepancies with the three actual heights) we arrive at the arithmetic mean, which is 177 centimeters in this case. The three committee losses associated with the individual optimal decisions are now 113, 65, and 50 (all in centimeters squared); these values are all larger than the attainable minimum, which is 38 square centimeters.

7.2.4. *The Desirability of a Symmetric Loss Matrix*

Our position can be briefly described in the following terms. The optimal committee decision is the $\mathbf{x}$ which minimizes the committee loss function (2.3) for some suitable choice of the loads d_g. We decided to confine the attention to the case in which these loads are functionals of the individual raw loss functions and it appeared that it is reasonable to impose certain constraints on the form of these functionals, see (2.7)–(2.9). Then we considered a simple example (mean and median as measures of central tendency of a frequency distribution) and it turned out that this is indeed a special case of the approach adopted here, but with

[1] This argument shows that it is better to say that the approach of the median is based on a symmetric loss matrix than on equal d's.

the following additional specifications: (i) the loads are not functionals of the raw loss functions but simply functions of the values which these functions take for particular argument values, viz., for all G individual optimal decisions; and (ii) the loads are chosen in such a way that the loss matrix becomes symmetric.

The question arises whether these specifications have certain merits with respect to our problem. Regarding (i)—functions instead of functionals—, we shall indeed adopt this restriction in what follows, partly on pragmatic and partly on intuitive grounds. We simplify the problem considerably by focusing on load functions rather than load functionals [1] and one should expect that the $G(G-1)$ off-diagonal elements of the loss matrix supply sufficient information about the structure of the individual preferences. Furthermore, one might argue that the individual optimal decisions $\mathbf{x}_1^0, \ldots, \mathbf{x}_G^0$ lie on the "edge" of the set of interesting decisions from the committee's point of view, since each is committee-optimal in the limiting case when the corresponding d_g is positive and all others zero. In fact, there is a considerable class of decisions which are not Pareto-optimal and therefore irrelevant from the committee's point of view; such decisions should preferably not affect the loads via the dependence of the latter on the individual preferences.

These considerations lead us to simplify our approach accordingly. Some notational simplifications are obtained by writing

$$\lambda_{gh} = l_g(\mathbf{x}_h^0) \tag{2.12}$$

for the raw loss inflicted on No. g by No. h's optimal decision, so that the condition of symmetry is then written as follows:

$$d_g \lambda_{gh} = d_h \lambda_{hg} \text{ for all pairs } (g, h). \tag{2.13}$$

Further, we shall write $\boldsymbol{\lambda}_g$ for the G-element column vector of elements λ_{gh} and $\boldsymbol{\Lambda}_g$ for the $G \times (G-1)$ matrix of all columns $\boldsymbol{\lambda}_h$ except the gth:

$$\boldsymbol{\lambda}_g = \begin{bmatrix} \lambda_{g1} \\ \vdots \\ \lambda_{gG} \end{bmatrix}, \quad \boldsymbol{\Lambda}_g = [\boldsymbol{\lambda}_1 \ldots \boldsymbol{\lambda}_{g-1} \; \boldsymbol{\lambda}_{g+1} \ldots \boldsymbol{\lambda}_G]. \tag{2.14}$$

---

[1] This argument of simplicity is comparable with that used for the restriction to linearity in best linear unbiased statistical estimation. The main reason why estimators should be restricted to be linear is that of convenience. See *Economic Forecasts and Policy*, Second Edition, pp. 489–490.

Then our functional f of (2.7) becomes a function φ of $\boldsymbol{\lambda}_g$ and $\boldsymbol{\Lambda}_g$:

$$f\{l_g; \mathbf{m}_g\} \equiv \varphi(\boldsymbol{\lambda}_g; \boldsymbol{\Lambda}_g). \tag{2.15}$$

Our problem is now to find an appropriate rule for the function φ. Of course, φ should be homogeneous of degree -1 in $\boldsymbol{\lambda}_g$, homogeneous of degree 0 in $\boldsymbol{\Lambda}_g$, and symmetric in the $G-1$ columns of $\boldsymbol{\Lambda}_g$.

We shall now consider the symmetry condition (2.13), for we have not yet given any cogent argument in its favour. Consider then any committee member, say No. k, and suppose that he changes his mind (i.e., his preferences are changed) or that he leaves the committee; or, as a third alternative, that he becomes a new member of the committee. We should of course in general expect that such a change alters the form of the committee loss function (and hence also the optimal committee decision). But we should not expect that this change will affect the loss functions $d_g l_g(\mathbf{x})$ of the other individuals. The raw loss functions will not be affected (since these are simply the basic ingredients of our problem); but we require that the loads be unchanged, or better their ratios, d_g/d_h, since these alone are relevant.

THEOREM 7.1. *Consider an arbitrary load function* $d_g = \varphi(\boldsymbol{\lambda}_g; \boldsymbol{\Lambda}_g)$ *with the following properties*: (i) *Its arguments are the vectors* $\boldsymbol{\lambda}_1, \ldots, \boldsymbol{\lambda}_G$ *as specified in* (2.14) *and the* h^{th} *element of* $\boldsymbol{\lambda}_h$ *is zero and all others positive and real*; (ii) *it takes real and positive values only*; (iii) *it is homogeneous of degree* -1 *in* $\boldsymbol{\lambda}_g$, *homogeneous of degree* 0 *in* $\boldsymbol{\Lambda}_g$, *and symmetric in the* $G-1$ *columns of* $\boldsymbol{\Lambda}_g$. *Then the symmetry condition* (2.13) *is necessary and sufficient in order that the following requirement be met: The load ratio* d_g/d_h, *for any pair* (g, h), *shall not be affected if some third individual changes his preferences* [*that is,* d_g/d_h *shall be invariant against changes in* $\lambda_{kk'}$, *involving the preferences of individuals other than No.* g *and* h].

To prove this theorem,[1] which can be regarded as a justification of the symmetry condition, we consider any pair of committee members whom we shall indicate as No. 1 and No. 2 for notational simplicity. Their load ratio is $\varphi(\boldsymbol{\lambda}_1; \boldsymbol{\Lambda}_1)/\varphi(\boldsymbol{\lambda}_2; \boldsymbol{\Lambda}_2)$, which should be independent of the preferences of any third individual. The consequence of this require-

[1] It is of course trivial to show that, if the loss matrix is symmetric, the load ratio for any pair of individuals is independent of the preferences of any third individual. We therefore confine ourselves to the proof of the necessity of symmetry in order that the load ratio be independent of the preferences of third individuals.

ment is that the load ratio can depend on λ_{12} and λ_{21} only:

$$\frac{d_1}{d_2} \equiv \frac{\varphi(\boldsymbol{\lambda}_1; \boldsymbol{\Lambda}_1)}{\varphi(\boldsymbol{\lambda}_2; \boldsymbol{\Lambda}_2)} \equiv \psi(\lambda_{12}, \lambda_{21}). \tag{2.16}$$

For if we take any other element of the $G \times G$ matrix $[\lambda_{gh}]$ we introduce the preferences of some third individual, either because it measures a loss inflicted on such a person (λ_{k1} and λ_{k2} for $1 \neq k \neq 2$) or because it involves his optimal decision (λ_{1k} and λ_{2k}) or both. Furthermore, we have

$$\psi(\lambda_{21}, \lambda_{12}) \equiv \frac{1}{\psi(\lambda_{12}, \lambda_{21})}, \tag{2.17}$$

because interchanging the arguments of ψ amounts to taking the reciprocal of d_1/d_2. We conclude from (2.17):

$$\psi(a, a) \equiv 1 \quad \text{for all} \quad a > 0. \tag{2.18}$$

[The second solution is $\psi(a, a) = -1$, but this would imply that either d_1 or d_2 is negative, which is excluded by property (ii) of the theorem.] We proceed to make use of the homogeneity properties and write:

$$\varphi\left(\frac{1}{\lambda_{12}}\boldsymbol{\lambda}_1; \frac{1}{\lambda_{21}}\boldsymbol{\lambda}_2, \boldsymbol{\lambda}_3, \ldots, \boldsymbol{\lambda}_G\right) \equiv \lambda_{12}\varphi(\boldsymbol{\lambda}_1; \boldsymbol{\Lambda}_1)$$

$$\varphi\left(\frac{1}{\lambda_{21}}\boldsymbol{\lambda}_2; \frac{1}{\lambda_{12}}\boldsymbol{\lambda}_1, \boldsymbol{\lambda}_3, \ldots, \boldsymbol{\lambda}_G\right) \equiv \lambda_{21}\varphi(\boldsymbol{\lambda}_2; \boldsymbol{\Lambda}_2).$$

Now the two φ's on the left have λ_{12} and λ_{21}-values which are 1, so that (2.18) is applicable (with $a = 1$). Therefore,

$$1 = \frac{\lambda_{12}\varphi(\boldsymbol{\lambda}_1; \boldsymbol{\Lambda}_1)}{\lambda_{21}\varphi(\boldsymbol{\lambda}_2; \boldsymbol{\Lambda}_2)} = \frac{\lambda_{12} d_1}{\lambda_{21} d_2},$$

i.e., the symmetry condition $d_1\lambda_{12} = d_2\lambda_{21}$. This proves the theorem, given that No. 1 and No. 2 stand for an arbitrary pair of committee members.

7.2.5. Symmetry Cannot Always Be Attained

It will be noticed that we have assumed that both λ_{12} and λ_{21} are positive [in accordance with property (i) of Theorem 7.1]. Suppose, however, that one of them (say λ_{12}) is zero while the other is positive. It is easily seen that No. 1 does not have a unique optimal decision in that case; for if there would be a unique $\mathbf{x}_1^0$, it must be equal to $\mathbf{x}_2^0$ because $\lambda_{12} = 0$, but in fact it is different from $\mathbf{x}_2^0$ because $\lambda_{21} > 0$. This means that our approach breaks down since the definition of the loss matrix requires unique individual optimal decisions.

Suppose now that λ_{12} and λ_{21} are both zero. When we have a two-person committee the loss matrix is a 2×2 zero matrix, which means that this matrix is trivially symmetric for any values of the d's. In other words, the symmetry condition does not lead to a well-defined committee loss function in that case—except of course when the individual raw loss functions are identical (apart from a multiplicative constant), in which case the committee loss function coincides with both. When $G = 3$, the specification $\lambda_{12} = \lambda_{21} = 0$ leads to the following loss matrix:

$$\begin{bmatrix} 0 & 0 & d_1\lambda_{13} \\ 0 & 0 & d_2\lambda_{23} \\ d_3\lambda_{31} & d_3\lambda_{32} & 0 \end{bmatrix}.$$

Assuming that the optimal decisions of No. 1 and No. 2 are both unique, we must conclude that they are identical and also that the corresponding losses suffered by No. 3, $d_3\lambda_{31}$ and $d_3\lambda_{32}$, are identical as well. Symmetry requires:

$$d_1\lambda_{13} = d_2\lambda_{23} = \lambda_{31} = \lambda_{32},$$

where d_3 is used as the *numéraire*. When these four λ's are all positive we obtain unique solutions for d_1 and d_2.

Summarizing, we can say that the case $\lambda_{gh} = 0$, $\lambda_{hg} > 0$ cannot be handled by our approach; that for $G = 2$ the case $\lambda_{12} = \lambda_{21} = 0$ leads to a well-defined committee loss function if and only if $l_1(\mathbf{x})$ and $l_2(\mathbf{x})$ are identical (possibly apart from a multiplicative constant); [1] and that for $G = 3$ this case leads to unique d-ratios and hence to a well-defined committee loss function when all four other off-diagonal λ's are positive. When we consider the case $\lambda_{12} = \lambda_{21} = 0$ for $G = 4$ we face the problem of "too many" symmetry conditions. In fact, this problem exists in general. The number of symmetry conditions (2.13) is $\frac{1}{2}G(G-1)$; that of the d-ratios—which should be adjusted in order that these conditions be satisfied—is only $G-1$. So we should expect that the loss matrix cannot in general be made symmetric as soon as the committee consists

---

[1] One can nevertheless regard the common optimal decision of No. 1 and No. 2 as the optimal committee decision even if $l_1(\mathbf{x})$ and $l_2(\mathbf{x})$ are different, since it is the only decision which meets the condition of Pareto optimality.

of three persons or more. There are exceptions, of course, as in the case of the mean and the median considered in 7.2.3; but in the general case it is not possible to realize symmetry for $G \geqq 3$.

Now if it is agreed that symmetry of the loss matrix is a desirable condition and if it is impossible to realize symmetry, then a plausible procedure is to approximate symmetry. This can be done in a variety of ways. Hence there is a certain amount of freedom as to the procedure to be used, but it has to meet the following requirements: (i) it leads to a symmetric loss matrix in case symmetry can be attained; (ii) it approximates symmetry in a well-defined sense in case exact symmetry cannot be attained; (iii) it satisfies the conditions set forth in 7.2.3, i.e., it leads to positive load ratios and the loads should have the appropriate homogeneity characteristics (homogeneous of degree -1 in the corresponding raw loss function, etc.).

VAN DEN BOGAARD suggested making corresponding row and column sums of the loss matrix pairwise equal: [1]

$$\sum_h d_g \lambda_{gh} = \sum_h d_h \lambda_{hg} \text{ for } g = 1, \ldots, G; \tag{2.19}$$

or in vector form:

$$\begin{bmatrix} -\sum \lambda_{1h} & \lambda_{21} & \cdots & \lambda_{G1} \\ \lambda_{12} & -\sum \lambda_{2h} & \cdots & \lambda_{G2} \\ \vdots & \vdots & & \vdots \\ \lambda_{1G} & \lambda_{2G} & \cdots & -\sum \lambda_{Gh} \end{bmatrix} \mathbf{d} = \mathbf{0}, \tag{2.20}$$

where $\mathbf{d}$ is the column vector of the loads $d_1, \ldots, d_G$. He proved the following

THEOREM 7.2. *For any* $G \times G$ *matrix* $[\lambda_{gh}]$ *with zero diagonal elements and positive and real off-diagonal elements there exists a vector* $\mathbf{d} = [d_g]$ *satisfying* (2.19), *which is unique apart from an arbitrary multiplicative scalar and which is the characteristic vector of the* $G \times G$ *matrix on the left of* (2.20) *corresponding with the (unique) zero root. This vector has elements whose ratios are all positive and ensures symmetry of the matrix* $[d_g \lambda_{gh}]$ *whenever a vector ensuring symmetry exists. For each* $g = 1, \ldots, G$, *the* g^{th} *element of this vector is homogeneous of degree* -1 *in the* g^{th} *column of the matrix* $[\lambda_{gh}]$, *homogeneous of degree* 0 *in all other columns, and symmetric in the* $G-1$ *columns of* $\mathbf{\Lambda}_g$.

---

[1] P. J. M. VAN DEN BOGAARD and J. VERSLUIS, "The Design of Optimal Committee Decisions," *Statistica Neerlandica*, Vol. 16 (1962), pp. 271–289.

The proof is as follows. By adding the G rows of the square matrix on the left of (2.20) we obtain a row consisting of zeros, which means that the rank of this matrix is at most $G-1$. Therefore, (2.20) has at least one nonzero solution for $\mathbf{d}$. To show that all components of this solution are of one sign (positive, say), we start by assuming that the first k components, $d_1, \ldots, d_k$, are negative or zero, all others being positive. (There is no loss in generality in taking the first k, since we can always rearrange the order of the committee members.) Hence $d_1 = -|d_1|, \ldots, d_k = -|d_k|$ with some or all $d_1, \ldots, d_k$ equal to zero. The first k equations of (2.20) can then be written as follows:

$$\begin{aligned} |d_1|\textstyle\sum\lambda_{1h} - |d_2|\lambda_{21} - \ldots - |d_k|\lambda_{k1} + c_1 &= 0 \\ -|d_1|\lambda_{12} + |d_2|\textstyle\sum\lambda_{2h} - \ldots - |d_k|\lambda_{k2} + c_2 &= 0 \\ &\vdots \\ -|d_1|\lambda_{1k} - |d_2|\lambda_{2k} - \ldots + |d_k|\textstyle\sum\lambda_{kh} + c_k &= 0, \end{aligned}$$

where $c_1 = \sum d_h \lambda_{h1}$, $c_2 = \sum d_h \lambda_{h2}$, and so on, the h-summation being from $k+1$ to G. Note that all c's are positive since they involve positive d's and λ's.

By adding these k linear equations we obtain:

$$|d_1| \sum_{h=k+1}^{G} \lambda_{1h} + \ldots + |d_k| \sum_{h=k+1}^{G} \lambda_{kh} + \sum_{h=1}^{k} c_h = 0.$$

Now $\sum c_h$ is positive as we just saw, except of course when $k = G$, in which case $\sum c_h = 0$. It follows that there is only one possibility for this result to be valid if $k > 0$, viz., when all d's are zero. But we know that there is a nonzero solution for $\mathbf{d}$ and for this solution, therefore, we must have $k = 0$; i.e., all its components are positive.

We must now show that this nonzero solution is unique. Let us assume that there are r linearly independent solutions, $\mathbf{d}^{(1)}, \ldots, \mathbf{d}^{(r)}$. We know from the preceding paragraph that the elements of all these are positive. The general solution can then be written as

$$\mathbf{d}^* = a_1\mathbf{d}^{(1)} + \ldots + a_r\mathbf{d}^{(r)}$$

for any choice of the a's. Now choose the a's in such a way that the first component of $\mathbf{d}^*$ vanishes; this is always possible for appropriate $a_1, \ldots, a_r$ not all equal to zero. But it follows from the result of the preceding paragraph that this implies that all components of $\mathbf{d}^*$ must be zero; and $\mathbf{d}^* = \mathbf{0}$ for $a_1, \ldots, a_r$ not all equal to zero implies linear dependence of $\mathbf{d}^{(1)}, \ldots, \mathbf{d}^{(r)}$, contrary to the assumption made. Therefore,

$r = 1$ and the ratios of the elements of the nonzero **d**-solution are thus unique and positive.

It is obvious that this solution ensures symmetry if this can be realized, for the **d** which satisfies $d_g \lambda_{gh} = d_h \lambda_{hg}$ satisfies (2.19) automatically. Finally, it follows directly from (2.20) that if we multiply the first column (say) of $[\lambda_{gh}]$ by some positive constant c, this leads to a replacement of d_1 by d_1/c and leaves all other elements of **d** unaffected. The symmetry condition is obviously satisfied, too.

7.2.6. An Application to the Dutch Economy in 1957

Our application is a straightforward extension of the analysis carried out in Chapter 6 on the Dutch economy. Thus we have a committee of three: a labour representative, a member appointed by the Crown, and an employers' representative. The committee has to face a number of constraints which formalize the mechanism of the Dutch economy; they describe certain noncontrolled variables linearly in terms of instruments (in a manner which was considered in detail in Chapter 6). Each of the committee members has his preference system, formalized by a quadratic preference function in instruments and noncontrolled variables (see again Chapter 6). By substituting the linear constraints into these preference functions we obtain three quadratic preference functions of the type (2.1), the instruments being the only arguments which remain. The corresponding raw loss functions are then:

$$(2.21) \qquad l_g(\mathbf{x}) = -\tfrac{1}{2}(\mathbf{x}-\mathbf{x}_g^0)'\mathbf{K}_g(\mathbf{x}-\mathbf{x}_g^0) \quad \text{where } \mathbf{x}_g^0 = -\mathbf{K}_g^{-1}\mathbf{k}_g .$$

Our problem is then: given the constraints and the individual preferences which lead to the three raw loss functions (2.21), how can we arrive at an optimal committee decision if these three individuals are the members of that committee?

There are two preliminary problems to be solved. One is the weighting problem. Should we interpret the present committee as a three-person committee whose individual preference functions are to be treated in the "impartial" manner of the preceding pages, or should we interpret the committee members as spokesmen of groups of different size? In what follows we shall adopt the former view. The other approach can be handled by assuming that there are three groups of size G_1, G_2 and G_3 respectively, that the G_1 employees have all the same preferences as their representative (similarly for the other two groups), and then proceeding with a loss matrix whose number of rows and columns is

$G_1+G_2+G_3$.[1] The second problem is the uncertainty aspect. The best line of action which is available to No. g is the strategy which maximizes the expectation of his own preference function; or alternatively, which minimizes the expectation of his own loss function. It is obvious that this expected loss is positive even for this maximizing strategy. In other words, even if we would apply the procedure of Theorem 7.2 to expected losses rather than actual losses, so that the uncertainty problem is solved, then we have nevertheless a new problem due to the fact that the diagonal elements of the expected loss matrix are positive. We shall solve it by measuring the expected loss of the strategy $\mathbf{x}$ as a deviation from that of the maximizing strategy:

$$\mathscr{E}_0 l_g^*(\mathbf{x}) = -\tfrac{1}{2}\mathscr{E}_0[(\mathbf{x}-\tilde{\mathbf{x}}_g)' \mathbf{K}_g(\mathbf{x}-\tilde{\mathbf{x}}_g)], \tag{2.22}$$

where $\tilde{\mathbf{x}}_g$ stands for the maximizing strategy of No. g.

TABLE 7.1

THE MATRICES K_g FOR THE THREE SETS OF INDIVIDUAL PREFERENCES*

	w	ΔT^{ia}	ΔT^{wa}	ΔT^{oa}	ΔG
			K_1		
w	−3.513	−2.173	0.159	0.893	0.690
ΔT^{ia}		−152.964	−8.210	1.812	15.660
ΔT^{wa}			−142.948	−1.926	12.861
ΔT^{oa}				−6.765	0.863
ΔG					−67.634
			K_2		
w	−3.537	−2.410	−0.321	0.916	1.302
ΔT^{ia}		−321.918	−12.849	2.040	21.579
ΔT^{wa}			−318.989	−1.464	24.828
ΔT^{oa}				−20.847	0.274
ΔG					−82.900
			K_3		
w	−3.358	−1.910	−1.276	0.559	2.120
ΔT^{ia}		−315.127	−15.728	1.883	22.062
ΔT^{wa}			−330.212	0.427	38.199
ΔT^{oa}				−301.257	−1.657
ΔG					−183.011

* Elements below the diagonal are obtained by transposition.

[1] This leads of course to many zeros in the loss matrix; reference is made to the beginning of 7.2.5.

In order to concentrate on the committee aspect of the problem we shall confine ourselves to the first year, 1957. This means that we remove the 1958 and 1959 variables from constraints and preference functions, so that the decision problem becomes static and the three K_g-matrices are all of order 5×5. They are presented in Table 7.1. To evaluate the loss matrix we then only need the three decisions which maximize the expectations of the individual preference functions. These are given in

TABLE 7.2

THE INDIVIDUAL AND COMMITTEE DECISIONS

	$\hat{x}_1$	$\hat{x}_2$	$\hat{x}_3$	$\hat{x}_C$
w	10.087	8.155	7.958	9.236
ΔT^{ia}	−0.188	−0.086	−0.085	−0.137
ΔT^{wa}	−0.051	−0.046	−0.087	−0.046
ΔT^{oa}	1.301	0.257	−0.094	0.337
ΔG	0.170	0.112	0.130	0.144

Table 7.2 and the resulting expected loss matrix, based on the definition (2.22), is as follows:

$$\begin{bmatrix} 0 & 9.082d_1 & 12.618d_1 \\ 17.654d_2 & 0 & 1.608d_2 \\ 300.747d_3 & 18.822d_3 & 0 \end{bmatrix}. \tag{2.23}$$

On applying the procedure of Theorem 7.2 we obtain

$$d = \{1 \quad 0.513 \quad 0.0421\}, \tag{2.24}$$

the normalization being such that $d_1 = 1$. The resulting matrix is

$$\begin{bmatrix} 0 & 9.082 & 12.618 \\ 9.050 & 0 & 0.824 \\ 12.651 & 0.792 & 0 \end{bmatrix}, \tag{2.25}$$

which, though not symmetric, is evidently close to symmetry. The next step is to construct the committee loss function:

$$l_C^*(x) = -\tfrac{1}{2}\sum_{g=1}^{3} d_g(x-\hat{x}_g)' K_g(x-\hat{x}_g). \tag{2.26}$$

Minimizing its expectation, we obtain the committee decision:

$$\hat{x}_C = \left(\sum d_g K_g\right)^{-1} \sum d_g K_g \hat{x}_g, \tag{2.27}$$

which is specified numerically in the last column of Table 7.2. Thus the committee decision implies a 9.2 per cent wage increase, which is to be compared with the individual policies of 10.1, 8.2, and 8.0 per cent of the employee, the Crown member, and the employer, respectively. Regarding the autonomous tax changes, the committee decision implies a 140 million guilder reduction of indirect taxes, a 50 million reduction of direct taxes on wage income, and a 340 million increase of direct taxes on nonwage income. If the employee alone had played the game, the result would have been a larger reduction (190 million) of indirect taxes, about the same reduction (50 million) of wage taxes, and a much larger increase (1300 million) of nonwage taxes. The employer would have applied reductions only: about 90 million for each of the three tax categories. The Crown member occupies an intermediate position. For indirect taxes he would apply about the same reduction as the employer (and, therefore, a smaller reduction than the employee and the committee as a whole); for wage taxes the reduction is of the same order of magnitude as that of the employee and the committee (and smaller than that of the employer); and for nonwage taxes he advocates a moderate increase, slightly larger than the committee increase but not nearly as large as the employee's increase. As to government expenditure on commodities, finally, we find that the committee decision is about halfway between the individual extremes; the smallest increase is that of the Crown member, the largest that of the employee.

These results show that the committee decision is more or less "in between" the three individual decisions and on the average rather close to the Crown member's decision. This feature can be analyzed in a less casuistic manner by substituting $\hat{x}_C$ into (2.26). The result is a committee loss of 6.404, which is the sum of three terms:

3.884 for the employee ($g = 1$)
1.219 for the Crown member ($g = 2$)
1.301 for the employer ($g = 3$).

This shows that the expected loss which the Crown member suffers in case the committee decision is imposed is less than the corresponding losses of the two other committee members; further, that the employee's part in the committee loss is larger than the sum of the other two parts.

7.2.7. Concluding Remarks

(i) It is perhaps good to stress that the proposals made in this section have no pretension of being satisfactory under all circumstances but only under the conditions which have been mentioned. This holds both for the symmetry approach and (in particular) for the approach which equates corresponding row sums and column sums. We may say that this situation is comparable with that of another area in the general field of aggregation theory, viz., price index numbers.[1] There we have a great many alternative approaches, such as those of Laspeyres, Paasche, Edgeworth and Fisher, and their relevance is determined by several factors (e.g., the availability of relevant data). Likewise, we should hope that future research will lead to a larger number of alternative approaches to the committee decision problem as well as to a clearer insight into their relative merits. In this connection it is worthwhile to add that symmetry of the loss matrix is not only a desirable condition with respect to changing preferences of any committee member (which was our justification of symmetry in 7.2.4), but also with respect to disaggregation. To show this, we suppose that the committee is spread over a number (n, say) of different locations and that it is considered convenient to split it up into n subcommittees, one for each location. Each subcommittee will then have its own loss function:

$$l_{C_r}(\mathbf{x}) = \sum_{g \in S_r} d_g^{(r)} l_g(\mathbf{x}), \qquad r = 1, \ldots, n, \tag{2.28}$$

where S_r stands for the set of individuals in the rth subcommittee. Now it would obviously be desirable if the sum of the n subcommittee loss functions were identically equal to the committee loss function:

$$\sum_{r=1}^{n} \sum_{g \in S_r} d_g^{(r)} l_g(\mathbf{x}) \equiv \sum_{g=1}^{G} d_g l_g(\mathbf{x}), \tag{2.29}$$

which implies that the subcommittee loads $d_g^{(r)}$ should all be equal to the corresponding loads d_g for the committee as a whole:

$$d_g^{(r)} = d_g \text{ for } g \in S_r, \quad r = 1, \ldots, n. \tag{2.30}$$

Let No. g and No. h be members of the same subcommittee S_r. Then the load ratio $d_g^{(r)}/d_h^{(r)}$ will be determined by the λ_{ij} with $i, j \in S_r$ and independent of the λ_{ij} with either i or j (or both) outside S_r. But the load ratio d_g/d_h will in general depend on all λ_{ij} without restrictions on

[1] For a survey of aggregation theory which is convenient in this connection, see H. THEIL, "Alternative Approaches to the Aggregation Problem," *Logic, Methodology and Philosophy of Science* (edited by E. NAGEL, P. SUPPES and A. TARSKI), pp. 507–527.

i and j. It follows that condition (2.30) can be satisfied only if we impose that d_g/d_h for $g, h \in S_r$ may depend only on λ_{ij} with $i, j \in S_r$, for $r = 1, \ldots, n$. If we now imagine all conceivable partitionings of the committee in subcommittees, and if we require that it be always true that the subcommittee loss functions add up to the committee loss function, then d_g/d_h can depend only on λ_{gh} and λ_{hg}, which as we saw implies the necessity of a symmetric loss matrix.

A more concrete picture of the situation is perhaps useful. Let us consider a committee of five persons, the first three being arranged in the first subcommittee and the last two in the second. Both subcommittees succeed in establishing a symmetric loss matrix (or order 3×3 and 2×2, respectively); the loss matrix for the committee as a whole may then be:

$$\left[\begin{array}{ccc|cc} 0 & 1 & 3 & 2 & 3 \\ 1 & 0 & 2 & 1 & 2 \\ 3 & 2 & 0 & 3 & 4 \\ \hline 4 & 2 & 6 & 0 & 4 \\ 6 & 4 & 8 & 4 & 0 \end{array}\right]$$

The rows specify the losses inflicted on any given individual, the columns specify the losses inflicted by the optimal decision of any given individual. Obviously, this matrix is only symmetric as far as the diagonal blocks are concerned, so that the problem is how we can relate the loads which fall under different subcommittees in such a way that the off-diagonal blocks are each other's transpose. In the present example this can be achieved by multiplying the loads of the second subcommittee by $\frac{1}{2}$, so that the followig symmetric loss matrix results:

$$\left[\begin{array}{ccc|cc} 0 & 1 & 3 & 2 & 3 \\ 1 & 0 & 2 & 1 & 2 \\ 3 & 2 & 0 & 3 & 4 \\ \hline 2 & 1 & 3 & 0 & 2 \\ 3 & 2 & 4 & 2 & 0 \end{array}\right]$$

The question arises how one can arrive at this symmetry with the smallest possible loss of the advantages accruing from the decentralization of the committee in terms of subcommittees. Suppose then that the following procedure is adopted. Each subcommittee decides on its own loss function, (2.28), and sends one of its members as a delegate to a meeting of all n delegates. What should these delegates do in order that condition (2.29) be satisfied? The answer is easily formulated in terms of our numerical example. Suppose that No. 1 and No. 4 are appointed as delegates by their subcommittees; then they can equate the losses which they inflict on each other, $d_1 \lambda_{14}$ and $d_4 \lambda_{41}$, and thus achieve symmetry for the loss matrix as a whole if this matrix can indeed be made symmetric. Thus the only thing we need is a meeting of delegates, one from each of the n subcommittees. Every delegate has to supply two pieces of information: the loss function of his subcommittee and his own (raw) loss function. The former functions are combined linearly and the latter supply the weights of the linear combination. This holds, of course, only if there exist positive loads $d_1, \ldots, d_G$ which make the $G \times G$ loss matrix symmetric.

(ii) The committee decision problem as it has been treated here can be said to consist of two stages. One is that of comparing the individual preferences (by means of the loss matrix) and the other that of maximizing a linear combination of the individual preference functions after the weights have been obtained from the first stage. The first is the problem of comparing and it may be considered worthwhile to define some quantitative measures for the degree to which we succeed in making the preferences comparable.

Let us start by defining the "preference distance" of any pair of committee members, say No. g and No. h, by $\frac{1}{2}(d_g \lambda_{gh} + d_h \lambda_{hg})$; then we measure the "incomparability" of their preferences by

$$I_{gh} = \frac{|d_g \lambda_{gh} - d_h \lambda_{hg}|}{d_g \lambda_{gh} + d_h \lambda_{hg}},$$

which is a number between 0 and 1 on the assumption that the two committee members do not agree as to the optimal decision (if they do, I_{gh} is of the indeterminate form 0/0). The incomparability of the preferences of No. g with those of all other committee members can be measured by

$$I_{g\cdot} = \frac{\sum_h |d_g \lambda_{gh} - d_h \lambda_{hg}|}{\sum_h (d_g \lambda_{gh} + d_h \lambda_{hg})},$$

which is also a number between 0 and 1. The same holds for

$$I_{..} = \frac{\sum_g \sum_h |d_g \lambda_{gh} - d_h \lambda_{hg}|}{\sum_g \sum_h (d_g \lambda_{gh} + d_h \lambda_{hg})} = \frac{\sum\sum_{g<h} |d_g \lambda_{gh} - d_h \lambda_{hg}|}{\sum_g \sum_h d_g \lambda_{gh}},$$

which measures the incomparability of all individual preferences in the committee as a whole. It is easily seen that $I_{g\cdot}$ is a weighted average of all I_{gh}, and $I_{..}$ of the $I_{g\cdot}$:

$$I_{g\cdot} = \frac{\sum_h (d_g \lambda_{gh} + d_h \lambda_{hg}) I_{gh}}{\sum_h (d_g \lambda_{gh} + d_h \lambda_{hg})}, \quad I_{..} = \frac{\sum_g \sum_h (d_g \lambda_{gh} + d_h \lambda_{hg}) I_{g\cdot}}{\sum_g \sum_h (d_g \lambda_{gh} + d_h \lambda_{hg})}.$$

It is instructive to apply these concepts to the example of 7.2.6. The matrix of preference distances follows directly from (2.25):

$$[\tfrac{1}{2} d_g \lambda_{gh} + \tfrac{1}{2} d_h \lambda_{hg}] = \begin{bmatrix} 0 & 9.066 & 12.634 \\ & 0 & 0.808 \\ & & 0 \end{bmatrix},$$

which shows that the Crown member occupies a position "between" the other two but that he is "closer" to the employers' respresentative than to labour's representative. The matrix of pairwise incomparability coefficients is

$$[I_{gh}] = \begin{bmatrix} \cdot & 0.002 & 0.001 \\ & \cdot & 0.020 \\ & & \cdot \end{bmatrix}$$

and the vector of individual incomparability coefficients:

$$[I_{g\cdot}] = \{0.001 \quad 0.003 \quad 0.002\},$$

while the committee incomparability coefficient is $I_{..} = 0.002$. The conclusion is that in this case the "comparability fit" is very good.

7.2.8. Summary

(1, 2) The problem is to formulate an optimal committee decision based on the preferences of the committee members. A brief survey of Arrow's and Harsanyi's contributions is presented; the approach followed amounts to maximizing a committee preference function which is a linear combination of the individual preference functions and the main problem is finding the appropriate weights (the "loads").

(3, 4) The loads are determined by the requirement that the loss matrix should be symmetric. The typical element of this matrix specifies the loss which any given committee member suffers in case some other committee member succeeds in imposing his own optimal decision on the committee. The condition of a symmetric loss matrix is based on a more fundamental postulate, which requires that the loads of any two committee members should not be affected when any third member changes his preferences.

(5, 6) The symmetry condition cannot in general be satisfied, because the loads are insufficient in number. It is then suggested to retreat to a weaker criterion, viz., the pairwise equality of corresponding row sums and column sums of the loss matrix. This procedure is applied to a three-person committee consisting of the labour representative, the Crown member and the employers' representative of Chapter 6.

(7) The symmetry condition has not only desirable properties with respect to changing preferences of some third committee member, but also with respect to disaggregation of the committee in terms of sub-committees. Some quantitative measures are proposed to determine the degree of comparability of individual preferences.

Bibliography

ARROW, K. J. *Social Choice and Individual Values.* Cowles Commission Monograph No. 12. John Wiley and Sons, Inc., New York; Chapman and Hall, Ltd., London. 1951.

ARROW, K. J., S. KARLIN and P. SUPPES (editors). *Mathematical Methods in the Social Sciences, 1959.* Stanford University Press, Stanford. 1960.

BANBURY, J., and J. MAITLAND (editors). *Proceedings of the Second International Conference on Operational Research.* English Universities Press, Ltd., London. 1961.

BOGAARD, P. J. M. VAN DEN. "On the Static Theory of Certainty Equivalence." Report 6010 of the Econometric Institute of the Netherlands School of Economics. March 28, 1960.

BOGAARD, P. J. M. VAN DEN, and G. ARNAIZ. "On the Sensitivity of Committee Decisions under Alternative Quadratic Criteria." Report 6107 of the Econometric Institute of the Netherlands School of Economics (also Report No. 7 of the International Center for Management Science). May 30, 1961.

BOGAARD, P. J. M. VAN DEN and A. P. BARTEN. "Macroeconomic Decision Rules for The Netherlands, 1957–1959." Report 5915 of the Econometric Institute of the Netherlands School of Economics. June 15, 1959.

BOGAARD, P. J. M. VAN DEN, A. MONREAL LUQUE and C. VAN DE PANNE. "Étude sur les implications des horizons alternatifs dans la programmation quadratique dynamique." *Revue de la Société Française de Recherche Opérationnelle*, Vol. 6 (1962), pp. 163–183.

BOGAARD, P. J. M. VAN DEN, and H. THEIL. "Macrodynamic Policy-Making: An Application of Strategy and Certainty Equivalence Concepts to the Economy of the United States, 1933–1936." *Metroeconomica*, Vol. 11 (1959), pp. 149–167.

BOGAARD, P. J. M. VAN DEN, and J. VERSLUIS. "The Design of Optimal Committee Decisions." *Statistica Neerlandica*, Vol. 16 (1962), pp. 271–289. [An abbreviated version of this article was published under the title "The Design of Socially Optimal Decisions" in *Proceedings of the Second International Conference on Operational Research*, edited by J. BANBURY and J. MAITLAND. English Universities Press, Ltd., London. 1961.]

BOWMAN, E. H. "Consistency and Optimality in Managerial Decision Making." *Management Science*, Vol. 9 (1963), pp. 310–321.

BURGER, E. "On Extrema with Side Conditions." *Econometrica*, Vol. 23 (1955), pp. 451–452.

CHERNOFF, H., and N. DIVINSKY. "The Computation of Maximum-Likelihood Estimates of Linear Structural Equations." Chapter X of *Studies in Econometric Method*, edited by W. C. HOOD and T. C. KOOPMANS. Cowles Commission Monograph No. 14. John Wiley and Sons, Inc., New York; Chapman and Hall, Ltd., London. 1953.

CHURCHMAN, C. W., and M. VERHULST (editors). *Management Sciences, Models and Techniques*. Two Volumes. Pergamon Press, Oxford, London, New York and Paris. 1960.

DEBREU, G. "Definite and Semidefinite Quadratic Forms." *Econometrica*, Vol. 20 (1952), pp. 295–300.

DEBREU, G. "Representation of a Preference Ordering by a Numerical Function." Chapter XI of *Decision Processes*, edited by R. M. THRALL, C. H. COOMBS and R. L. DAVIS, John Wiley and Sons, Inc., New York; Chapman and Hall, Ltd., London. 1954.

FISHER, W. D. "Estimation in the Linear Decision Model." *International Economic Review*, Vol. 3 (1962), pp. 1–29.

FRISCH, R. "Numerical Specification of a Quadratic Preference Function for Use in Macroeconomic Programming." Mimeographed report of the University Institute of Economics, Oslo. 1957.

FRISCH, R. "A Complete Scheme for Computing All Direct and Cross Demand Elasticities in a Model with Many Sectors." *Econometrica*, Vol. 27 (1959), pp. 177–196.

GORMAN, W. M. "Separable Utility and Aggregation." *Econometrica*, Vol. 27 (1959), pp. 469–481.

HARSANYI, J. C. "Cardinal Welfare, Individualistic Ethics, and Interpersonal Comparisons of Utility." *Journal of Political Economy*, Vol. 63 (1955), pp. 309–321.

HICKS, J. R. *Value and Capital*. Second Edition. Oxford University Press, London. 1946.

HOLT, C. C. "Decision Rules for Allocating Inventory to Lots and Cost Functions for Making Aggregate Inventory Decisions. "*Journal of Industrial Engineering*, Vol. 9 (1958), pp. 14–22.

HOLT, C. C. "A General Solution for Linear Decision Rules." Mimeographed report of the Carnegie Institute of Technology, Pittsburgh, Pennsylvania. 1960.

HOLT, C. C. "Linear Decision Rules for Economic Stabilization and Growth." *Quarterly Journal of Economics*. Vol. 76 (1962), pp. 20–45.

HOLT, C. C., and F. MODIGLIANI. "Firm Cost Structures and the Dynamic Responses of Inventories, Production, Work Force, and Orders to Sales Fluctuations." *Study of Inventory Fluctuations and Economic Stability*, Congress of the United Statates, Joint Economic Committee. 1961.

HOLT, C. C., F. MODIGLIANI and J. F. MUTH. "Derivation of a Linear Decision Rule for Production and Employment." *Management Science*, Vol. 2 (1956), pp. 159–177.

HOLT, C. C., F. MODIGLIANI, J. F. MUTH and H. A. SIMON. *Planning Production, Inventories, and Work Force*. Prentice Hall, Inc., Englewood Cliffs, N. J. 1960.

HOLT, C. C., F. MODIGLIANI and H. A. SIMON. "A Linear Decision Rule for Production and Employment Scheduling." *Management Science*, Vol. 2 (1955), pp. 1–30.

HOOD, W. C., and T. C. KOOPMANS (editors). *Studies in Econometric Method*. Cowles Commission Monograph No. 14. John Wiley and Sons, Inc., New York; Chapman and Hall, Ltd., London. 1953.

HOUTHAKKER, H. S. "Additive Preferences." *Econometrica*, Vol. 28 (1960), pp. 244–257.

KALMAN, R. E., L. LAPIDUS and E. SHAPIRO. "The Optimal Control of Chemical and Petroleum Processes." Pages 6–17 of *Proceedings of the Joint Symposium on Instrumentation and Computation in Process Development and Plant Design*, published by The Institution of Chemical Engineers, London. 1959.

KLEIN, L. R. *Economic Fluctuations in the United States, 1921–1941*. Cowles Commission Monograph No. 11. John Wiley and Sons, Inc., New York; Chapman and Hall, Ltd., London. 1950.

KOOPMANS, T. C., and W. C. HOOD. "The Estimation of Simultaneous Linear Economic Relationships." Chapter VI of *Studies in Econometric Method*, edited by W. C. HOOD and T. C. KOOPMANS. Cowles Commission Monograph No. 14. John Wiley and Sons, Inc., New York; Chapman and Hall, Ltd., London. 1953.

KOYCK, L. M. *Distributed Lags and Investment Analysis*. Vol. IV of Contributions to Economic Analysis. North-Holland Publishing Company, Amsterdam. 1954.

MANSFIELD, E., and H. V. WEIN. "Linear Decision Rules and Freight Yard Operations." *Journal of Industrial Engeneering*, Vol. 9 (1958), pp. 93–98.

MARSCHAK, J. "Rational Behavior, Uncertain Prospects, and Measurable Utility." *Econometrica*, Vol. 18 (1950), pp. 111–141.

MARSCHAK, J. "Elements for a Theory of Teams." *Management Science*, Vol. 1 (1955), pp. 127–137.

NAGEL, E., P. SUPPES and A. TARSKI (editors). *Logic, Methodology and Philosophy of Science – Proceedings of the 1960 International Congress*. Stanford University Press, Stanford. 1962.

NEUMANN, J. VON, and O. MORGENSTERN. *Theory of Games and Economic Behavior*. Third Edition. Princeton University Press, Princeton. 1953.

PANNE, C. VAN DE, and G. J. AEYELTS AVERINK. "Imperfect Management Decisions and Predictions and Their Financial Implications in Dynamic Quadratic Cost Minimization." *Statistica Neerlandica*, Vol. 15 (1961), pp. 293–318.

PANNE, C. VAN DE, and P. BOSJE. "Sensitivity Analysis of Cost Coefficient Estimates: The Case of Linear Decision Rules for Employment and Production." *Management Science*, Vol. 9 (1962), pp. 82–107.

RADNER, R. "Team Decision Problems." *Annals of Mathematical Statistics*, Vol. 33 (1962), pp. 857–881.

REITER, S. "Surrogates for Uncertain Decision Problems: Minimal Information for Decision Making." *Econometrica*, Vol. 25 (1957), pp. 339–345.

ROTHENBERG, J. F. *The Measurement of Social Welfare*. Prentice Hall, Inc., Englewood Cliffs, N. J. 1961.

ROTHENBERG, T., and C. T. LEENDERS. "Efficient Estimation of Simultaneous Equation Systems." Report 6216 of the Econometric Institute of the Netherlands School of Economics. June 19, 1962.

SAMUELSON, P. A. *Foundations of Economic Analysis*. Harvard University Press, Cambridge. 1953.

SCHLAIFER, R. *Probability and Statistics for Business Decisions*. McGraw-Hill Book Company, Inc., New York, Toronto and London. 1959.

SIMON, H. A. "Dynamic Programming under Uncertainty with a Quadratic Criterion Function." *Econometrica*, Vol. 24 (1956), pp. 74–81.

STROTZ, R. H. "The Empirical Implications of a Utility Tree." *Econometrica*, Vol. 25 (1957), pp. 269–280.

THEIL, H. "Econometric Models and Welfare Maximization." *Weltwirtschaftliches Archiv*, Vol. 72 (1954), pp. 60–83.

THEIL, H. "A Note on Certainty Equivalence in Dynamic Planning." *Econometrica*, Vol. 25 (1957), pp. 346–349.

THEIL, H. *Economic Forecasts and Policy*. Second Edition. Vol. XV of Contributions to Economic Analysis. North-Holland Publishing Company, Amsterdam. 1961.

THEIL, H. "Alternative Approaches to the Aggregation Problem." Pages 507–527 of *Logic, Methodology and Philosophy of Science – Proceedings of the 1960 International Congress*, edited by E. NAGEL, P. SUPPES and A. TARSKI. Stanford University Press, Stanford. 1962.

THEIL, H. "On the Optimal Management of Research: A Mathematical Approach." Report 6212 of the Econometric Institute of the Netherlands School of Economics (also Report No. 17 of the International Center for Management Science). May 10, 1962.

THEIL, H. "On the Symmetry Approach to the Committee Decision Problem." *Management Science*, Vol. 9 (1963), pp. 380–393.

THEIL, H., and J. C. G. BOOT. "The Final Form of Econometric Equation Systems." *Review of the International Statistical Institute*, Vol. 30 (1962), pp. 136–152.

THEIL, H., and E. KAPTEIN. "The Effect of Forecasting Errors on Optimal Programming of Production-Inventory and Anti-Depression Policies." Report 5906 of the Econometric Institute of the Netherlands School of Economics. February 25, 1959. [An abbreviated version of this article was published under the title "The Effect of Forecasting Errors on Optimal Programming" in *Management Sciences, Models and Techniques*, Vol. 1 (pp. 295–322), edited by C. W. CHURCHMAN and M. VERHULST. Pergamon Press, Oxford, London, New York and Paris. 1960.]

THEIL, H., and T. KLOEK. "The Operational Implications of Imperfect Models." Chapter 8 of *Mathematical Methods in the Social Sciences, 1959*, edited by K. J. ARROW, S. KARLIN, and P. SUPPES. Stanford University Press, Stanford. 1960.

THRALL, R. M., C. H. COOMBS and R. L. DAVIS (editors). *Decision Processes*. John Wiley and Sons, Inc., New York; Chapman and Hall, Ltd., London. 1954.

TINBERGEN, J. *On the Theory of Economic Policy*. Second Edition. Vol. I of Contributions to Economic Analysis. North-Holland Publishing Company, Amsterdam. 1952.

TINBERGEN, J. *Economic Policy: Principles and Design*. Vol. XI of Contributions to Economic Analysis. North-Holland Publishing Company, Amsterdam. 1956.

VAN DE PANNE, C., *see* PANNE, C. VAN DE.

VAN DEN BOGAARD, P. J. M., *see* BOGAARD, P. J. M. VAN DEN.

VERDOORN, P. J., and C. J. VAN EIJK. "Experimental Short-Term Forecasting Models." Mimeographed report of the Central Planning Bureau, The Hague. 1958. [This report was a paper read at the Bilbao Meeting of the Econometric Society in 1958.]

VON NEUMANN, J., *see* NEUMANN, J. VON.

INDEX